RICK BARRY: GOLDEN STATE SUPER- STAR

****

by Sam Goldaper and Jay Searcy

tempo
books

GROSSET & DUNLAP
Publishers • New York

For Robert, Brenda and Martha
For Jackie, Mike and Mark

Chapter One

Keith Wilkes, the newly-named NBA rookie of the year, burst through the door of the Golden State Warriors' dressing room in Landover, Md., and shouted, "We're champions of the world." Al Attles, the coach, grabbed him by the hand and together they danced a jig. There was singing, and uncontrolled laughter and champagne showers. And, for Rick Barry at least, there were tears.

Barry, bone-weary and sweat-drenched, had his head buried in his hand and was crying unashamedly. Cliff Ray, the Warriors' towering center, stopped celebrating when he noticed his captain sitting alone on the bench near his stall, walked over and patted him softly on the head. Barry didn't look up. Ten years of professional basketball frustration welled inside him and burst out in the flood of tears.

He had been called traitor, money hungry, arro-

gant, cry baby, selfish, temperamental and moody.
Now he had been named the most valuable player in
the playoffs and suddenly they were calling him the
greatest player in the NBA, the man who took the underdog Warriors to four straight stunning victories
over the Washington Bullets for the 1974-75 National
Basketball Association championship.

The Warriors, given no chance of getting to the
playoffs before the season began, had completed eight
unforgettable days in May and Barry had been the
man most responsible. It was only the third four-game
sweep in the 29-year NBA playoff history. Only the
1959 Boston Celtics and the 1971 Milwaukee Bucks
had accomplished the feat before.

When Barry finally regained his composure and
joined his teammates in the Capital Centre victory
celebration, he said, "It was the most rewarding season I've ever had. We were supposed to be a run-of-
the-mill team, but instead of the Bullets beating us
four straight, we beat them four straight. It was
tremendous. Everything fell into place. It was really a
fantasy kind of year."

Rick Barry agreed that Golden State wasn't a super
team, but that didn't interfere with the Warriors'
success.

"We realize we got here through hard work, determination and a lot of guts," he said.

The upset had been witnessed by millions on television and by the thousands who managed to get seats
at the Cow Palace in San Francisco, and at the Capital Centre. They had seen Rick Barry, the perfectionist, at his 10-year best, setting up his teammates with

pinpoint passing, fighting for loose balls, rebounding, and hustling for baskets. And, with every basket, his right arm had shot skyward in a boyishly enthusiastic salute. He was the leader, the inspiration, the superstar on the top-to-bottom team of "no names."

In the 17 games on the road to the championship Barry scored 479 points, dealt out 103 assists, and grabbed 94 rebounds. He also made 50 steals during the playoffs, eight against the Seattle SuperSonics, both league records, and walked away with a flock of accolades.

Tom Heinsohn, the Boston Celtics' coach, called him "the best all-around player in the game," and another coach said, "I don't think I've seen Barry play better basketball than he is this season. He's doing everything, and through his example, the other players are following his lead. Don't forget most of them are new to the team. Nobody gave them a tumble when the season opened, and now they are the champions.

This was the same Rick Barry who had left behind a trail of friends and critics as he traveled from the NBA to the American Basketball Association and back to the NBA, five different teams in 10 seasons of fun, pain and legal maneuvers. At times it appeared he had spent as much time in the courts as on them. Law suits pursued him in the ABA sites of Oakland, Washington, Virigina and New York. He was under contract to two teams at the same time, and only a court order forced him back to the Golden State Warriors from the New York Nets.

Over the years he had been bad-mouthed on the east and west coasts and booed in between. He had been accused of shooting the ball too much and showing an indifference to playing defense. Even before Barry had turned pro there were those who said he was "flaky", a cry-baby, that he didn't have the muscle nor the fight to make it in the NBA.

The federal courts had ripped away his Nets uniform three years before (1972) and Barry, suffering yet another crushing setback, had vowed to retire. But as the unpredicatable and controversial Barry had done so often since 1965, he changed his mind when the Warriors, who had been his first pro team, offered a reported 3-year, $1.6-million contract.

Now he was walking through the dressing room at the Capital Centre, his eyes wet and red, and congratulating the teammates who had placed their faith in him. He hugged Derrek Dickey, a no-name who had led all the shooters in the championship series, and who had done a job on Washington's Elvin Hayes.

"My man," said Derrek and together they sipped champagne and laughed. Then he turned to Steve Bracey, the 12th man on Rick Barry's no-name team and Bracey laughed and poured champagne on Barry's head. "I'll take it, I'll take it," said Barry and they laughed and hugged. Cliff Ray, who came to the Warriors at the start of the season in a deal for Nate Thurmond, wiped the champagne off Barry's face.

The team that played together, worked together, stuck together and won together was now celebrating together, with teamwork. Coach Al Attles was talking to the television people; Joe Roberts, the assistant who took charge on the bench after Attles had been ejected in the opening minutes of the game by the officials, was talking to writers; Bill Bridges, who had earned his first NBA championship ring in 12 years of professional basketball, was hugging Charlie Johnson, the little no-name of the backcourt; Phil Smith and Charlie Dudley, the other backcourt no-names, were guzzling champagne like veterans.

Barry stated, when he finally found his voice, "One of the most unique teams in all of basketball history. A team that cares for each other. The most beautiful individuals I've ever been associated with. I don't know how anyone can top it. The championship is everything. I never thought at the beginning of the year we could achieve it. This team has character. This is the most rewarding thing, the happiest thing that's ever happened to me. It's everything. I only wish I was in a position to retire now."

The man who has been equally regaled and vilified for his activities on and off the court, lifted the champagne glass and took a long drink as the sweat and champagne ran off his 6-foot-7-inch frame. At the same time, the boy in Barry recalled how his father would shout to him as he practiced running backwards ... "Get back ... Don't look at the ball when you dribble." He remembered those nights in the gym at the University of Miami when he would practice alone, sometimes past midnight, and how his teammates used to scoff at him.

In his third season with the Warriors since his return from the Nets, the longest one-town stint in his professional career, no longer could Barry be called a superstar who couldn't help a team win a championship. Barry had matured. He hadn't got caught up in helpless arguments with officials as he had done so many times before. He had actively campaigned to become the team captain before the season began and amazed even himself by his conduct. He took another long drink of the sparkling wine.

He had not even drawn a technical foul in the entire playoffs ("It took me 10 years to realize you can't win an argument with an official," he said), not even when Mike Riordan of the Bullets had tried to draw him into a fight early in the fourth game of the championship series.

Barry, who had averaged 30.6 points during the regular season, second to Bob McAdoo of the Buffalo Braves, had been matched with the 6-4 Riordan in the three regular season games. Mike, who had grown from a 12th round draft pick to one of the NBA's outstanding small forwards, clearly won the regular season battle against Barry. He limited Rick to 8 points in one of the meetings and held his average against the Bullets to 16.3 points. In the one game Riordan had missed, Barry scored 34.

Pro basketball is clearly a game of match-ups, and even before the Golden State-Washington final series had opened, the Barry-Riordan match-up was considered one of the key factors. When it was all over Barry left no doubt that he was the master in the first three games. Then, three minutes into the final game, Riordan precipitated a fight and was charged with a foul, and Barry coolly walked away from it.

"I amazed myself at my restraint," Barry said.

Riordan denied that he had attempted to get Barry

involved, and perhaps ejected from the game and insisted that he was simply playing "aggressive" basketball. A younger Barry might have fallen for the ploy and fought Riordan, but this year it was Captain Barry and he had his team to think about. He let Coach Attles take up the battle.

Rick's temper, no-compromise attitude and fierce competitiveness have born many tales. Of all the barriers Barry had to overcome, one of the hardest was his raging temper, and it was Bruce Hale, his coach at the University of Miami and his father-in-law, who warned him of the importance of controlling it. "What I tried to teach Rick was how to behave on the court," Hale said. "The game of basketball reflects life. What you do on the court reflects you as a person outside. People may not hire you for a business job if you act up on the court. The image you develop on the court will stay with you later on."

Barry tried to understand what Hale was saying, and he made conscious efforts to control his temper, but the ghost of the old Barry reared its head from time to time throughout his pro career and he lived with the reputation of a referee-baiting, elbow-throwing flake who had a star complex. Barry fought two kinds of fights. He battled the referees verbally in an effort to attract attention to fouls committed against him and he fought players to keep from getting butchered. "You have to fight back," Barry said. "You can't just stand there and take it. You have to let them know you're in the game."

It has often been intimated, written and said, especially during all the years that Wilt Chamberlain played and never fouled out of a game, that officials protected superstars.

Why then was the same protection not afforded Barry?

Rick is an emotional player who oftens plays best when he is angry. When he is upset by a call, he lets the official know immediately, and like the players who don't like his criticism, the officials, too, don't like Barry showing them up. Thus, he probably gets manhandled more without fouls being called than any non-center in the NBA.

"My game is to drive to the hoop and try to draw a foul," Barry explains. "When I feel the initial contact I start to twist and turn to get the shot off. What happens is that the refs lose sight of the body contact sometimes because they follow the flight of the ball. The only thing that really gets my goat is when the opposition gets indignant when they're caught for butchering me and they act as if they never touched me. Or what's even better is when they get angry when I foul them. They have to be kidding."

Much of Barry's unpopularity has come primarily because, when he is asked a direct question, he has always answered honestly, never considering the consequences. He has spoken out in the past against the NBA Players' Association, for the merger between the NBA and ABA when it was unfashionable to do so, and has said that athletes were overpaid.

When he came back to the Warriors, after his playing days in the ABA, he told an interviewer that Sidney Wicks of the Portland Trail Blazers was a better forward than Spencer Haywood of the Seattle Super-

Sonics, but that Julius Erving of the Nets was probably better then either of them. The remark did not sit well with either Wicks or Haywood.

Barry's outspokenness may have cost him the 1974-75 regular season MVP award. The vote figured to be a closely contested battle between Bob McAdoo and Barry. It wasn't. Instead, Barry finished a distant fourth and it was suggested that the players who did the voting remembered his frankness and criticism of them.

Players do not like criticism, especially from a peer, and throughout the years Rick has played the role of critic in the print media and as the 1974 NBA television playoff color commentator. He was honest, and in private some of the players expressed disenchantment with that honesty.

Al Attles was among the first to admit disappointment that Rick had not been selected as the MVP.

"I don't see how any man could be more valuable for the successes of his team than Rick," said Attles.

But the outspoken Barry said, "I'm not surprised, because centers always get it." And, then in a move that would not endear him to McAdoo, he said he had voted for Dave Cowens of the Boston Celtics who had finished third in voting.

"Cowens does more things," said Barry. "There is too much emphasis on scoring."

But being anything else would mean changing his style, and that wouldn't be Rick Barry.

But for that all-important fourth playoff game, the Barry temper, which had caused so much trouble in years past, had been conquered, along with the Washington Bullets.

Soon the Warriors began to dress and rejoin their families and friends who were waiting outside. Then there would be more celebrating.

"This is a team that doesn't know how to die," said Cliff Ray, and everyone agreed.

"I guess no one took us seriously," said a smiling Al Attles.

For years the Warriors had been losers, especially at the box office. It was a financially troubled franchise kept together by Franklin Mieuli (pronounced Muley), an eccentric nice guy who had been taking the rap for a long time. For years it was the Los Angeles Lakers this and the Lakers that, and to make matters worse, the heralded Bill Walton from UCLA was moving into the Pacific Division for the 1974-75 season.

Before the Warriors opened training camp, few people in the Bay area were buying season tickets, or even cared if there was a pro basketball team in the area. But by season's end, the Warriors were again playing before screaming fans, something that had not happened in a long time.

The Golden State fans had cut down the nets after the Warriors won the third straight game of the championship series, but after the fourth and clinching victory, they stole owner Franklin Mieuli's hat and broke through police lines at San Francisco International Airport.

"We're No. 1, we're No. 1," an exuberant crowd of 3,000 chanted after having waited up to five hours for their heroes return from Landover, Md. When the team finally showed up, it was by taxi.

A minor malfunction had forced their plane to land in Oakland and the management decided to reward the noisy fans by bringing the Warriors across the bay by taxi. The crowd had to be restrained by a cordon of police until they caught sight of their heroes.

Sixty San Mateo County sheriff's deputies and airport police stood by helplessly as the fans surged past them, swarming over taxi cabs for a better look at the Warriors. Police said it was the biggest airport crowd to greet a local sports team since the San Francisco Giants returned home with the 1962 National League Pennant.

The fans waved signs such as "Go Warriors Go" and "Only the Warriors do things right in Washington," and called the sweep the biggest sports upset of the year.

When Barry finally got his chance to address the crowd, he said, "They said we would fold, but the Bullets were the ones who folded."

The fans responded with wild cheers. No one had expected the Warriors to be taking those cheers. The preseason prognostications were for Golden State to finish fourth in the five-team division.

Meanwhile, Mieuli scanned the group hoping to catch a glimpse of his checkered deerstalker cap. "Somebody stole my hat," the owner muttered. "It was my security blanket. I don't know why anyone else would want it. It's really soggy. Rick Barry soaked it with champagne twice after the final game.

"There will be a substantial reward if I get that hat

back. Whoever has it can have a ride on my boat, season tickets to the Warriors' games next year, a ride on my motorcycle and a lot of love. They can take their pick."

Mieuli, one of the few remaining one-man ownerships in the NBA, had waited a long time for this celebration. He had tossed good money after bad, had been maligned, but he watched the average attendance soar from a measly 2,000 to 10,000 as Barry led a team shorn of other stars, studded with rookies and upgraded reserves, to a championship.

Mieuli could look back to the day he hired Dick Vertlieb as the general manager prior to the start of the 1974-75 season. Vertlieb had done well at Seattle and he would do far better in his new role wih the Warriors.

General managers don't sell tickets, but the moves they make do. Upon his hiring, Vertlieb vowed to do what apparently seemed to be a hopeless possibility for all who had preceded him. He promised he would sign the Warriors' first-round draft pick, a forward out of UCLA named Keith Wilkes, who had played second fiddle to Bill Walton. The Warriors had not signed their first draft choice in five years, and when Vertlieb got Wilkes' name on a contract, it was the beginning of the changing of the guard.

Chapter Two

When Barry walked into training camp, his initial reaction was that he was to be the link with the past in a rebuilding season. There was no reason to dispute those feelings.

The names on the Warrior roster were conspicuous for their anonymity—Phil Smith, Charles Dudley, Derrick Dickey, Clifford Ray, Charles Johnson, Steve Bracey. "You've go to be kidding," was the typical reaction.

Dudley, a guard, had been doing graduate work at the University of Washington the year before, playing pickup games at the gym. The Warriors had drafted him in 1972, then waived him, and he signed with Seattle, where he was cut after 12 games.

Smith? A rookie guard from the University of San Francisco. Dickey? A second-year forward out of Cincinnati. Johnson had been a sixth-round draft choice from the University of California in 1971. Bracey was a third-year pro from Tulsa by way of the Atlanta Hawks. Bill Bridges, old and past his prime, had been signed as a free agent and Ray came to the Warriors from Chicago for veteran center Nate Thurmond, with $500,000 cash and a first-round draft choice. "To be honest," said Vertlieb, "we traded Thurmond because I needed cash to carry out some other things. We got Ray, but I was just hoping to maintain the team. I didn't think he would improve it. And Dudley—shoot, I was just doing a favor for a friend who suggested we give him another tryout."

A sportswriter, cornering Phil Smith in the dressing room, once asked, "Who are you?"

"What?" Smith asked.

"Who are you? I mean, if you had to introduce yourself to the American public, what would you say?"

Smith thought a moment. "Well, I'd say, 'Hi, I'm Phil Smith from the University of San Francisco.'"

Al Attles was certain of only one starter, Rick Barry. Over all, he was a much better player than the young superstar who had left the Warriors in 1967 for the ABA. When he returned after five years in the new league, he was bigger, stronger and wiser.

"He looked around and saw the players we had and the talent on the club," Attles said of Barry, "and he realized what he could do to make us an even better club. He is so much more mature now than he was back in 1966. People looked to him to score then and he did. Now the pressure is off and he is a complete player. He's still as smart and as quick as he was before but he's filled out a lot more physically. He has a lot more muscle and strength than he did in his rookie season. Back then we would have hesitated to put him on a really big forward. We don't now."

Barry was 30 years old as he prepared for his 10th season of pro basketball. "The most frustrating thing about sports," he said, "is the paradox of experience. For nine seasons I have steadily matured and improved every phase of my game. But just as experience had developed me day by day, my body has been deteriorating day by day. If I had the energy that some of the young kids on this team have, I'd be a monster, really a monster on the court."

For the first time in 15 years the Warriors would open the season without a superstar-caliber center, either Wilt Chamberlain or Nate Thurmond, and everyone knows, a team doesn't win consistantly in the NBA without a super center.

The Warriors were young, Barry and the 32-year-old Jeff Mullins had a combined total of 18 pro seasons and the rest of the Warriors had logged only 15 in all.

From the old guard, Cazzie Russell had played out his option and signed with the Los Angeles Lakers, and Nate Thurmond, big, mean and always promising, was new in Chicago. In return, the Bulls sent some much-needed financial replenishment and 6-9 Cliff Ray, with his 8.3 scoring average. There were those on the West Coast who joked that if Ray, standing at the edge of the Coney Island Pier, took 10 shots at the water, maybe he would hit on six of them.

In training camp Attles was to tell his young Warriors, "It's going to be a big change without Thurmond. We're going to miss Clyde Lee, too. We'll have to put in a lot of work to get it together, but it won't be as bad as most people think. I think we'll be all right.

If Attles was playing the role of the optimist, Barry was not.

"I was very pessimistic when we began camp," he said. "It looked as though I was going to finish my career playing on a team trying to rebuild. But after a while when I saw the enthusiasm and the attitude, I became more and more optimistic. I began to feel we'd be competitive."

There is a big difference between being competitive and winning the NBA championship.

For some unexplained reason, the infectious spirit began to take hold, and Barry, looking back at the season, was to say, "This was like a college team. The spirit and enthusiasm was contagious. Nobody cared what we did, or what stars we had. The only thing we cared about was winning."

In the back of everyone's mind was the thought that if the Warriors hadn't made it to the 1973-74 playoffs wih Thurmond, Russell and Lee, how could the possibly do it without them?"

Out of the gloom pieces slowly began to fall into place. Attles decided, no matter what, to start Wilkes at forward alongside of Rick Barry. Cliff Ray could make a full-time career of being the big, bad, mean center. The job of scoring points was left to Barry and Wilkes.

Attles and Vertlieb talked Jeff Mullins out of planned retirement. Though Mullins opened the season with a broken hand, he slowly regained his form, and in the playoffs, where experience wins games, he was highly visible and effective.

During the regular season Attles relied heavily on a backcourt team of Butch Beard, playing for his fourth team in his five year pro career, and Charlie Johnson.

"It's funny how a championship happens," said Barry looking back. We played real good ball early in the season, slumped around All-Star time, then finished with a little momentum. As we started to win games in the playoffs, we all started to get certain feelings that maybe we could pull it off."

Cliff Ray agreed. While playing for the Bulls, he said, "the coach (Dick Motta) played one center against the other. I don't think he really understood the players. Here we've got one center (George Johnson, his backup man) rooting for the other. Everybody cheers for everyone else.

"The coach here talks to you. A lot of coaches don't. Al doesn't make you guess what he's going to do with you. Motta played a guessing game, always keeping you in suspense.

"We had a good team in Chicago, but some people cared about bettering their average. All they could do was shoot. People are dumb. They look at the stats, see a guy who's scoring 25 points a game, and say he's a great player. He may be a lousy player. Rick

Barry's a great player, and he doesn't have to score to be great."

The transformation of Barry began with his captainsy. Al Attles had appointed him to the job for the preseason schedule, and his teammates made it offical with an election before the first regular season game. Rick took his new role so seriously that he carried everyone else with him.

"I'd never been captain before," said Barry, "anywhere. And I thought, if I ever was going to be, this was the year. Physically I relied on self motivation, but having the vote of confidence from the guys you're playing with forced me to excel. I have very badly wanted to be captain of the different teams I'd played for over the years, but it never came, and I didn't want to force it. I can't express the feeling I have about this honor."

It was the most enjoyable situation of Barry's career because of the totally new atmosphere. "The difference this season," said Barry, "is that I've come to see the insignificance of winning a scoring championship and the other guys on the team this year are the kind that can see it's not important that I am scoring most of the points."

"There's a strange chemistry sparking on this team," Attles added with a smile, as if he knew something was about to happen.

"It was an attitude I felt almost from the day we opened training camp," said Barry. "You could see it happen. Being captain of this bunch of guys suddenly became more than just going out and shaking hands with the opposing captain before the start of a game.

By my taking an active role and pointing out the mistakes, I think we were more successful. I would criticize them at times but it was constructive criticism. They accepted it and no one got upset.

"This was a unique team, a team that cared. They put the team ahead of themselves. Team success was what everybody was dedicated to. I never saw a guy down on himself after he had a bad game, as long as we won. In the past a player might have been concerned with his poor shooting rather than if the team won or lost."

Right from the start no team received a greater individual effort than the one Barry gave Golden State. As the season neared the halfway mark, Barry led in scoring with a 33-point average, having gone over the 40-point mark six times in 21 games. Sixteen times he had gone over the 30-point barrier, hitting 48 on his best night. He became the franchise in just about every aspect of the game.

The statistics were only the trimmings. The beauty of Barry was the Bay-blue uniform with gold piping leaving the field behind on a fast break, soaring high above all defenders to unleash a classic jump shot, threading between bodies, forcing a lane where no lane existed, shoveling in a two-handed, under-hand layup. There were nine other players on the court at all times. But the man everyone noticed was Rick Barry.

"I don't know how much more a man could do for a team," Attles said. "This is the best I've seen Rick play in all phases of the game."

Barry scored, rebounded, passed off and stole the

ball with such regularity that he inspired the Warriors to play better basketball than any one of them
knew he could.

The Warriors finished the regular season with a
48-34 won-lost record, and Barry's name showed up
as a leader in a number of the statistical categories.
His 30.6 scoring average was second best. He was the
NBA's best free-throw shooter, led the league with
228 steals and tied Pete Maravich of the New Orleans
Jazz for fifth place in assists, with a 6.2 average.

The new Barry, and his pride, was even more evident during the NBA All-Star game in Phoenix, Ariz.
Along with Sidney Wicks of the Portland Trail
Blazers and Nate Archibald of the Kansas City-
Omaha Kings, they were out there running, diving for
loose balls and trying to win. The same could not be
said for his Western Conference All-Star teammates.
While Barry fought, and berated the officials, the
players did not appear concerned about winning or
losing an exhibition game.

The day of the All-Star game, Ray Scott, the coach
of the Detroit Pistons, in cool analytical terms, explained the evolution of Rick Barry.

"It isn't hard, it's simple," said Scott, who could
trade with the sharpest elbows in the NBA during his
playing days. "Basketball is a game of ego. Subtract
four egos from five and what you have left is a man
who knows where he is going. Before he had too
many egos to think about. Now they have to think
about him and he is player enough to make them see
it is worth the time.

"He is the captain. They tell me it means a lot to

him and I believe it, because he plays like it does. Right now he's playing as well as anyone has ever played this game. It isn't easy coming where he's coming from . . . all the talk, all the word-of-mouth reputations."

As the season progressed the Barry booster club grew.

Mike Newlin of the Houston Rockets called him, "The best basketball player I've ever seen. There is nothing Rick can't do with the basketball. He is probably the best outside shooter in the game. He dribbles and passes as well as any guard, and he knows how to move without the ball to get open."

Larry Siegfried, the assistant coach of the Rockets, added "He's the heart of the team. Rick is absolutely super. He's always aware of where the ball is. I don't see how a man can play better . . ."

And from his teammate, Jeff Mullins, came, "It appears to me Rick performs best when everything rests on his shoulders. When he's most needed, he delivers. Last season there was some doubt. If Rick missed his first five shots or so, Cazzie (Russell) would come in. The situation would upset him.

"Now there is no question in my mind that this is the best I've seen him play, with more desire, intensity and leadership. He is the key. Everyone expects him to get the big basket. He can carry a team to great heights and he has shared himself with the younger players. I'm his biggest fan. He's a pleasure to watch."

Al Attles, who played with Barry when Barry was a rookie and who has played or coached in the NBA for

15 years, agreed. "You can't believe what Rick has done for this club," said Attles. "When the guys named him captain, he accepted it as sort of a mandate. You see him scoring 30 to 40 points a game, and he's also in double figures in rebounding and assists. Hell, he's doing it all."

Barry has often said, "Whenever I do something I always want to be the best. I hate to be second best. I have personal pride."

Bill Sharman, currently the coach of the Los Angeles Lakers, but Rick's coach when the Golden State Warriors were still called the San Francisco Warriors, recalls the time Rick missed a putt on the golf course.

"He became furious," recalled Sharman, "and threw his clubs away. Another time I recalled when he played in a summer basketball league. Rick would explode if he missed an easy shot. He would kick the ball real hard or throw it at the basket."

During his rookie season in a game against Baltimore, Buddy Jeannette, then the Bullet coach, was harrassing the officials and was slapped with a technical foul. Barry, being the best foul shooter, went to the line to shoot the technical. He took a shallow knee bend and flipped the ball underhand.

As the ball missed the basket Barry spun around and began talking to himself.

What did he say?

"Stupid I told myself," said Barry later, "You did not concentrate."

During the championship season, wherever Barry played, opposing coaches lamented and newspaper headlines in the 18 NBA franchise cities told the story of the havoc he inflicted.

In Seattle it was, "Barry's Hot Hand Crushed Sonics"; in New York, "Barry's Too Much;" in Atlanta, "Rick Barry Takes Charge;" and in the Bay area, "Rick Is Doing It All For Golden State."

After his 41-point performance in Atlanta, Cotton Fitzsimmons, the Hawk coach said, "It didn't matter who the Hawks put on Barry, it didn't make much difference. It wasn't a matter of who I put in to stop him, as long as he was in the game it didn't make a difference. Barry's playing the greatest ball of anybody in the NBA. He's not just shooting well, he's passing well and doing everything well."

And when the Warrior Express stopped over in Seattle, and Barry collected 45 points, Don Fair wrote in the Post Intelligencer. "It has been verified and notarized that Rick Barry did not: (a) Collect tickets; (b) Sell hot dogs; (c) Cater drinks; (d) Sing the National Anthem.

"Disdaining such mundane duties, Barry settled for 45 points, six assists, eight rebounds, two steals and flawless leadership as he helped Golden State strengthen its grip on the Pacific Division lead."

Bill Russell, the Sonics coach who created his own havoc when he wore the Boston Celtics Green and was the dominant force in leading the Celtics to their 11 championships, said after the Barry show, "No, he doesn't remind me of anybody else. He's one of a kind. He had a hell of a game, and, listen, Leonard (Gray) played well against him. Barry moves so damn good without the ball. Rick has had 45 before quite a few times and he'll do it again ... quite a few times."

Barry is a great admirer of Red Auerbach, the president and general manager of the Boston Celtics, who like Rick has a hatred for losing.

Barry has often said, "I love to play against the Celtics and I love to watch them play. To me, they epitomize the game of basketball."

Sometimes Barry has strange ways of showing his appreciation. One night during the 1974-75 season he scored 31 points against the Celtics, 11 in the last 6½ minutes of the game to bring the Warriors back from an early 16-point deficit to a 102-101 victory.

But of all the teams that felt Barry's wrath during the Warriors' championship season, none felt it more than the Knicks.

Madison Square Garden is a tough place for visiting ballplayers. They face a fiercely knowledgeable, fiercely partisan crowd. Visiting teams are enemies of the Knicks. But this one night Rick won over the Garden crowd.

Barry started flying right at the start. Nine seconds after Cliff Ray, the Golden State Warrior center, outreached Tom Riker for the opening tap, Barry arched a sweeping hook for the game's first two points. Nineteen seconds later he scored a jumper from the corner for two more points and by half time he had hit on 12 of 17 shots and had added two free throws.

The cheers were grudging at first, but by the fourth quarter they were out of pure respect, even awe. With just 5:17 to play, Barry bent low, scooped a loose ball from between Harthorne Wingo's feet, exploded three strides ahead of the field, jumped high above the rim and stuffed the ball. The 6 foot 7 Barry finished the night with 44 points, four assists and handled the ball like he was 7-5. He kept his hands in the middle of the Knicks' offense and generally played like an MVP as the Golden State Warriors won easily, 126-108. It was the eighth game in which he had scored over 40 points and the season was only 29 games old.

The Knick dressing room turned into a Rick Barry fan club with accolades of, "Very fast, very quick, very agile, very great, a very great passer, a very great ballhandler and very, very smart."

"He moves very well without the ball," said Wingo, one of the Knick forwards who was matched against him. "Like he fakes down very well and comes back to get the ball. He cuts so quick. You can try to slough off on him but it's hard to 'cause if he sees someone open he'll get the ball there. He's also very unselfish. On every play, no matter who scores, he handles the ball at least one time. He makes them happen."

Walt Frazier said, "He's the spark, the life of the team. He's a forward who is the quarterback of this team, and that's never been done before. He has developed great consistency. In the past he's been great in games in spurts, but lately I've noticed he has been great all the way."

Barry's 25-footers, spinning lefthanded hooks, lefthanded drives, twisting two-handed scoops forced Phil Jackson, another of the Knicks who tried to stop

Barry, to remark, "It takes great timing to run plays down to perfection like he does. A ballplayer like Bob McAdoo (of the Buffalo Braves) eventually comes right down at you, where Barry would catch the ball and shoot in one mid-air motion.

"He has the ability to communicate with just his eyes, and he has the ability to see how his man is playing him and when to make the correct break. It's pretty difficult to stop him because he can get the ball just about anytime he wants."

And, from Red Holzman, the Knick coach, "Barry knows how to set his man up for what he wants to do. He's a very smart player and when he gets the ball he can cash in. That's the thing."

In the Warrior dressing room, as newspaper men crowded around Barry, his young teammates sat by themselves and watched the attention being given Rick. Did they resent it? No way. He was their leader in every respect—on the court and off, and they said so.

"I see Rick giving 100 per cent," said Cliff Ray, "and I say to myself that if he can do it, so can I."

Ray recalled how he was traded from Chicago and arrived in Oakland without furniture.

"I didn't have a TV set or anything," he said. "Rick offered me his stereo and Butch Beard, his TV. There are always two or three guys together. Never anyone alone. If Rick and Jeff Mullins are going out, they ask the other guys if they want to come along. I've never seen anything like this."

If the young Warriors enjoyed Rick, he enjoys them even more.

"This is the way basketball is supposed to be," said

Barry. "It is supposed to be fun and it has been, because everyone has been pulling together playing as a team."

Barry and Mullins were the only white players on the team. Thrown together as much as the 12 are, race is treated in what outsiders might regard as an indelicate manner.

"On a plane trip a stewardess asked, 'What team is this?'" Barry recalled. "I told her, 'The Harlem Globetrotters plus two.' Then Cliff Ray spoke up and said, 'Yeah, the only reason we brought these two along is so we could be accepted.'

"I think the fact we can kid each other and not worry about it is great. Let me add this: My contract calls for me to have a single hotel room and most of the guys on the club room alone. It's probably best. One guy wants the room warm, another cool. You might need two TVs to keep them happy. But if I had to have a roommate, I'd want it to be Clifford Ray."

Being a tough competitor, Barry plays hard against every team, but somehow it appears he saves his best for the Knicks. It's almost as if it was a personal vendetta. With his every drive to the basket, long jumper or rebound, Barry reminds all that once, more than anything, he wanted to play for the Knicks.

After all, he had grown up across the river from Madison Square Garden, and his father, his first coach, had once played basketball with Eddie Donovan, the Knicks' general manager.

Barry had played the Garden three times during his

college career, twice in the National Invitation Tournament.

"During the quarter-final round of the 1962-63 N.I.T. against Providence," recalled Barry, "we were losing by 18 points with five minutes remaining in the game. But we made a remarkable comeback and cut the Providence lead to four with a minute and a half to go.

"Ray Flynn of Providence, later voted the tournament's most valuable player, had the ball and we had him cornered. He dribbled the ball off his foot and I picked it off and was driving for a layup when I heard a whistle. When I was charged with a foul, my fifth, in utter disgust I lost my temper and heaved the ball against the rim.

"The referee called a technical foul on me, and you might say it was another good lesson in the education of Rick Barry. Providence won the game, 106-96.

"Later I read where Ned Irish (then president of Madison Square Garden and the Knicks) said I was 'flaky'. He hadn't even met me, but judged me on this one moment of anger."

To this day Barry firmly believes the incident was responsible for the Knicks not picking him in the 1964-65 college draft.

"Rick has always been largely misunderstood," said Bob Green, a 6-0 guard for the U. of Miami Hurricanes and Barry's roommate at Miami for two years. "He is so intense that he is hard to like at first. The first impression is rarely a good one because you have to have time to get into his shell. What people forget is that Rick was very, very young in college. He started when he was 16, so he was at least a year younger than everybody and that had a bad psychological effect.

"To get attention, he had to excel in something, do something to be different and that's why he became so competitive. He's the most competitive person I've ever known, in athletics, academics or whatever he was doing. He's really a self-made man. He wasn't too big to ask somebody for help, but whatever challenge he met he was going to work out himself.

"I know he has been criticized by a lot of people, but they don't know him. I'll say this, I have never seen him refuse an autograph, either when he was at Miami or since he turned pro. He came to our house in Vincennes, Ind., to visit after they won the championship and everywhere we went kids were around him and he signed autographs. He always had time, or took time. He's really a warm and sincere person when you get to know him."

What Green said showed up during the 1974-75 season when he did everything asked of him in leading the Warriors to the NBA championship.

In fact at Christmastime, he did something that wasn't asked of him—he played the unfamiliar role of Santa Claus.

Carrying out an idea he helped formulate, he visited underprivileged children in the Bay area.

Accompanied by his wife, Pam, Rick brought gifts to youngsters who ordinarily would not have had them.

"It was an idea I've had for a while," Barry said at the time. "I was sitting around one night with a neighbor at Lake Tahoe, and we started discussing the idea. We got an Oakland restaurateur involved in the idea and it blossomed."

With the help of Pam, who did much of the leg work, and many of his Warrior teammates, Rick solicited funds from many of his rich friends, in addition to his own contributions.

Then Rick contacted a manufacturer who sold him the toys at a discount, and while the Warriors were on the road, Pam, in the family station wagon, gathered up the toys and had them all ready for Rick and some of his teammates, who helped him play Santa Claus.

"I know how much Christmas meant to me when I was a kid," said Rick. "And I figured these kids wouldn't have much of a Christmas without presents.

"To me, there's nothing more enjoyable than giving a person something when he doesn't expect it. There really isn't much I can get for my family, and everything I need I can go out and buy. But there are so many people, particularly young people, who don't have much. And when they get something, their surprise and happiness is really rewarding."

That he conceived the idea and carried out the entire operation without any thought of publicity, was a further indication of a new, happy Rick Barry.

Almost four months later, Barry would play Santa Claus again, this time for all the Bay Area, leading the Happy Warriors in the playoff series against the Seattle SuperSonics, then the Chicago Bulls and finally against the Washington Bullets.

When Rick Barry plays his game, there's nothing

the other side can do. That was never demonstrated any more clearly than on Monday, April 14, in Oakland when the Warriors, looking for Barry every time they had the ball, rolled over the Seattle Supersonics 123-96, in the opening game of the Western Division semi-final series.

Barry scored 39 points and there was no question he might have collected at least a half a dozen more. But with Golden State ahead by 30 points, Al Attles took him out of the game midway through the final period.

"With a big lead, there was nothing to be gained by wearing Rick out," said Attles. "He did his job. It was just another one of his outstanding games. He is such a great player and a big help to all those around him."

Barry didn't spend his entire evening gunning for the basket. While he had many opportunities to shoot, he passed off enough to throw Seattle's defense off stride and finish the game with a high of 11 assists and 8 steals.

Barry was proud of his performance but he gave credit all around.

"It may have looked like a one-man show, but it was far from that," he said. "We won the game on defense as much as we did on offense. We cut them off inside and made them shoot outside and you don't win NBA games that way."

This was just one of the many times that Barry had credited his teammates with a helping hand.

"There are a super group of guys on this team," said Barry. "Players who put the team ahead of self. I think basketball is the epitome of team sport anyhow, and we've got players now who complement one another for the sake of the team."

Bill Russell, the Seattle coach, had locked his dressing room door for more than 15 minutes afer the game but later said it was not to berate his players.

"Our meeting," Russell said with a smile, "was an intellectual dissertation. The boys felt bad enough about losing without my having to chew them out. Obviously, we didn't play good defense and we had virtually no rebounding. It's tough to win games that way, but we'll come back. I've been in enough play-offs where we lost the first game and came back."

Russell was correct. The Sonics won the second of the four-of-seven-game series, 100-99, and play moved from the friendly confines of the Oakland Coliseum Arena to hostile Seattle territory.

Barry figured the odds were against him in Seattle, but nothing he couldn't handle: something like 14,-000-to-1.

"I spoiled 14,000 people's evening," Barry gloated after he led the 105-96 Warrior triumph with a 33-point effort. "You can't let the fans bother you. If anything, it gives you more incentive."

After the physical first 15 minutes, in which four fights almost erupted, Russell said, "I guess everybody was going to establish that no one was going to be pushed around. I guess we got that established."

The Warrior coach used the word "intensity" to describe the game.

Russell promised adjustments for the fourth game

and when he asked what those would be, he answered with a sly grin, "That's for the next game.

Russell must have made the correct adjustments because the Sonics triumphed and the series returned to Oakland for the fifth game, which the Warriors won easily, 124-100.

With George Johnson, the reserve center, replacing the foul-plagued Cliff Ray, and playing the best game of his career, the Warriors clinched the series.

There was no celebrating after the Warrior victory in which Johnson scored 18 points, hitting on 8 of 10 from the floor, grabbing 15 rebounds and blocking 8 shots. A number of Seattle partisans turned on the Warriors after the game. Attles, his assistant, Joe Roberts, and several players were kept on the court while police tried to clear the corridor leading to the dressing room.

"This is basketball?" fumed Rick Barry, who was the game's high scorer with 31 points. "What do these fans think it is, a soccer game in South America?"

Barry was hit by a woman and also doused with beer and soft drinks as he tried to get to the dressing room.

"As I was going out, somebody tripped and hit me with something," said Barry, who nursed cuts on both knees. "When I turned around, I couldn't believe it was a woman. I grabbed her jacket and pushed her away. If it wasn't a lady, I would have swung. It's bad enough to be hit by a guy, but a lady? That's ridiculous."

Attles, who got into a scuffle with a fan, said, "It's unfortunate a great effort by the Sonics has to end like this. It puts a black eye on the league when a few fans do something like this. The fans should be above it."

The next Warrior stop in their trip to Fantasy Land was against the big, strong Chicago Bulls, who had ousted the Kansas City—Omaha Kings, 4 games to 2, in their Western Conference semi-final.

The Bulls also had the misfortune to wrap up their semi-final series on the road. Late in the final game at Kansas City, the Chicago players were targets for fans throwing ice, cans and even a pair of shoes. They started into the stands after one particularly rowdy heckler.

"We don't care who we play now," said Bulls' coach Dick Motta, "We're the best team in pro basketball."

The Bulls, the Midwest Division champion, had beaten the Warriors in three of the four regular season meetings, but Golden State took a chance and elected to play the first game at home and the next two in Chicago.

The Bulls, who thrive on defense and led the league in that department, limited their opposition to 95 points a game. But in the opener, it was the Warriors who were the defensive experts with an easy, 107-89, triumph.

"They were great," said Jerry Sloan, the Chicago guard, "They forced us into mistakes we usually don't make."

Motta added, "They outshot us, outrebounded us and outhustled us. It was like a high school team against a college team."

Individually, the show belonged to Rick Barry, who not only lives with pressure, but thrives on it and Bob

Love, who was a Warrior nemesis during the regular season with a 32 point average.

"Pressure is something you create if you think about it," said Barry after his 38-point performance. "There is no pressure if you go out and play the game and do what you are supposed to. If you don't think of pressure, this game was no different than any others."

Love, who scored 37 points, collecting 14 of the Bulls 15 second quarter points, said, "I always get charged up when we play on the coast. It's also a big lift to play against someone like Rick. You don't want to be embarrassed by a guy like Rick, so you work harder."

For the first time in the playoffs, the young Warriors got their own taste of pressure, as the Bulls won the next two games. In the third game Golden State overcame an 11-point deficit to win, 108-101, but when the series resumed in Oakland, the Bulls were doomed. The Golden State comeback was even more incredible, since the Bulls had bolted to a 35-18 lead after the first quarter and increased their margin to 19 points early in the second quarter.

It was now the time for Rick Barry, the Knight in Shining Armor, to ride in and undo all the Warrior wrongs, and he did. Barry scored 26 of his game-high 36 points in the second half.

"It was done on hustle, guts and determination," Barry said after the 111–106, victory. "We can all be proud. We didn't fold when we could have. When we got behind that much I was concerned to say the least. I was playing lousy and couldn't hit my shots.

But then Bill Bridges came in and gave us a lift by working his tail off."

As Golden State lost for the third and final time in the fifth game, an 89–79 defensive struggle, it became more evident that as Barry goes, so go the Warriors. In the three losses Barry had been held to 26, 21 and 20 points, connecting on just 38 per cent of his shots from the floor.

"If I'm shooting well and others are having difficulties," he said, "we seem to be better off then if I'm shooting poorly and the others are shooting well."

The Warriors went into the sixth game knowing that if they didn't come out blazing they would go on vacation until October.

The Warriors tied the series with an 86–72 victory as Barry was back to his old self. To go with his 36 points, there were six steals and two assists. Five of the steals came in the first half when he scored 20 points, and he added an assist, a steal and a blocked shot to go with 16 second-half points.

But this time, Barry was a firebrand from start to finish. His 12 points in the second quarter ignited a Warrior spurt which erased an early 25–18 deficit and moved them to a 46–38 halftime advantage.

"For the first time in six games," explained Barry, "the Bulls had to play Warrior basketball. That means we run and they can't set up their defense. Our defense was so good that by default, I fell into it. I don't think I played any different on offense, but my shots were going in this time. When I'm shooting well, it worries them and they have to do other things defensively."

Barry, who sent only two of his first 15 shots, turned from bad to good, in time to lead an 83–79 victory and give the Warriors a berth in the final against the Washington Bullets who had eliminated the Boston Celtics, the defending champions, in a six-game series.

"I made up my mind when I was sitting on the bench," said Barry. "Those guys were looking for me to help."

Help he did. He scored 14 points in the final quarter and finished with 22.

Before the series with the Bullets began, the prognosticators, who had picked Golden State for a fourth place finish before the start of the season, were at it again. This time they were saying Golden State would be target practice for Washington, a powerful, deep team.

The team that didn't know how to die, came back three times during the four-game sweep, erasing Bullet leads of 13 points or more. Only in game three did Golden State establish itself early, but Butch Beard, who has since been traded to the Cleveland Cavaliers, said at the time, "That was the trademark of our team. We were down in quite a few games this season, but we held together through adversity. We win it together or lose it together. This is a team with a lot of courage."

Washington had gambled on the playoff schedule, but it didn't seem to matter. The original setup called for the first two games to be played on the Bullets' home court, the next two in Oakland and the remaining games to be alternated. Then it was discovered that the Ice Follies had been previously booked to play the Coliseum.

Who had expected the Warriors still to be playing basketball in May?

Franklin Mieuli had the answer after this team had won the opener, 101–95. "Like Phoenix," he said, "we have risen from the ashes."

With Barry scoring 36 points, Golden State rushed back from a 13-point deficit and won the second game, 92–91, as Washington missed two shots in the final six seconds. The Warriors made it 3-0, by winning, 109–101.

Toward the end of the third game, the Bullets, whose coach, K. C. Jones, learned about playoff pressures as a Boston Celtic, looked bad and disorganized. Washington was manhandled by Barry, who got 38 points, and by George Johnson, who came off the bench as Cliff Ray's replacement and added 10 points and grabbed nine rebounds.

Before the fourth game, Wes Unseld of the Washington Bullets, who had won the Atlantic Division title with a 60–22 record, was to say, "It's very important that we get a couple of victories even if we lose the series. We need it for the future. For next year, for our state of mind."

The Warriors had battered the Bullets on the boards and choked off their running game. When someone asked how could the Warriors, who had traded away Nate Thurmond, outrebound a team like Washington which had Wes Unseld, the league's best rebounder, and Elvin Hayes.

Someone remembered that the Warriors had led the league in rebounding.

"We didn't have that one big rebounder," said Al Attles during the off season. "What we had was eight guys getting eight rebounds each. Sometimes I think when you have that one big rebounder, everyone else has a tendency to stand around."

Much of the come-from-behind success may, in the ultimate, be credited to the tactics developed by Al Attles in the early days of the regular season.

Attles sent his troops in waves at the Bullets and outhustled and outscrambled them.

"We went at them 12 different ways," said Attles. "They didn't know who was going to do what, or what to expect from whom."

While Attles was making use of all his players, K. C. Jones primarily countered with six. And the sixth man, Nick Weatherspoon, a forward, after a torrid 59 per cent floor shooting against Buffalo and Boston in the earlier playoff rounds, failed to hit even 20 per cent in the final. In the first three games Warrior reserves outscored the Bullet reserves, 115–53.

"If you expect people to play for you in the playoffs," Attles said, "you have to play them in some critical spots during the season and hope they're ready. They have to be ready mentally, and fundamentals are important to this sport. That's not something you can turn on like a water faucet.

"The lack of recognition given some of the players, and the team as a whole, bothered me. People tended to overlook them completely, but I'm not going to argue about what people think."

Why should he, or any of the Golden State Warriors be concerned? They earned $110,000 for beating
the Bullets and divided $330,500 in playoff money,
not bad for a team that was ridiculed before the season began.

And during the summer when Barry, the celebrity,
wasn't making money, he had time to reflect on that
championship season.

"After we beat the Bullets in the first two games, I
could see it begin to happen," he said. "Our guys began to get that dazed look in their eyes. The Bullets'
faces went from expressions of smug confidence to
masks of fear and disbelief.

"I recently got a chance to watch for the first time
some game films of the fourth and final game with
Washington. Looking back on it now, it seems like a
case of destiny. Wes Unseld gets a rebound and for no
reason it bounces off his knee out of bounds. Dick
Gibbs misses an uncontested lay-in and we win the
game. Fate played a major role," and with a smile and
a pause he added, "as did the coaching of Al Attles."

Chapter Three

After having achieved his last major basketball goal, the NBA championship, Barry reached a new high in national popularity. Since his rookie debut in 1965, he had been the NBA rookie of the year, the only player ever to win scoring championships in both the NBA and ABA, most valuable player in an NBA All-Star game, and had played with championship teams with both leagues.

But none of these honors had brought Barry the new image and the financial opportunities made available after the Golden State Warriors' fairy-tale season of 1975.

Muscle, speed and intelligence may have accounted for Rick's transformation on the basketball court. But that infectious smile, his good looks that make women palpitate, and his self confidence, coupled with his banner season, opened the door to a flood of endorse-

ments, celebrity events, and radio and television appearances like never before. He became, in fact, a
celebrity to celebrities.

He joined the elite group of high-priced, commercially sought athletes that is usually dominated by
New York based players such as Joe Namath, Catfish
Hunter and Walt Frazier. Few athletes have ever
reached that commercial plateau without the help of
the New York media.

While he is happy to be back in the Bay Area
where he started, Barry looks to Madison Avenue for
his future. The cheers that he draws in the 18 NBA
franchise cities reverberate back to Madison Avenue,
and as Walt Frazier of the New York Knicks once
said, "Money, that's what New York means: money,
endorsements, commercials.

"But it isn't for everybody. You have to have this
bit of charisma, like Catfish, Namath and myself.
People have to take to you."

They have taken to Rick Barry.

At the height of Barry's most popular summer, he
was drawing choice sportscasting assignments, was
making the rounds of network TV celebrity shows,
and was making commercials. He also hinted at retirement, but quickly dispelled that idea.

"Nobody knows," said his mother in Roselle Park,
N.J., one August afternoon. She was sitting in her living room waiting for Rick and Pam to appear as guest
contestants on CBS-TV's Tattletales game show.

"You never know what he'll do next," she said. "He
gave us that TV set for Christmas and he didn't say
anything about it. They just delivered it one day

about two months before Christmas and I almost sent them away. They called the store to see if they had the address right and said this is where it goes. That's the way Rick is, full of surprises."

She looked at the magnificent new Motorola color set as her son appeared on the screen. "You see, they ask Pam a question but Rick can't hear the answer. Then they ask Rick the same question and if their answers are the same, they win." She listened as Bert Convy, the show's host, introduced Rick, ". . . and from the NBA champion Golden State Warriors," Convy said, "Rick Barry, and his lovely wife, Pam."

"Look at his nose," said Rick's mother. "It's crooked. Broken playing ball. He's had so many injuries. I don't see how he's taken them. You should see him after games some times. Scratches all over him. Welts and bruises. I can't sleep some nights when I know he's playing. I toss and turn sometimes till 2 or 3 in the morning. I always said that when he retires it will be the happiest day of my life. They make it rough for you when you're on top, and he's so injury prone." She turned back to the TV as Convy asked Pam the first question:

"Here's the situation," said Convy. "Rick is watching television and it goes on the blink. He kicks it and it works again. Later it goes on the blink again, and again he kicks it to make it work. It happens once an hour for four hours. The question is, what would Rick do? Continue kicking it as long as it worked, or would he call a TV repairman?"

Pam studied. "I think he would tell me to call a repairman." she said.

"Pam's right," said Rick's mother. "That's exactly what he would do. He's such a perfectionist. I'm that way and his dad's that way, too. If I'm knitting something and I make a mistake, I'll rip it out 16 times if I have to, to get it right. It hurts to know somebody can do something better than you. That's the way we all are. An apple doesn't fall far from the tree, you know."

"What would you do, Rick," Convy asked, "continue kicking the TV or call a repairman?"

"Well," said Rick, "since my motto is don't do anything today that you can put off until tomorrow, I guess I'd keep kicking it."

"Oh, you would not," Pam said in surprise. "I can't believe you said that."

"Riiiick," said his mother as if she were scolding a child. "Oh, Rick, you know you're not that way."

She was silent a moment, then said, "He called us when they were on this show and told us they didn't do very well. This is on tape, you know. He calls us now and then just to see how everybody is.

"Of course, we don't see him much, but that's the way it is with everybody when they grow up and get their own family. We go see him play when he's playing in New York or Philadelphia, but he's so busy, so involved . . ."

Convy was asking Pam another question on TV: "Which came first in your relationship, friendship or love?"

"Well," said Pam, "It wasn't either, really. I didn't like him at first, so I guess the answer would have to be friendship. It sure wasn't love."

"He'll get that right," said Rick's mother. "He knows she hated him at first because he was pesty to her, treated her like a little girl. He was a freshman at Miami and she was still in high school, you know. He was 16 or 17 and she was about 15. He says he didn't like her. His brother, Dennis, was the one who introduced them. Well, not introduced exactly, but he was the one who got him interested. He kept telling Rick he was crazy. 'Have you looked at her, Rick?' he kept asking him. "Have you really stopped to look at her?' So he must have looked at her and liked what he saw." Rick's mother laughed about it and waited for Rick's TV answer.

"It would definitely have to be friendship," he said, "because she hated me when we first met."

"Rick didn't date much when he was in high school," said his mother as the show broke for a commercial. "There was just one girl he saw very much. He took her to the prom and sometimes they would go dancing down at the high school, a place they called the Rec. You know, pay 25 cents and then they would dance to records or sometimes they would have a band.

"But he never brought a girl home, not as long as he was in high school, I guess. He was mostly playing sports, something all the time. And anything he did, he had to be better than anybody else, no matter what.

"You ever hear of tetherball? He was the tetherball champion of Union County. Always something. Of course, he had things he had to do around the house because I was working. He washed dishes, carried out

the garbage and kept his room clean, made beds. He
was pretty good about it but he hated washing dishes.
He always said he wouldn't wash another dish once
he got out on his own. Always said he'd be rich someday. We were at the table one night and he said, 'I
don't know how I'm going to do it, but one day I'm
going to be rich.' Of course, we didn't think anything
about it. All kids think that. We were just as shocked
as anybody by his success.

"He didn't have much extra money growing up. He
would shovel snow and things like that for extra
money. We gave the boys an allowance every week,
but it wasn't much. I don't think it was as much as a
dollar. Dad didn't have much of a job then and things
were tight, but he never complained. But even then
he had expensive tastes. He liked only imported ham
and cheese, and he could tell the difference, too. One
day we were having ham bologna and he said, 'Hey,
this isn't imported.' He could tell the difference. He
always wanted the best.

"Ever since he was old enough to understand us
we tried to have both make their own decisions and
he has always said what he thinks. I remember when
he was going to college, we didn't want him to go to
the University of Miami because it was so far away,
but he said if he couldn't go to Miami, he wouldn't go
anywhere. He had met Coach Hale and he liked him
and he said it was going to be four years and he
wanted it to be with somebody he liked. So he went
to Miami. His decision.

"It was the same way with all the trouble about
jumping leagues. He never discussed it with us or

asked for advice. He said, 'You brought me up teaching me to make my own decisions.' So he made them himself. I was angry at the beginning the way it was turning out, his deal with Pat Boone. But I guess it's the same with Pat Boone or anybody. Business is business. It always seems to turn out all right, I guess."

She turned back to the TV show as Convy asked a final question. This time Rick was to answer first.

"Which would Pam consider more important," Convy asked, "your approval or your love?"

"I hope Pam listens carefully to this question," Rick said, "because I hope it would be love."

"Which would it be," Convy turned to Pam, "his approval or his love?"

"Well," said Pam, "I live just for him, so I would guess it would have to be his approval. Yes, I would say his approval."

The Barrys lost and Rick's mother shook her head. "Pam should know better," she said, hating the defeat. She turned off the television. "It was strange seeing him on television for awhile, but you get used to it. He's a celebrity, but it hasn't changed him, and it hasn't changed my life. The only thing is that a lot of people ask me for pictures of him. I keep a stack of his autographed pictures and when I run out he sends me some more. And whenever he calls he always asks us to tell everybody here hello for him. He keeps in touch with home."

The basketball education, drive and motivation for Richard Francis Barry III, born March 28, 1944, began when he was five years old, two blocks from his

home, in the Sts. Peter and Paul gymnasium, and at
Brophy Field, next to Public School 13 in Elizabeth,
New Jersey.

"Don't bounce the ball until you're ready to go
somewhere with it," Rick's father would shout while
he worked with Rick and his brother, Dennis, who
was four years older. "Use the right pass: chest pass,
bounce pass, overhead pass. Hit the open man . . ."

From these words emerged one of the finest front
court talents in basketball. Rick was a high school
standout at Rozelle Park, N.J., and became the nation's leading scorer at Miami (Fla.) University before joining the pro ranks in 1965.

Richard Francis Barry, II, his father, was by far the
greatest influence on Rick's life. A phone company su-
perintendent, Rick's father didn't superintend phones
all day. He played semi-pro basketball for local club
teams and coached Rick's parochial grammar school
basketball team. In the evenings he practiced basketball with his sons; on weekends it was more basketball practice with his sons and at the supper table the
three males of the family would sit and talk continu-
ously of basketball.

"My mother had to tolerate it all," Barry has said.
"She did not understand the game."

At the Plaza Hotel in New York, a few days after
Barry had been named the NBA's most valuable
player of the 1975 playoffs, his father stood in the
background while Rick was being surrounded by
hundreds of people—advertising executives, television
crews and newsmen, photographers and autograph
seekers.

"He's come a long way, hasn't he?" said the elder Barry as Pam nodded agreement.

At that moment, Mr. Barry's thoughts must have wandered back to those early days in New Jersey when he, too, had wanted to become a basketball star, but had no help.

Basketball had dominated the elder Barry's life from the day he went out for basketball in junior high, was laughed at and eventually cut from the squad. He made two vows after that sad experience. He vowed to learn the game and he vowed that if God ever blessed him with children, he would teach them the things he had been denied.

He learned basketball wherever he could, with whatever pickup team would have him—YMCA, Jewish, Polish, Spanish, Italian—because his funloving father had no interest and no time for him.

He was quite pleased at having two sons and promised himself to be a good father, not like his own, who never saw him play a single game in any athletic event.

Rick practically learned to dribble as he learned to walk and the learning never really stopped.

"My father was a strict fundamentalist and disciplinarian," Barry recalled. "He is responsible for my being a perfectionist. He was one, and he drilled the fundamentals of the game into me. He made sure I knew how to dribble without looking at the ball, how to pass and how to run backwards."

Barry has always insisted that basketball was never forced on him.

"I would always get interested first," recalled Barry.

"I would ask my father to show me, and he would. Take the way I shoot free throws. He taught me to shoot them underhand. He never forced me to do it that way. He just would say, 'I'd like you to try it this way,' and he'd shoot fouls underhand.

"Dad wouldn't let me shoot that way until my hands were large enough to get over the top of the ball. He asked me to give it a good honest effort, and then if I didn't feel it was better I could go back to the overhand way. I tried it and it worked. There is nothing exaggerated to the shot. Just a gentle flick of the wrist. It's a very relaxed shot, a very soft shot that can hit the rim and still bounce in. To this day I think I'm a better free throw shooter because I shoot underhand.

"I know a lot of the older fans enjoy seeing me use it. It brings back memories for them."

Barry is the only consistent underhand free throw shooter in the league, and he takes great pride in being one of the best in all of pro basketball.

"I try to make about 90 per cent of my free throws," said Barry. "It's the only goal I've ever set for myself. After all, it's the same distance each time, the same shot and there is nobody there to bother you. That's why I get so upset when I miss even one.

"I'm surprised more players don't use the underhand method, I think it could revolutionize free throw shooting. Part of the problem, I guess, is proper instruction. Coaches are getting younger and younger. They never shot that way so they wouldn't be able to teach it."

When Bill Sharman coached Barry during his second pro season in San Francisco, they had a personal duel going that Rick once described as "the battle for the world's free throw shooting title."

As opposed to Barry's underhand shooting, Sharman shot the more popular one-handed, over-the-head way. His credentials were as good as Barry's when he played for the Boston Celtics. He led the NBA in free throw shooting for seven seasons and left behind an 88.3 percentage career mark.

"We really had some real free throw shooting contests before and after our practice sessions," remembered Barry. "We would start out shooting 10 each, but usually we had to shoot more because both of us would make all 10. I guess we each won the same number of times, but then we would try shooting with our eyes closed, and I think I had a big advantage there."

Barry's home-bred basketball education enabled him to make the parochial school team that included seventh and eight graders and one fifth grader. The fifth grader was, of course, Rick Barry.

It was not easy for Barry to cope with having to play against older and stronger youngsters.

"My father would take me out of the game," Barry said, "if I made an error on the court. After a while I got so that I tried never to make an error on the court. Nobody likes to be taken out of the game."

So was born Rick Barry, the perfectionist, son of perfectionist parents. It has stuck with Barry all his life.

"He was the most disciplined person I have ever known when we were growing up," said Arthur

Smith, Barry's closest friend at Roselle Park High School. "We did a lot of bowling, playing miniature golf and things like that in the summertime, but no matter where we were going, he would practice basketball first. Basketball always came first. When that was done, then he would have his good time.

"He was fiercely competitive, but more so with himself than with any of us. I remember when we bowled he would loft the ball halfway down the alley and get furious if he didn't get a strike. He had to keep beating his own records, especially in basketball."

Challenges make up Rick's life. Everything is a contest with him. He drives his sports cars like he's on a fast break. In 1969 when Barry was leaving Oakland to join the Washington Capitals, he drove across the Nevada desert at a 150 mile-an-hour clip while Pam held the baby and looked out the rear window as if she were expecting to see someone gaining on them.

"Even when he eats," Bill Sharman noticed when they were on road trips in Rick's early days with the Warriors. "it is a contest to see who finishes first. He checks into the airport first when we're traveling, and is the first one to get his hotel key. He has to be first."

The challenges may have begun even before he started to tag after his brother Dennis to play ball with the older kids. Rick was enrolled in school when he was four years old, and he says with a laugh, "My mother wanted to get rid of me. The idea was, if I did well in the first grade, they would keep me in school. If not, I'd stay out a year." He got good grades and stayed in school, and that's when he started competing against older kids. He never stopped.

Challenges beget pressures, and not all the excitement of a kid's basketball court can dissipate them all. Pressures beget hostilities, and as a kid in New Jersey, Rick had more than his share of fights.

"One kid, his name was George [Zalinsky, his next-door neighbor in Elizabeth], galled me," Rick recalls. "He would talk about a friend of my brother's in a mean way. It would kill me. I'd tell him to shut up and he'd call me a big baby, and I'd hit him. We had lots of fights. If George walked in right now, I'd hit him.

"George wasn't the only one. One kid had a dirty mouth," Rick remembers. "He called everybody dirty names. He got my best friend in trouble because of the things he said about him. I got into a fight with this kid. He tried to run away, but I caught him and threw him down, and I was yelling, 'Stop saying that! Stop saying that!' He hit me in the stomach. I tried to pull away, and my stomach—the skin of my stomach—stretched out this far. I started to pound his head against the sidewalk. Finally my brother saw what was happening, and he pulled me off the kid before I killed him. That was the worst. Something got into me, and I couldn't stop."

Rick's mother didn't know about all his boyhood fighting until his book was published in 1972.

"A mother has no way of knowing everything her

son does," she said. "I didn't always know who he was with or what he was doing. How could I? But if my son fights somebody, then that somebody has done something to him, because Rick never went looking for a fight."

Although Rick's heavy schedule prevents him from seeing his family often, the Barrys still are close. Mrs. Barry, who was born Alpha Monique Stephanovich, went to Rick's house to stay through the 1975 championship series while her husband went to the games in person. Dennis, once a teacher but now a mortgage banker in Miami, vacationed with Rick before the start of the 1976 season.

Everything Dennis did, Rick wanted to do, and from the time Rick was 5 years old, he tagged after Dennis. "He didn't chase me," said Rick. "I played basketball with him and his friends. I guess I could keep up with him because I was much taller than kids my own age."

"Dennis was an unusual brother," said Rick's mother. "Most older brothers don't want a little brother tagging along, but Dennis encouraged it. So I guess Rick was always with older boys. It was a help, too, because I worked and Dennis was good about looking after him."

Dennis, who grew to a handsome 6-3, became a standout basketball player in high school, but a knee injury prevented his playing at St. Mary's College after a few games.

It was Dennis who kept Rick straight when the influence of older boys sometimes threatened to change

Rick's lifestyle. Before the family moved to Roselle Park, Rick began running around with a group of loosely disciplined friends in Elizabeth Park and before long Rick was smoking—at age 12.

One day Dennis drove by a neighborhood youth hangout and spotted Rick playing a pinball machine, a cigarette dangling from his lips.

"I stopped the car, ran in and slapped the cigarette out of his mouth," said Dennis in Rick's book, with Bill Libby, *Confession of a Basketball Gypsy*. "Then I dragged him out to the car and drove off.

"Look, you dumb cluck," Dennis yelled. "I may be smoking but I'm nothing. You've got everything ahead of you. If I ever catch you hanging around joints like that smoking and killing your wind, I'll kick your tail all around the block."

Rick gave up smoking.

Not everyone could keep Rick's energy contained all the time, however.

At the Polo Grounds once, Rick jumped over the wall from the stands and ran on the field to shake the hand of Willie Mays as Mays was walking out toward the center-field clubhouse.

When Rick went home that night Dennis said something about having seen some thoughtless kid running on the field to shake May's hand on television. Rick never told on himself until years later because he had cut school to go to the game.

Barry idolized Mays throughout his boyhood and from the time he was a junior in high school, he wore Willie's number 24, the number he wore in college and in every pro city since. Ironically, Mays was playing center field in San Francisco when Barry arrived as an NBA rookie in 1965 and they shook hands a second time.

Chapter Four

Barry began to flirt with stardom in his junior year at Roselle Park High, although he was less than happy. "I almost quit basketball," he recalls. "I hated my high school coach. That man did nothing for me. After a game, or a practice, I'd go home and I'd want to cry. He had no idea how to handle players. He made life miserable for everybody on the squad. One day he didn't like the way we practiced, so in the next game he started the substitutes. We were losing by 31 points when he finally sent in the first team. We cut it to one point, but we lost. He was later fired."

The coach, Tom Murtha, was young and had been schooled under the old "be tough" coaching philosophy, and although Barry didn't like him, Murtha's discipline demands probably helped the developing star. Murtha's primary concern was the team, however, not Barry's development.

Today, Murtha lives in Wanamasa, N.J., and is coaching at Monmouth College.

Perry Preckwinkle, now a contractor in Roselle Park, was captain of the high school team Rick's senior year. "We all felt pretty much the same way about the coach," he said. "He had a temper and was stubborn. There would be games when we would do something wrong and he would take the whole team out and we'd end up losing by 1 or 2 points. He was so stubborn that if something didn't work, he'd just keep trying it and telling us, 'We're going to keep doing it until we get it right.' We didn't have that bad of a team, but we had a mediocre record—about 13-12 or something like that.

"Once we did something in a game, I think, or at practice, and he didn't like it so he started the junior varsity to punish us. Then he put the first team in when we were way behind and we lost by a point or two."

Preckwinkle was a 6-1 guard and remembers how he used to watch Rick move around the basket to get open. "I'm not trying to pat myself on the shoulder or anything," he said, "but we had a play going that just happened without anybody signaling or anything.

"I'd be way out at the key and he'd make a move and I'd loft the ball right up to the rim and he'd go up, the timing was just right. I got just as much of a kick out of that as I did from scoring a basket.

"Rick was our center, but he wasn't a pivot center. He'd rove out and shoot from the corners. He was a good ballplayer in high school, better than average, but he really matured in college. I saw him play in the N.I.T. when he was a sophomore at Miami and I could really see a great change in him. I knew right then that he would be a pro. We were seniors together, but he was a year younger and he did a lot of growing up in college. But even in high school he had great reflexes and he always seemed to be in the right place at the right time. People call it garbage points, but that's just being where the ball is, and that's what the game is all about. We both had pretty good averages, but his was higher. I averaged about 16 or 17. One game I'd be high and next game he'd be. We weren't really competing but in high school you're always aware of how many you get. But he was the star. Not like in college, but he was the star.

"I knew he'd be a pro. I kid everybody. They say, 'I understand you played basketball with Rick Barry,' and I say, 'No. He played with me. I was the captain and I taught him everything he knows.' They laugh."

Even under the unhappy conditions, Barry began to make his mark that eventually led to stardom. A gawky kid, he grew from 6-1 in his junior to 6-4½ by the time he was a 15-year-old senior. He averaged 16 points as a junior and 28 as a senior and began to draw the attention of the college coaches. Barry has often said that he had a long way to go both as a person and an athlete when he graduated from high school.

"I had talent as a basketball player," Barry said, "but it was not developed by my high school coach, but rather my college coach."

"It wasn't a good basketball team in high school," said Rick's hometown friend, Arthur Smith, "and Rick wasn't THE star. Perry Preckwinkle, the captain, was also a star and there was another good player named Charlie Grob, a 6-9 center from Roselle High, who got most of the headlines in Union County. He later played with Rick at Miami.

"Rick was not real popular in high school. He was somebody who knew he wanted to go on to college, as several of us did, and he didn't necessarily fit in with the common rank of people. But he was friendly, sincere and the finest host. Always when we would go over to his house to watch television, he would bring out these big bowls of potato chips.

"I don't remember him dating but one girl in high school—maybe two or three dates—with Cheryl Boone, and she was a knockout."

Smith, now living in Devon, Pa., keeps in touch with Rick and is one of his biggest fans.

"I see him play whenever he comes to Philadelphia," Smith said, "and everytime he goes home he calls my parents. Whenever anybody asks me about Rick Barry, I tell them he's just like everybody else I know who makes $30,000 a week."

Roselle Park, a commuter town about 30 minutes from New York City, had made a few contributions to history before Barry became famous. Charles E. Stone's Grocery Store on Westfield Avenue, just a few blocks from Rick's house, became the first building in the world to be lighted by electricity. The store was wired by Thomas Edison.

Also, the A&M Karagheusian weaving plant was erected on the site of the Marconi Wireless Station and Eddie Cantor made his first radio broadcast from there.

And there was an athlete who graduated from Roselle Park High ahead of Barry who went on to attain fame in professional football.

His name? Roosevelt (Rosie) Grier.

The high school attended by Grier and Barry is now the Middle School. A new high school, completed in 1963, is in the same general neighborhood, within walking distance of Rick's house.

The Barrys live today where they lived when Rick was at home, in a well kept but modest two-story frame house at 55 West Colfax Avenue in an old established working class neighborhood. Everyone in town (population 14,277) seems to know Rick and it upsets many of them to read that he is from Elizabeth, not Roselle Park.

"Rick was involved in a lot of things when he was here," said his mother. "He was in the scouts for a time, he had the lead in the Christmas play, he was an altar boy when we lived in Elizabeth, delivered the Elizabeth Daily Journal and sold pretzels. And he would rarely buy candy with his money. It was always fruit with him. Every Saturday morning Rick and Dennis would go to the movies. Those were hard times in a way, but they were good times. We had an old Chrysler then, a car we drove for 17 years."

Today, Rick lives in a sprawling two-story house in Alamo, Calif., an Oakland suburb of 14,000 residents, with Pam, four sons and an adopted daughter and he drives a $10,000 De Tomaso Pantera. The children, Rick IV, age 9, Jon Alan, 6, Brent, 3, Drew, 2 and

Shannon Lee, 1, "think their daddy hung the moon," said Rick's mother.

Barry's base salary with the Warriors for the 1975 season was reported to be $218,000 a year, which, he says, does not put him among the top 25 among pro basketball's salaried elite.

Barry received about 40 college scholarship offers, including an alternate appointment to the United States Naval Academy, after his senior season in high school. But Bruce Hale, the coach at the University of Miami, and later to become Rick's father-in-law, heard about Rick from a friend who coached the local parochial high school team. Hale came to Roselle Park, met Barry and his family, and before long, Rick had a grant-in-aid contract in the mail, which he signed without visiting the Miami Campus. It was a surprise to many since the Hurricanes were not and had never been a national basketball power. Rick toyed with the idea of going to Wake Forest, but he discovered, during a campus visit, that the dormitory rooms were very small with two athletes per room "and I have claustrophobia," Rick said.

"Coach Hale seemed interested in me as a player and as an individual," Rick said. "We hit it off right from the start."

In a sense it was the most significant move of his life, and not just because the living facilities at Miami were roomy and pleasant. "Coach Hale put my game together," said Barry. "He helped me get rid of my temper. I used to stew or pout on the court. I would get mad easily if something went wrong or if I thought an official made the wrong call against me.

Defense was non-existent for me. I would never run back on defense. I stopped playing. Coach Hale explained that I had to mature and not be a kid all my life."

Barry's temper had been a source of embarrassment to his family at high school games sometimes and it may have kept him off some all-star teams, although he did make the All-New Jersey team his senior year.

His temper probably kept him from accepting an appointment to the Naval Academy. As he said later, "I'd probably punch someone who told me what to do."

Barry scored 489 points as a freshman at Miami, and while he impressed Coach Hale, he failed to make an impression on his daughter, Pam. He met her soon enough, because Coach Hale frequently had his players visit him at his home, but, as befits a young man who had grown up inculcated with the basic American belief that only toadies play up to the boss's daughter, Rick dunked her in the pool and chased her around. For a year or so Barry and Pam pretended to hate each other. It was only after Barry had secured a berth on the starting five as a sophomore that they began dating. But they were never planned dates.

"Rick used to come over to talk to dad, go for a swim and then, sort of as an afterthought, ask if I wanted to go to a movie," said Pam. "I never thought he really liked me." Her opinion changed one night. As usual, Barry was visiting her father when Pam came out dressed for a date.

"How do I look?" she asked Rick. Fumbling at the thought of her going on such a big date with anyone else, Barry picked her up, tossed her into the pool and answered, "You look wet." It was Pam's last date with anyone other than Rick Barry.

Besides being very young and immature, Barry had developed a complex because of his teeth. "They were like baby teeth," said Perry Preckwinkle, his high school teammate. "Really bad. When he spoke he covered his mouth with his hand and he smiled with his lips together all the time. I rarely saw him laugh. His teeth weren't rotten or anything like that, just real spacy, far apart and it looked bad. Maybe that's why he wasn't in any of the high school cliques. He was pretty much a loner. But not all the time. I would say he was just moody a lot of the time. He just kind of went his own way, but he was very intelligent. Had no trouble with the books and all. The teeth didn't affect his mind."

Perhaps it was because of his parent's financial situation or perhaps he hadn't wanted braces on his teeth to hamper his basketball, but he never asked to have the teeth fixed until Pam suggested it.

Pam was about ready to break up with Rick when he returned to campus for his senior year with beautiful straight, white teeth.

"Maybe it's wrong," said Pam, "but I'll have to admit my feelings changed toward him after he got his teeth fixed. I'd been away, and when I came home ready to break up with him, all of a sudden he looked terrific. I mean, he was sun-tanned and had let his hair grow and his mouth was fine and he was beautiful."

Barry scored 455 points as a sophomore, 870 points in his junior year and as a senior he tallied 973 points, an average of 37.4 points a game, tops in the nation. He was selected on every All-American team.

The Hale style of play readied Barry for the pro world in two ways. At almost any other school, Barry, still growing at 6-7, would have played center, his back to the basket. But Miami had a 7-foot center named Mike McCoy, so Barry was a passing, driving forward. Playing facing the basket, Barry began to pile up points and rebounds.

Hale also prepared Barry for the grueling physical side of pro ball. The coach would station himself and a couple of assistant coaches and two or three players between Barry and the basket, toss the ball to Rick and say, "Come on through."

Barry would hurl himself into the sweaty wall of flesh, elbows and knees flying, and drive for the basket. In another exercise, Hale would slap the ball against the backboard. Barry would leap for the rebound as two men, one on each side, smashed into him. Barry learned to handle himself in rough company.

His growth as a player began to show in his junior season when he averaged 32 points and 16 rebounds. He twice scored 50 or more points in a game.

In four years at Miami, Barry never played on a losing team. His freshman team won 18 straight while the varsity was struggling through a 14-12 season, and during his first varsity season, as a sophomore, the Hurricanes won 23 and lost 5, scored 100 or more points six times and received the school's first invitation to the National Invitation Tournament at Madison Square Garden.

As a junior, Barry led Miami to a 20-7 record and another N.I.T. bid, and the Hurricanes scored a season high 134 points in a game against Tampa. Miami had its best team when Barry was a senior. The team had a 22-4 record but was ineligible for the N.I.T. and N.C.A.A. tournaments. The school had been placed on probation because a teammate's father had given a basketball prospect a ride to Miami in his private plane.

Besides his 37.4 point average, Barry also averaged 18 rebounds that year, scored 40 or more points 11 times and 50 or more six times.

George Gallet, sports information director at Miami, said, "Nobody could touch him. He was the greatest thing ever to hit this part of the country, and still is. He was miraculous. There's never been anyone like him before or since."

Miami dropped varsity basketball after the 1970-71 season but Barry's records fill a page in the university's athletic brochure today.

"You can't believe what he did for a school that had never had much of a basketball team," said Gallet. We didn't even have a fieldhouse. We played our games at the Miami Beach Convention Hall, the Miami Beach Auditorium and at a junior college gym. Rick's career high was 59 points against Rollins, which is a school record, and he scored 20 or more points 61 times. Before he came, we were drawing a few hundred fans average and before he left we played many times before packed houses of 6,000 or 7000."

During his senior year, Barry and the Hurricanes played St. John's University at Madison Square Garden. Miami lost by 2 points, but Rick scored 39 points. The late Joe Lapchick, then coaching St. John's, cornered Barry in the corridor and told him, "Young man, you are one of the finest basketball players I've ever seen, and I go back to 1912 in basketball."

Even today, after all Barry has accomplished, he considers that remark the greatest compliment he ever received.

But all was not roses at Miami. He was resented by many of his teammates, he was chastized after a game incident in which he threw a punch and fractured an opponent's cheekbone and he was criticized for shooting so much.

Mike Volkman, a reserve on those Miami teams who has an insurance agency in Evansville, Ind., today, remembers.

"He was awfully young, but a good ballplayer. He was of the superstar mold. He had trouble getting along with the other guys but we all realized that he was far and away the superior athlete. Anything he tried, he'd be good at in a few days—billiards, ping pong, you name it.

"He was very hard to like. We all had our differences with him, you know. It seemed like he got most of the credit for everything, which he probably should have. You know how that goes—leading scorer in the nation and everything. He didn't carouse

around or drink or anything like that. He wasn't one
of the boys. He was interested in making the pros,
whatever it took, and he said that. The rest of us
were just down there playing ball, getting an education and having a good time. I realized I didn't have
the ability he had. If I had, maybe I'd been more like
him.

"Here was a guy who was 6-7 and the quickest man
we had, and we had two quick all-state guards from
Indiana. He could come off the defensive board with
a rebound, dribble the length of the floor and stuff it.
Nobody could keep him from scoring.

"One time we kind of decided to keep the ball
away from him and he still ended up making about
45 points. That was a long time ago. I don't have anything but praise for him now. I was with him at a
party—about six of the old Miami players got together
after the Warriors won the NBA championship—and
he's changed. He's top notch now. I think he was just
young before.

"But we used to get a kick out of the fact that he
wasn't supposed to be treated any different from anybody else, but we noticed him driving the university
basketball car and things like that. We'd give him
some flak about it at practice. At practice sometimes
he'd just quit if he thought everybody else wasn't trying hard. He did pretty much what he wanted to, but
when it came time for him to get it, he was right
there."

During Barry's final season, the night he scored his
2,000th career point, officials stopped the game and
presented him the game ball. The crowd stood to ap-

plaud him, "but not one of his teammates congratulated him," wrote Phil Pepe in the New York Daily News.

"I don't remember that," said Volkman, "but it's probably true. I guess we were just jealous, but he was such an intense person then, he was really hard to like."

Out of that resentment, Barry's image suffered. He was branded a selfish player who cared little for his team, an image that has followed him much of his pro career.

"He didn't deserve that," said Bob Green, his roommate for two seasons at Miami. "If people only knew how hard he worked to get where he is. Gene Seybold, the manager of the team in Miami, became good friends with Rick and he used to open the gym for him at night so Rick could practice alone—two, three hours—after a two hour practice session in the afternoon. I've gone in with him many times at midnight to practice—just the two of us. But if I didn't go, he'd go by himself and stay until he worked some little thing out.

"He got a lot of bad publicity and it wasn't always his fault. I remember one time he was misquoted in a Miami paper. He had told the writer, 'If people come to see me shoot, I'm going to shoot, but we're going to win at the same time.' When it came out in the paper it read, 'People come to see me shoot and I'm going to shoot.' Period. I couldn't believe it."

Green, now general manager of Green Construction Co., a concern owned by his father in Vincennes, Ind., took Barry home with him during two summer breaks in college and Barry worked first as a gardener and general handyman around the Green home and later as a heavy equipment operator on a construction job. "After a hard day's work," Green said, "he would train—jog, sprint or find a place to shoot baskets. He's really a self-made man."

During Barry's junior year, he became involved in a fight with Johnny Erb, who played for Loyola of the South, and it attracted national attention. Erb had been roughing Barry throughout the game and once, when they went up on a jump ball, Erb pushed him in the face and Barry punched him. Erb was carried off the floor unconscious and spent five days in a hospital with a fractured cheekbone.

"He just got tired of it," Green said. "People shoving him, hitting his elbow on shots. But nobody felt worse about it than Rick. He took him a box of candy at the hospital next day not realizing that Erb's jaw was wired. The two of them laughed about the incident. Erb told him to forget it, that it wasn't everybody who could say he had his cheek broke by Rick Barry."

Junior Gee, a 5-10 sophomore guard on the 1965 Miami team, was one of Barry's biggest admirers. He sat in his living room in Loogootee, Ind., and watched Barry and the Warriors on television through the 1975 playoffs. "Those interviews they had with Rick just put cold chills down my back," said Gee, "because I knew the NBA championship was his ultimate goal. I kind of felt I was right there with him.

"But I told my wife, 'you know, I wouldn't be surprised if there were several people sitting at home just like we are watching the ball game hoping that Rick plays bad and that his team loses. Some of his former teammates.' Some of them were envious, you know.

"I would have to say he was disliked by the less dedicated ballplayers and we had a few. But I always thought a lot of him because I was a dedicated athlete myself and I think I understood him more than a lot of guys. I'm sure some of the players were envious of his abilities. I will say that Rick was his own man, so to speak. Being in athletics, you find more self-centered people, I guess, and Rick was a little that way and so was I.

"If people could realize what an athlete goes through, they would be more understanding. Rick was egotistical, but to me that was understandable. I think he is the most dedicated athlete I've ever been associated with. I admired his dedication then and I admire it now."

Gee, now a 30-year-old independent insurance agent in his hometown, said if team members ever tried to keep the ball away from Barry, he wasn't aware of it. "And I doubt that none of us congratulated him the night he went over 2,000 points," he said. "I don't remember specifically, but I'm sure that I would have congratulated him."

The one complaint Gee had with Barry was his attitude at practice. "To be very honest," he said, "Rick practiced when he wanted to. I personally believe that you play the way you practice, but of course, Rick disproved that with his performances. But I used to get a little upset with him for not going 100 per cent in practice, when I knew that I was. But when you're averaging 37.8 points a game and leading the nation, you can do whatever you want to do, I guess. But he's the type of guy you're proud to say, 'I was a teammate of Rick Barry.' And I am proud."

There was other disappointment for Rick. During the trials for the 1964 Olympic Games, Barry hardly got a look. Many believed the team had been selected before the trials got under way. He was told to play defense and play defense only. Barry, of course, is a consummate scorer, one of the best the game has ever seen, but he went out and played defense as they asked him and shut off his man with just one point. He did not make the team. A certain balance—geographical, racial, amateur-collegian—seemingly had been determined before the first trial session began.

Barry has outlived the bad-guy reputation but he hasn't lost his intense desire, nor his perfectionist attitude. He has learned to be loose, to joke around with people, to become the person he always wished he could be. But there are limits to what he will do for friendship's sake.

Recently Frank Gifford was sent to one of Barry's basketball camps to get some film clips of Frank and Rick playing a little one-on-one basketball for an evening news show. The cameras were going to catch Gifford putting the ball in the basket against the great Rick Barry. But when Gifford went up for the shot, Rick stuffed the ball down his throat.

"I'm sorry about that," Rick said later, "but nobody is going to make any shots off me. I happen to be a very competitive person. It's that way on the court.

It's that way on the golf course. I even hate to play tennis against my wife because I don't want to pitty-pat the ball across the net. I want to win. I have never done anything where losing doesn't eat me up."

Whatever Rick's failings may be, a lack of courage isn't one of them. He still says what he thinks, and that includes his opinions of his NBA peers, a boldness that has engendered some resentment among some pros. At an exhibition benefit game in 1972, when it was undecided whether Barry would leave the Nets and return to San Francisco, some Nets' fans held up a poster that read: "DON'T GO RICK." One of the players whispered to another, "They left out one letter."

If Barry has changed, it is because he has nothing more to prove. He has learned how to open up to people, how to inspire teammates rather than irritate them.

"I think I've changed in that I've gotten a little wiser as I've gotten older," he says. "But I'm still the same type of ballplayer people either love or hate. I've always played the same and it seems to create a reaction in people. I never know if it will be good or bad. But I still always get some kind of reaction."

And he still has his super ego.

"Is there anyone in the league you can't score against?" he was asked after he had established himself as a super scorer in the pros.

"No." he replied emphatically. "If you can't, you shouldn't be here. Some make you work harder, but you just have to concentrate more then. You adjust to different people. If the defensive man is shorter, I shoot over him. If he isn't, I try to move him into a screen and shoot over it, or move a lot. Get him going one way, and then go to the other. You just have to work.

"I'm not a great shooter. I think I'm a good scorer and I know how to get points, but I don't think of myself as a great shooter. A great shooter is someone who can stand outside all night and pop in better than 50 per cent of his shots. I can do that on a given evening, but not most of the time. I drive to the basket a lot and draw a lot of fouls. I think you have to go to the foul line about 10 or 12 times a game to be a big scorer. And I make the most of my scoring opportunities."

The ego that turned off his teammates at Miami was a help to him in the pros. "He has the good ego, all right," said a former Barry teammate. "All the good ones do. Rick and Jerry Lucas didn't get along very well when they were on the Warriors, for instance. One reason is that they got to roughing it one time, and Lucas threatened him and Rick threatened him right back. But the big reason, I think, is that Rick had burned Lucas a few times, scored on him, and Jerry didn't like it. Jerry had a pretty good ego, too."

Rick wears a sweatband on each wrist when he's playing to protect his sensitive hands from moisture. When the game begins, his hands are always moving, always searching for the ball, reaching for a steal, a loose ball, changing the dribble from side to side, going for the basket hard, his long fingers doing miraculous things in close with spins and over-the-shoulder shots. He is one of the great one-on-one players.

Bill Sharman has been asked if there would have been room for Barry on the great Boston Celtics teams of the nineteen-fifties, for which Sharman starred. "Listen," said Barry's former coach, "he could make any team there ever was. The thing is, he is never satisfied."

On the first Monday in March, 1965, Barry played his final college game, and he didn't want to leave. The game had been over for more than an hour when he walked out of the locker room. He did not walk into an empty corridor. When he walked out he was greeted by almost two dozen children who had waited for one last glimpse of the great man, one last autograph before he left Miami to become one of the greatest pro players of all time.

As graduation time approached, Barry's thoughts turned to the NBA and to Pam Hale. As he waited for the pro draft, he talked seriously of marriage. Pam had been more than a girlfriend in college. She was a knowledgeable basketball critic, having been exposed to the game all her life and much of the time they had spent together had been in basketball conversation, about his future in the game.

Pam, too, had considered a career in sports, for she was an excellent swimmer and had worked, one summer, in the Billy Rose Aquacade at the World's Fair in New York. She also had auditioned for a Broadway show as a dancer and had been offered the job, but turned it down. She wasn't so sure about marriage at first.

"He was a small-town boy," she recalled her thoughts later. "I was afraid of that. I mean, he came from a solid, quiet family in a small town and he was the sort who wanted to marry the girl next door right away and settle down for life. He was shy and hadn't dated much."

She was a tall, slender girl with light brown hair and a pale blush for a complexion which deepened when people complimented her startling blue eyes. She had practiced basketball with him, played golf with him, the perfect companion.

In May, Rick received a Business degree. In June, Rick Barry and Pamela Hale were married, an event that created such a stir in Miami that a local television station carried the ceremony.

They spent their honeymoon in Hawaii, compliments of Franklin Mieuli and the San Francisco Warriors, who had made Barry their No. 1 draft choice.

Chapter Five

Though Rick Barry had led the nation's collegiate scorers, he had been downgraded by the pro scouts.

Earl Lloyd of the Detroit Pistons said he wasn't mean enough to play in the NBA. Arnold Heft, then the owner of the Baltimore Bullets, had joined the Barry rap parade with, "We had three different scouts who looked at him and decided he couldn't make it. We figured he couldn't take the belting."

The Knicks, besides disliking his attitude, had questioned the durability of the 195-pound Barry. Still others had made light of the 973 points he scored during his senior season and maligned the University of Miami schedule as being too easy.

The 1965 college draft, for which Barry was eligible, was a complicated one.

The expansion boom had not yet started. The NBA had nine teams, rather than its present 18. The Knicks

were buried in the cellar and the San Francisco Warriors, once the Philadelphia Warriors, had moved to
the West Coast for the 1962–63 season, but drew few
fans. The Boston Celtics, with Bill Russell, had won a
seventh straight championship, but most of all, there
was not the $9-million in television money that the
franchises currently divide annually that helps the
struggling teams survive.

In an attempt to strengthen the league from top to
bottom, a plan was devised in which the Knicks, last
in the four-team Eastern Division, and the San Francisco Warriors, who had won a total of 17 games in
the Western Division, would be awarded the four top
draft choices. A coin toss decided the order they
would select, and the Knicks earned the right to pick
first and fourth.

While Barry was a senior at Roselle Park High, an
austere kid from Missouri, named Bill Bradley, was
the going high school thing that year. Four years
later, the two vied for the No. 1 pick in the college
draft. The Knicks chose Bradley from Princeton, although he had told them he could stand a couple of
years without basketball, though the Knicks couldn't.

Barry had neither an alternative nor the desire for
one, and he was selected by the Warriors. The
Knicks, who had to do without Bradley for two seasons while he attended Oxford University in England
as a Rhodes Scholar, used their other selection for
Dave Stallworth of Wichita State. San Francisco
chose Fred Hetzel who had turned Davidson College
from a perennial loser into an instant winner.

Although Bob Feerick, the then general manager

of the Warriors, had played basketball at Santa Clara with Bruce Hale, he had never seen Barry play for Hale at Miami. The Warriors first scouted Rick at a college All-Star game in Kentucky.

"We knew Barry could score points," Feerick said, "but that was all we were sure of. Alex (Hannum, Barry's first pro coach) went to the All-Star game in person, and I saw the game on television, and we both came away with the feeling that the kid had what it takes. He got in there and mixed it up with the best in the nation and came away looking great. He's strong, quick, and as I said, he can shoot."

After that game Hannum was to comment, "Outstanding players like Elgin Baylor and Oscar Robertson would often make their final move a flip back away from the basket. Not Barry, he went to the hoop, even better than Bob Pettit did. He showed me right away he was familiar with pro moves. Give Bruce Hale the credit for that, but I could also see that Rick would be outstanding as a stock broker, lawyer, doctor or any profession he chose."

Ironically, Barry's idol was Pettit, but in his junior year at Miami, Rick, a marketing major, switched allegiance to Elgin Baylor.

"He, like I," Barry said at the time, "played forward, and I learned a new move from him every time I would watch him play."

Hannum learned more of the things he needed to know about Barry in a 1965 exhibition game between some U.S. college players and the Russian National team. Watching Rick clinically, again with the thought that pro scouts had said he could not take a belting, Hannum quickly found out about Barry's durability. He saw Nicolai Volnov push Barry all over the court, then his eyes widened. When the Russian angered Barry, Rick responded with twisting layups, soft hook shots, and arched in jumpers from every angle. He ran up 14 quick points. The Warriors had the answer, Barry could take a beating in close from such giants as a 280-pound Wilt Chamberlain.

"The Americans won in overtime because of Barry," recalled Hannum, "but more important, we knew we had a draft choice who could take care of himself."

No matter what you have been led to believe, the Warriors signed Barry for a $3,000 bonus and $15,000 for his first-year salary. Consider that Rick earns more than $200,000 annually, the average salary in the NBA is better than $65,000 and the minimum is $20,-000.

"Most kids," recalled Bob Feerick, "when they come in the first time, they want to hedge. They want no-cut contracts, things like that. Rick just said something like, 'give me the money and when do we start.'"

Barry wasn't long in establishing himself as a starter. In preseason training, he was thrown against Nate Thurmond, and the notoriously tough center came away from the first scrimmage and said, "He's not as frail as he looks."

Maybe Hannum and Thurmond were sure, but even after Barry had started his rookie season as a regular, the skeptics still thought he was out of place in the NBA.

Early in his rookie season Barry met up with Ben

Warley of the Baltimore Bullets. Warley bounced, bumped, banged, elbowed Barry and generally shoved him all over the court. After the game, Warley announced triumphantly, "I all but stuffed him in the basket."

Warley was a hard-nosed veteran, but no one had ever accused him of throwing his weight around, primarily because he had no weight. He was slightly shorter and slightly lighter even than Barry.

The average NBA corner-man, in Rick's rookie days, weighed between 225 and 240 pounds. Here Barry had been black-and-blued by Warley, and he was to face Dave DeBusschere, currently the Commissioner of the ABA, for a first time. The doubters went to work before that meeting and again expressed concern whether Rick could stand up through the punishment of an 80-game schedule.

DeBusschere, the Detroit Piston player-coach at the time, was a 6-6, 225-pounder, who played a clean but tough game of basketball. His forte was defense and he shut off opposing players with his determination and rugged approach.

DeBusschere, who had taught tougher and stronger forwards a lesson, had one for Barry in their first meeting. Dave limited Rick to 8 points and later said, "Barry should send away for some muscles. He can't push you out of the way, so he has to go around you. And we don't think he's that fast or maneuverable."

Barry had his early problems, but they were short lived. DeBusschere, and the rest of the NBA was quickly to learn of Rick's fighting spirit and determination to be the best.

Barry not only found ways to take care of himself, but also to make his opponent look bad. Against the Boston Celtics he was involved in a scramble for a ball near the sideline. Suddenly a Celtic player dropped to the floor in pain. "All I did," Barry said later, with a look of innocence, "was try and bank the ball off his knee so it would bounce out of bounds and we'd get possession."

Guy Rodgers, his teammate, listening to Barry tell the story, laughed and added, "Yes, but it seems you got the ball a little high and caught that boy right in the belly."

In the next Barry-DeBusschere meeting, Rick proved to Dave that he had been a bit premature in his judgment. In less than 30 minutes of playing time, Rick scored 23 points against DeBusschere and proved among other things that he had enough quickness and maneuverability to get open for his shots and make them, and that he belonged in the NBA. Barry had set a pattern which he still retains 10 years later. Challenge him and he will retaliate.

Another time against the Pistons he got knocked to the floor during a scramble for the ball. Instead of slugging it out with the players, he found another way to even the score.

What Barry did was to spring high in the air to spear the next defensive rebound. He pitched out to Guy Rodgers, the Warrior backcourt man, who sprinted up court, and scored on a layup at the end of the fast break. Moments later Rick fed Rodgers underneath afer another dash up the floor. He finished the night with 36 points, 11 rebounds and four assists.

In a game against the Knicks he scored 33 points and excelled off the offensive boards. After his all-around play and, in particular his shooting touch from the corners, had impressed Harry Gallatin, then the Knick coach, said, "He looks like he could be a real star, maybe a superstar."

Gallatin didn't stay around very long as the Knick coach, but his prophecy came true. Other coaches began agreeing with Gallatin, including Dick McGuire, who replaced him as the Knick coach.

"The kid is just great," said McGuire, currently the Knicks' chief scout. "Just when you think he's getting tired, he's by you for 2 points."

Red Auerbach, then the Celtic coach, said, "Barry knows how to get the ball, and he knows what to do with it when he gets it."

The Kansas City Kings were the Cincinnati Royals at the time and Jack McMahon, their coach, said, "Barry sure knows why the hoop is up there. He has more moves toward getting 2 points than any rookie I have seen in a long time."

And, from Hannum, his own coach, "One big plus about Rick is that he is never satisfied. Even when he scored 40 points, he will go home and think about the shots he missed and when he comes to practice he will work on those shots so that he won't miss them again. Heck, he could be the first player never to miss a shot."

Barry's deceptive moves and deceptive looks contributed to his success. "High school kids look older than him and you have a tendency to relax a little," said Dave Gambee of the Philadelphia 76ers. "The first time I did that he had 22 points off me in two periods. He may be skinny, but once he has his hands on the ball, you don't get it away from him. He's got great hands."

By late February Barry had become the highest-scoring rookie forward in NBA history. He surpassed the mark of 1,739 points Elgin Baylor had racked up in 69 games as a rookie. When Barry was told about the feat he asked quizzically, "What record?"

Barry knew nothing about the mark he had set. In fact, he didn't even appear impressed with his play. He said, "I'm fortunate to be scoring, but I'm not pleased with my shooting. I still missed too many shots from the outside."

By the end of the season Barry had scored 2,059 points for a 25.7 average. He became only the fourth rookie in NBA history to score 2,000 or more points. He joined an exclusive club that had included Wilt Chamberlain (2,702) who began his career with the Philadelphia Warriors, Walt Bellamy who scored 2,-495 points for Chicago and Oscar Robertson's 2,165 point performance with the Cincinnati Royals.

During Barry's rookie season he became the highest scoring forward in the then 20-year history of the NBA, and his 57-points against the Knicks was the second best one-game performance by a first-year player. Only Wilt Chamberlain had bettered the mark during the 1959-60 season by scoring 58 points.

Barry was the only rookie to make the 1965-66 All-Star team and was the sixty first season player ever chosen for the All-Pro team.

The pros may have bounced Rick Barry around a

little, but they quickly learned to respect him. Of the 86 ballots cast for the rookie of the year, Barry polled 84. The other two went to Billy Cunningham of the Philadelphia 76ers.

Barry's selection as the top rookie gave Bob Feerick and Franklin Mieuli, the men who were most on the spot when they made him the Warriors' top draft choice, a chance to gloat.

"After every game," Feerick recalled, "I would swear that he couldn't get any better. But every game he showed me something new."

Mieuli added, "All this talk about his being skinny bores me. They spoke as if we paid Rick as much money as we've paid anyone except Wilt Chamberlain, and then suddenly discovered he was frail. Malarkey. Here's an athlete whose played maybe 400 games in his life and never had a bad injury. Barry's as flexible as a whip."

A sports writer who covered the Warriors at the time made an interesting observation after Barry was fouled on a shot attempt and the ball rolled off the rim. "That play made Rick madder than anything else on the court," remembered the writer, "because he had missed a three-point play and had to settle for only two."

If there was a weakness in Barry's rookie season, it was in his defensive play.

"On defense," said Hannum, "he's not Bill Russell. Rick had played his college ball for an offensive-minded Miami team and sometimes found he lacked the experience and the muscle to keep his opponent from scoring on him."

There were times when Barry wondered whether he'd make it. At first, he'd stay up until the wee hours of the morning after a game and replay it mentally trying to review all his mistakes. Hannum felt Rick was worrying too much and that his anxiety had drained his energy.

Barry finally learned to work his problems out during Warrior practice sessions. He also learned to conserve his strength.

"You begin to see things that throw off your game," Barry said. "I won't take a shower the day before a game because the hot, then the cold water sapped my energy and made me feel tired and sluggish."

The 80-game schedule took its toll more than anything else. The lack of energy tormented him.

In mid-February, though he had been piling up points, he said, "I was down to 190 and worried whether I was strong enough to take a whole season in this league—you could count my ribs—when we got this week's rest. I started taking this new supplement they gave people in hospitals and I began to feel my strength coming back."

Gradually Rick built his weight up over the 200-pound mark again.

Rick and the other players discovered though, that his scoring could be up even when his weight was down.

"You don't have to be 240 pounds to make it up front in this league," said Barry. "If you work on your timing to get in to the bucket, it can make up for a lot of weight."

But the biggest thing Barry did for the NBA was to

bring new life to a sport that had been dominated by deadpan pros such as Elgin Baylor, Wilt Chamberlain and Oscar Robertson. In Barry, the Warriors came up with an unmistakable box-office attraction.

With his loose, controlled body movements, Barry would snake through defenses and then sink a dazzling hook shot or toss in an acrobatic flip shot. His quick jump shot was deadly from all angles and distances. When Rick went underneath, his timing and spring often enabled him to tip in missed shots. And, too, he was one of the best foul shooters in the league.

Off the court, Barry was personable and in appearance flawless. He wore blue blazers, conservative sport jackets and subtly razored haircuts that cost $6.50. He would answer the telephone with a poise and articulation that appeared almost excessive.

Every afternoon when the Warriors were at home, "Supersoph," as one local newspaper called him, folded his frame behind the wheel of his red Porsche sportscoupe and drove to a local radio station for his daily five-minute sports show delivered in a well-manicured baritone.

When he was at the University of Miami and began to realize that he had a good chance of making the pros, he increased the number of radio and television courses on his schedule. His instant popularity in the pros also brought him a rash of commercial endorsements ranging through candy bars, a laundry bleach, sportswear, a bank and sneakers.

In the days before expansion, NBA teams would barnstorm through various cities, not only seeking extra money, but also as a testing barometer for future franchises.

During Barry's sophomore season in the pros, the Warriors and the St. Louis Hawks played the brand new Veterans Memorial Coliseum in Phoenix, Ariz.

Phoenix was to get a team of its own for the 1968-69 season, but for that night, the only drawing attraction appeared to be Rick Barry, who had taken on the image of the NBA's newest star and glamor boy.

Some 5,500 fans paid their money and Barry did not disappoint them. He came on with the aura and the insistence of a star. His blond hair was carefully shaped, he was clean cut and handsome and he moved like a whippet: agile, fast and intense.

In one three-minute stretch he stole the ball and outraced Lenny Wilkens, then one of the fastest men in the league, for a layup. Then he hit on two jump shots from 20 feet out, including one coming fast across the keyhole, stopping suddenly, faking his man up into the air, faking him again when he came down and then putting up a soft hook that cleared without touching the rim.

The Warriors won the game, 124–106, and Barry hit on 19 of 46 shots from the field and missed only two of 14 free throw attempts for a 50-point evening.

Before the start of Barry's second season the Warriors underwent two major changes. First, the Warriors fired Alex Hannum and replaced him with Bill Sharman as the head coach. The Warriors had one of the worst records in the league, 35 victories and 45 defeats during Barry's rookie season. Only the Knicks

(30-50) and the Detroit Pistons (22-58) had worse records.

Next, the Warriors traded Guy Rodgers to the league's newest team, the Chicago Bulls, for Jim King and Jeff Mullins.

Both moves were considered stunners. Hannum, who wound up succeeding Dolph Schayes as coach of the Philadelphia 76ers, had a fine reputation, while Rodgers was one of the most sensational playmakers in the league.

The effect of Hannum and Rodgers leaving the Warriors brought the critics out again. The assumption was that without Rodgers' playmaking, San Francisco's playing style would change and that Barry would score less.

The Warriors' style changed drastically, but Barry scored more. Bill Sharman had the big men up front play with the ball more, instead of waiting for the feed from Rodgers. He instituted more of a running game and the ballhandling responsiblity was spread around. Barry, working with the ball more, shot more and better from the outside, while still retaining the skills he developed when Rodgers was running the fast breaks. Rick's moves cut him loose at the proper instant and he scored in the 30s and 40s from the start.

"As a rookie," said Barry, "until the end of the season, the last month or so, I played most of the time without the ball. When you don't have the ball, there's just so much you can do."

"Guy controlled the ball. I have nothing against

Guy. He's a great basketball player. But we're all moving the ball now, and it's a different game.

"When the forwards get the ball out on the sides, Nate rolls and things happen. It's easier for us to score. Occasionally I force a shot: everybody does. But they know I'll give 'em the ball if I see 'em in the clear. Playing with the ball, I get to see what the defense can do. I see what gets 'em off balance. A guy plays you a lot different when you don't have the ball."

Tom Meschery, the Portland Trail Blazers' assistant coach, but then a teammate and one of the greatest admirers, said at the time, "His ability is obvious, and it creates openings for the other guys. Rick is always a threat out there and it pressures them a little—like Oscar Robertson of course. Rick is the fastest 6-7 I've ever seen, probably the fastest 6-7 ever in basketball. He really is like a greyhound. He runs like a guy 6-3."

Jim King, quickly establishing himself with the Warriors, had spent three seasons with the Los Angeles Lakers where he played with Jerry West and Elgin Baylor. King, the new coach at Tulsa University, was asked at the time to compare Barry with Baylor and West.

King was concise. "Rick goes to the basket rather than away," he said. "Baylor usually falls away when he shoots. No one outshoots Jerry under pressure. Rick's a better passer than I had anticipated. He's not selfish, but I don't think anybody can outshoot Jerry West. Barry is like West in that both are explosive. They are liable to shoot an entire quarter without missing a shot."

Bill Sharman, commenting on Barry's play at the time, added, "At first, they were guarding him as though he was just another good player. Suddenly it changed, and they were all over him. I told Rick that if they concentrated on him like that, we're going to use him more and more as a decoy. The thing is—everybody knew it—he also was a good passer."

After a two-point loss to Philadelphia, in which Barry played with a tightly taped ankle and scored 30 points, Rick slumped in front of his locker, stripped off one soggy shoe and smashed it against the concrete dressing room floor.

Barry scowled, thinking of his last play, when he had cut toward the basket, with nine seconds to go, for the 2-points that would have tied the score. The dribbled ball had struck the hounding Philadelphia guard, Larry Costello, currently the coach of the Milwaukee Bucks, on the foot and caromed out of control.

"Breaks," Barry ranted. "Rotten breaks. Costy fouled me and they didn't even call him for kicking the ball."

As Barry rolled up huge point totals, he brought the crowds back to the San Francisco Civic Auditorium.

One night against the Cincinnati Royals, while he was driving towards the basket, he collided with a pair of opposing players. They hit hard and Barry fell. He landed with a loud thud, then writhed in pain. The capacity crowd fell silent and Franklin Mieuli turned pale. If Rick Barry was hurt, the Warrior franchise would be hurt even worse.

It took almost one minute and a half, but for Mieuli it appeared like a month before Barry got to his feet, limped for a few moments and continued his night's work. He scored 36 points and the Warriors won in overtime to increase their Western Division lead to 6½ games.

After the Royal triumph, the Warriors' fifth game in five nights coast to coast, Barry admitted to being tired. And he should have been. His road show produced 203 points in five games, including 47 against the Knicks in New York, his 50-point performance in Phoenix and a 49 pointer against the Los Angeles Lakers.

"He has improved more and quicker than I hoped for or even imagined possible," said Sharman. "This guy, he's so coachable. He adjusts so quickly. He'll do anything he has to do to help us win and improve himself.

"During that stretch when he hit for 203 points in five nights, he had 21 against the Baltimore Bullets. That's a good night for most fellows, but it's not much for Rick. We talked things over. He wanted to know why his shots were not going in. I had a few suggestions and he wanted to hear them. They must have worked because the next night he got 50 against Phoenix."

Rick's startling success in pro basketball has been due to his great desire to be the best and to win. And that was never more evident than the night of November 11, during his second pro season.

The game was between the San Francisco Warriors

and the Los Angeles Lakers, and the matchup, Barry against Rudy LaRusso.

There was no peace that night—Barry barreled into LaRusso, one of the toughest men in the league, and smashed Rudy flat. When he was charged with a foul, Barry turned his baby face and those pale brown eyes and innocently spread his hands, as if to say, "How could you?" LaRusso had to be helped to his feet.

In the opening minutes, he drove on the Lakers, drilled a shot from point blank range, and turned around to tear up the court. Jerry West stood in his way, hobbled by a sore heel, and Rick banged into him, hitting his face against West's shoulder. Barry's nose bled but he refused to leave the game. Instead, he grabbed a rebound, dribbled to the sideline, and after he seemingly was trapped, managed to turn the corner on his man, and drive down court again and score again. This time Barry was fouled, and as he walked to the free throw line, blood still pouring from his nose, Jerry West came by and patted him on the back.

This was Rick Barry, or part of him. Al Attles, his present Warrior coach, but then his teammate, and the oldest player on the squad, had watched forwards play for the last seven seasons. He was asked, "What made Rick so special?"

"His quickness," Attles was to say. "He is quicker than any forward around. The difference between his first and second seasons, is his keener awareness of the game as a whole."

Bill Sharman had been around longer, and when he was asked what made Barry tick, he said, "He's 6-7, with long arms and very quick. He is quicker than the big men who guard him; he can fake past them and he is too big for "little" men like John Havlicek. He has quickness and agility above other forwards. He has great body balance. He is intelligent and is a great competitor. There is a strong chance he may end up the greatest forward ever to play the game."

What Bill Sharman had predicted during the 1966-67 season, Red Auerbach, sitting around before the Maurice Stokes Memorial Game at Kutsher's Country Club, in Monticello, N.Y., almost a decade later, concurred with his former star.

"He is the best there is," said Auerbach, "and the best there ever was. And more important, this was the kid they said couldn't play defense. Defense is probably one of the strongest parts of his game."

Sharman lent a helping hand in Barry's improvement as a shooter. Most coaches those days taught their players to aim their shots at the front rim of the basket. Sharman insisted his men aim at the back rim.

"It gives you a leeway of seven or eight inches if your short," Sharman explained. "If you're long, you may get lucky off the backboard. If you aim at the front rim, and your short, you've had it."

Barry aimed at the back rim and his shooting improved enough to win the 1966-67 scoring title with 2,277 points, a 35.6 average, and to end Wilt Chamberlain's seven-season reign as scoring champion.

As he scored 30, 40 and even 50 points a game, Barry faced accusations of being a gunner, and needed Sharman, an outstanding shooter during his Boston Celtic playing days, to defend him.

"They always say the shooter is selfish," said Sharman, "But that's his job, to shoot. Did they ever say Bill Russell was selfish for taking all the rebounds?

"I consider Rick the best passing forward in the league, as well as the best scorer. If he wasn't such a good passer, they could sag and two-time him more. We look for Rick and feed him as much as we can. But our guys know that he'll give the ball back when they get loose."

Nate Thurmond, whom Barry replaced as the most popular Warrior, also came to Rick's defense.

"He gives the ball up real well," said Thurmond, who had also played with Wilt Chamberlain. "There is a great difference between Wilt making 40 and Rick making 40."

Barry's second pro season had many of the markings of the 1974-75 Warrior championship season. Although there was a run on adjectives that described Barry's shooting, rebounding, passing, speed and breathtaking moves, nobody dreamed that San Francisco would win the Western Division title. All that had been predicted for the Warriors was that they would be better than their 35-45 record of the year before.

The San Francisco remarkable success story wasn't all due to Barry. Although Rick was the pulse and the soaring spirit, Nate Thurmond, in his fourth pro season, had established himself on a plateau with Wilt Chamberlain and Bill Russell, the league's best centers.

"Thurmond has done for our team what Russell has done for the Celtics," Sharman said at the time. "Nate is a tremendous defensive player in the Russell mold and is a better shooter than Bill. Like Russell, Thurmond has an intimidating effect on the opposition. He forces the other team to get the ball away quickly and to take bad shots."

Many admirers of Thurmond resented Barry's rise to fame, but Rick would respond with, "It's very simple, the most important guy on the Warriors is Nate. You can't win in this league without a good center, and Nate is a great one now. I missed three games earlier in the season and we won all of them. If Nate misses any we don't win."

San Francisco won the Western Division title with a 44-27 mark and went all the way to the final round to be beaten by Wilt Chamberlain and the Philadelphia 76ers, 4 games to 2. The 76er triumph ended the Boston Celtics' seven-season reign as champion. As for the Warriors, they would not win another division title until the 1974-75 season when Barry would again be the key.

Despite Barry's improvement in his second pro year, he was highly critical of Coach Sharman. Barry said Sharman was fanatical about basketball, singleminded, unrealistically professional—all terms which could have been used to describe Barry's devotion to the game.

"I didn't dislike Sharman's coaching," Barry says today, "only his attitude and philosophy towards practices. It made it seem so much like work, as if that's all that counted. Of course, some people will condemn me and say, 'Well, that's your job.' But I never had it that way before. It had always been fun

for me and I was able to do well. I don't think he's
the same way now as he was that first year (1967). I
think we had only three days off the whole year and
we were in first place. You have to admire his dedication. People have taken things out of context and concluded that I hate Bill Sharman, which isn't true."

Of the many thrills Barry has had in his 10 pro seasons, he calls the 1967 NBA All-Star game in San
Francisco, "The game I'll never forget." Barry was
voted the most valuable player in the game after he
scored 38 points, hitting on 16 of his 27 shots from the
floor in 34 minutes of playing time. He also grabbed
six rebounds and passed off for three more baskets.

But that isn't the reason he said would always
remember. In an interview with Art Spander, a San
Francisco reporter, Barry said, "I've stressed a lot during the current season, as I have before, that basketball is the epitome of the team game. The sport that
requires the individual to curb tendencies to do
things on his own if he wants to win.

"That's why the game I remember most was not
where I played my best, although I certainly did have
a good game, but rather one that emphasized the ultimate team concept."

In being selected for the All-Star team for the sec-
ond time in his two pro seasons, Rick played on the
West team with Dave DeBusschere, Elgin Baylor,
Jerry West, Guy Rodgers and Nate Thurmond.

Because of players like Wilt Chamberlain, Bill Russell and Oscar Robertson, the East was favored to
win.

"But we came out and played a game that was as

near perfect as any game I've ever been in—or may ever be in—" Barry told Spander. "And we won, 135-120.

"It was a fantastic team game. Dave DeBusschere, who was then playing for Detroit, got us going. He was hot and we got him the ball. And when I got hot, I got the ball. In other words, we worked the ball to the man who was shooting well. We didn't force up shots.

"Nate Thurmond played super defense and got the boards—18 rebounds. We got the ball out and ran. For guys who hadn't played together, we actually played like we'd been together all our lives. It was super. It was fun to play, a great game, a game played the way I feel basketball should be played. The guy who got the hot hand got the ball. Nobody tried to do anything himself.

"I've played a hell of a lot better in other games, on both ends of the court. But nothing holds a candle to the All-Star game. It shows how well people can play together and how much fun a game can be. Fred Schaus coached us, and we went out there and executed the game plan almost flawlessly. Every All-Star Game should be played like that one was played. In some, guys are just out there trying to do their own thing. We had a team effort."

There is no fixing Rick Barry's image in your mind. He is never what he appears to be.

Pam Barry once was quoted as having said, "He twitches like 100 electric eels when he sleeps."

Lou Carnesecca, who coached him for two seasons while he played for the New York Nets, once said,

"Rick is always thinking, his mind is so active, he must even sleep with his eyes open. He is a perfectionist, a worrier."

Under all of Barry's elegance is a man with a terrible temper, often brought about because there probably is not a more intense professional athlete. He won't accept mediocrity, nor will he tolerate anything short of victory.

His perfectionist attitude also has its bad side effects. "I wish I could be loose, take things easy, not be so serious," Barry said. "I would love to be able to fool around with people, tell jokes. That's the type of person I've always wished I could be."

Once the biggest referee baiter in both leagues, Barry tried hard to control his temper during the championship season. Against the New Orleans Jazz, he was called for a personal foul and quickly flashed his old look of anger and disgust at the official. A few seconds later he was called for another foul and acted as though he were Mr. Cool.

When Barry loses control of his temper, it usually upsets him and gets the best of him, and he often comes up looking bad and a loser.

Such was the case during the 1974-75 season in a game against the Knicks at Madison Square Garden.

After 42 seconds of play had gone by, Charley Johnson of Golden State was about to throw an inbounds pass when Bill Bradley elbowed Barry. It was a culmination of shoving, pushing, elbowing and handchecking that had gone on between the two forwards from the opening buzzer.

Barry swung at Bradley, and though there was a

slight swelling under Bill's eye, the Knick forward would not admit the punch had landed.

"I will have to look at the film," Bradley said with his sly grin.

From that play on, Barry became the villain. He found out quickly that you don't hit Rhodes scholars before a capacity crowd of 19,964 at Madison Square Garden and get away with it. Barry was roundly booed and it seemingly effected his game. Rick, who had scored 110 points against the Knicks in three previous games, including 44 the last time he played the garden, was held to 18 points. He made half of his 16 shots, and commited 10 of the Warriors 34 turnovers. He also left New York $50 poorer when he was slapped with a technical foul for arguing with an official on an outbounds play.

"I think he was upset," said Walt Frazier, the Knick captain, with a smile after the game. "I never saw him miss so many free throws."

Barry still was not satisfied. In the Warrior dressing room, after his team had been beaten, 99-98, he charged, "Bradley can't play defense unless he holds you and shoves you. If he does things like that, he has to expect to get hit back. It's all right to play a guy aggresively, but that guy plays dirty. Did you ever see me have a fight with Dave DeBusschere? He's aggressive, but a good defensive player."

In his 10 pro seasons Barry's combatants in the pros have read like a page out of the Ring record book: Rudy LaRusso, Dan Spark, Bill Bridges, Bill Bradley, Butch Komives, Dick Van Arsdale, Jerry Chambers,

Jeff Congdon, Spencer Haywood, Charlie Scott and many others.

Barry has maintained that many of the so-called fights were nothing more than heated shoving matches, often provoked by his aggressive play.

"My game is to drive to the hoop and try to draw a foul," Barry has often explained. "When I feel the initial contact I start to twist and turn to get the shot off."

During the 1968-69 season, Barry's first in the ABA, Dan Sparks, a Floridian reserve, had engaged in a shoving match with him the first time the Oakland Oaks had played in Miami. When the team arrived for a second meeting, a headline in a Miami newspaper read: "Sparks To Fly As Floridians Take On Barry."

Thirty seconds after Sparks got in to the game, Barry feinted by him and drove for a layup. Sparks slashed him across the back, slamming Barry into the backstop. Barry whirled and threw a punch at Sparks and players came off the bench. The crowd jumped up booing and people raced down the aisles and crowded 10 deep around the courts. The police had to form a ring around the court to restore order. In three minutes of playing time, Sparks was charged with five personal fouls, four of them against Barry.

Another time, trying to get past Tom Hawkins of the Los Angeles Lakers, when the Warriors still had the San Francisco label, Barry slapped out at Hawkins' hands. Hitting back, Hawkins was caught and thrown out of the game and Barry didn't bat an eye.

Instead he said, "If I know somebody's going to give me the works, I give it to them first."

A couple of weeks later Barry and Dick Van Arsdale of the Knicks got into a pushing match. While both were being restrained, Barry said that Willis Reed had decked him with a right cross.

The next day the newspapers talked about how Van Arsdale had "held" Barry to 22 points.

"They're making a lot of defensive geniuses these days out of guys who don't score," Barry said at the time, "But they don't stop you in this league. There are a lot of guys who work hard at defense, they play you close and they make you work for every shot. But it all comes down to whether you can put them in or not. In the final analysis, it is not them stopping you but you missing it. There is nobody, who can stop the top scorers when they're hitting."

Rick's court anger isn't always directed at opponents or at the officials after they've made what he thinks is the wrong call. More than often it is directed at himself. He will berate himself for an error, be it on the basketball or tennis court, as if Rick Barry isn't supposed to be human. The crowds even boo him when he's scolding himself. They also boo him when he goes into one of his Barrymore performances on a contact play.

Barry is known for play-acting on the floor, much like Walt Frazier of the Knicks, and other players with charisma.

Sharman once said, "There is no one around, not Chamberlain, Russell or Baylor, who can turn on a crowd like Barry. He can do it with his ability or by a gesture to the crowd.

Barry's zestful drives to the basket sometimes lead to resounding mid-air collisions that often find Barry flat on his back, either stone-motionless or writhing in seeming torment.

"When Rick drives for a layup and hits the floor all sprawled out and moaning," said a former teammate, "you'd bet your last dollar he'd never make it back to his feet. But all the referee has to do is signal that Rick has some foul shots coming and you'll see the quickest medical recovery known to man."

Another of his teammates added, "You should have seen Rick all in Oakland, you never saw such carrying on. I thought he was going to go into shock."

One night during the 1971-72 season, his last with the Nets and the ABA, Barry was belted to the floor and came up cursing and clutching his left eye, a grimace of pain wrinkling his handsome face.

Pam Barry, sitting in the stands, turned to Mike Recht, then of the Associated Press, and currently the publicity Director of the Spirits of St. Louis of the ABA, and said, "I hate it when he does that."

"I've seen him get hit and do some kind of double flip to the floor and moan and groan. You'd think his back was broken. And it only turns out to be a sprained ankle."

"Right now, he's more angry because no foul was called than because he is hurt. And all those kids in the stands can hear him. He embarrasses me. My husband the hypochondriac."

It's not that Rick Barry hasn't had his share of serious injuries. During his brilliant career he has had two knee operations and a broken foot which caused him to miss much of two seasons.

Pam also said her husband seemed always to have some minor ailment. "He's accident prone, I guess, a lummox. Even at home, whenever I ask him to do something he hurts himself. He twists a light bulb and breaks it. He hits his thumb with the hammer. When he barbeques, he burns himself.

"He knows it. But that's his hangup. It's not something you can turn on or off and change."

"Most men are babies," said Mrs. Barry. "Rick feels a twinge of pain and he dies. As soon as he gets hurt, he thinks the worst.

"Sometimes I worry when he falls ... when he lands with a thud. I don't worry about what he does afterward. I've seen him get a cramp and grab his leg and go into a big painful ordeal. I know he doesn't do it purposely. He's just scared and he panics. Maybe he just has a low tolerance for pain."

Although she admits she didn't see Rick suffer his knee injuries or his broken foot, she has seen him take the kind of battering few players have ever received. She has seen him shoved, pushed and belted since his playing days at the University of Miami, and she frets and worries and sympathizes like any wife. "I believe it hurts him but it is so difficult to give sympathy all the time."

As the game progressed, she added, "Look, he's limping now, but I would be surprised if his foot is physically bothering him. It's in his mind. During a game he doesn't limp, but when he's just walking, he limps. If a doctor tells him his foot is okay, he walks out of his office fine. If the doctor says something is wrong, he walks out limping.

"Maybe if I knew what it was like to be incapacitated like he was with the knee, I might better understand. The knee was a traumatic experience."

"He was never injured in college and it hit Rick worse than it would others. It was his first time in the hospital, his first operation. After the operation, he was lying in bed saying 'I can't feel the leg. I'll never walk again.' Then one of those stout-hearted orthopedic nurses—you know, 6 feet tall and 180 pounds—told him to try to walk, and he kept saying 'no, I can't do it, I can't do it.' But he did.

"The injuries have really depressed him. He's lost a lot of enthusiasm because of them. He kept thinking about injuries after he hurt the knee. He would only jump a few inches off the floor, except for a few times he would forget himself.

"He knew what he could do before he was injured, but every time he starts to get back into form he gets injured again. He hasn't played well all year, and I know it's bothering him."

"He's like a spirited race horse. He kicks and bites, but he'll put out for you. He has his quirks, but he puts out for you, and you can't complain."

Pam Barry has seen her husband play most of the games when his teams were at home, and she watches with more knowledge than the average fan.

When Barry was playing for the Nets, at times she would tell her husband: "Willie Sojourner (of the Virginia Squires) was muscling in on Billy Paultz;

you didn't box your man; you dribbled too much in the back court and that's why you had the ball stolen."

Rick has always called Pam, "my severest critic, but there has been times that she has complimented me, especially when I play well defensively. She is very basketball defensive-minded."

There is nothing strange about Pam Barry's basketball knowledge.

"I have always been exposed to basketball," she says proudly. "When I was born in San Francisco, my dad was playing pro basketball with the Fort Wayne Zollner Pistons. He later coached in the pros, and in 1954 he became Miami coach."

Barry was a sophomore at Miami and she was in high school when they met.

"It was all basketball talk when I used to come to the Hale home," said Barry. "My father taught me the fundamentals and dedication to basketball and to shoot fouls underhand. Bruce did the rest."

"He was one college player I was sure would make it in the pros," Hale said. "How well I didn't know. But he was a good listener and a student of the game, and he was willing to put in the time."

Barry also was full of surprises, as his mother had always said, and as the basketball world would soon discover.

After the 1966-67 season, when the Warriors had reached the NBA championship final and appeared on the threshhold of NBA greatness, Barry jumped from the Warriors to the Oakland Oaks of the new American Basketball Association. The move by Barry, which came on June 20, 1967, surprised Mieuli, the Warriors and the NBA, and it changed the direction of Barry's life and the structure of professional basketball.

From that day, much of the admiration for the rising NBA superstar turned to hate. Sportswriters ripped him for being disloyal and greedy. His image became that of a selfish ego-maniac, a user of people, a dangerously ambitious, immature man. Even today, few people know the real reasons Barry left the Warriors, why he made what he would later call "my sacrifice."

Barry did not elaborate at the news conference on the day of the jump. "The offer Oakland made me was one I simply couldn't turn down," he told newsmen. "I'm not at liberty to reveal its exact terms, but I think it makes me one of the highest paid players in pro basketball."

And Mieuli responded: "This is the saddest day of my life, and also the most frustrating. I had and still have real affection for Rick Barry, but there is nothing I could do to hold him. I feel the whole structure of sports as we know them has been shaken by Barry's move. If it can happen to the Warriors, what's to prevent it from happening to any other team? We are starting a suit immediately. Imagine what baseball would be like if Joe Di Maggio jumped from team to team as he pleased."

On June 23, 1967, the Warriors filed a $4.5-million suit against the Oaks, declaring that Barry's 1966 contract prohibited him from playing for another team before 1968. Barry owed the Warriors an option year, Mieuli claimed.

The Oaks countered by saying the NBA reserve clause violated anti-trust laws and thus was invalid. Barry was crowded into the rough legal fight between the two organizations in what was to become a five-year nightmare.

In the next five years Barry would bounce around the new league from the Oakland Oaks to the Washington Capitals to the Virginia Squires (all the same unsteady franchise) to the New York Nets, and he would be forced by court order to sit out the entire 1967-68 season. A string of lawsuits would follow him wherever he went.

He would play some of his greatest basketball in high school gyms and out-dated, leaky arenas, often before crowds of only a few hundred. He would draw boos and cheers in every city in which he appeared, would scream and stomp at officials as never before, but he would emerge as a pioneer and a great athlete, if not a national idol.

The relative obscurity of the new league and the nagging court battles threatened to blot Barry's career. But he was an artistic success wherever he played, no matter what the conditions, no matter how unhappy he became. Basketball always came first.

Barry's decision to jump to the ABA surprised many people, primarily because they figured that his competitive nature would rule out his playing with an inferior league. There was a scattering of other NBA players jumping to the ABA, but no stars, certainly no player with Barry's credentials.

The ABA, formed because a considerable vacuum existed for pro basketball in the mid-nineteen-sixties, had planned to capitalize on an abundance of top players with well publicized reputations coming out of the nation's colleges each year, eventually gaining parity with the established NBA. There were a number of cities with big league arenas that had no NBA franchises. The opportunity for a new league seemed great. But for young athletes with big talents, it was a risk.

The NBA, in 1967, was looking forward to its most prosperous season, and with good reason. It had added two teams (San Diego and Seattle); the Philadelphia 76ers, under Coach Alex Hannum, had broken the Boston Celtic monopoly, creating fresh interest; Los Angeles was moving into its new arena; the league's television program was healthy and player-management relations were calm.

Mieuli was ecstatic with Barry and his Warriors and he was walking around San Francisco in May repeating his favorite line: "I've captured lightning in a bottle."

But even as Mieuli talked, the saucy young ABA was gaining financial muscle and was preparing to make a grandstand play for the newest, youngest superstar in basketball—Rick Barry of the San Francisco Warriors.

When the Oakland Oaks began investigating Barry, here's what they found:

In his second professional season, Barry had made $43,000 in salary and a bonus plus about $20,000 in related endeavors and he was ready to command one

of pro basketball's top contracts—maybe even in the
$100,000-a-Year-class with Wilt Chamberlain and Bill
Russell, the super centers.

He lived in a posh $1,400-a-month, glass-walled,
two bedroom apartment on Green Street in the exclusive Marina section of San Francisco with a spectacular view of the bay and the bridge. He drove a flashy
red Riviera and was awaiting delivery of a metallic
wine Porsche. "What a break," Barry had said, "to play
ball in a great town instead of someplace cold and
dirty and smoggy. My wife was born here and her father played his college basketball at Santa Clara. We
intend to buy a house and live nowhere else."

Rick seemed completely happy, except for a restless
gnawing that's inside every perfectionist. He had
proved to his critics, including himself, that he could
make it big in the pro ranks, and he seemed intent on
discovering the full measure of his greatness. He
didn't drink, he didn't smoke and he seemed to be in
near top physical condition year-round. He was
tanned from playing golf and tennis and water skiing
in the California sun and he was a straight, striking,
assured—yes, cocky—figure. "He was young and handsome and so sincere it made women cry and men
vomit," wrote a critic, Glenn Dickey, of the San Francisco Chronicle.

The man who turned Barry's ambitious head was
Pat Boone, then a 33-year-old singer, movie star and
principal owner of the Oakland Oaks. Boone had
originally invested lightly in the franchise and then
took over to protect his investment. He had already

hired Bruce Hale, Rick's father-in-law, as coach and general manager.

Also, Boone appealed to Barry's show-business ambitions. Barry had always wanted to be a movie star. Boone talked of drama lessons and indicated that Barry could have a future in the movies with the proper influence—Pat Boone, for instance.

The three-year personal service contract accepted by Barry, it was later revealed, was for $75,000 a year, 15 per cent ownership of the Oaks (for $5,000) and 5 per cent of the Oaks' gate receipts above $600,-000, not to exceed $10,000.

There were other reasons why Barry favored Boone's proposal. With Hale as the Oaks' coach, it would bring the family closer together, Rick thought, and there had been some unsteady moments in his young marriage with Pam. Also, he did not like playing for Bill Sharman, the Warrior coach who often had demanded that he practice on the days of a game.

And finally, Barry's pride had been wounded by Mieuli, who had offered him, it was later learned, far less than Barry was worth—$40,000 plus fringe benefits—in a preliminary negotiating session shortly after Barry had completed the greatest NBA season that anybody had in 1966-67.

It had been Mieuli's strategy, some speculated, to give Barry a lesson in humility. At any rate, Mieuli seemingly ignored the advances by the ABA and sailed for Europe to visit his daughter. Before he returned a month later, Barry had been persuaded to leave the NBA.

On June 17, shortly after Mieuli's return from Europe, Barry was signing autographs at a San Francisco shoe store:

"As a joke," Mieuli said, "I got in line with the rest of the people and handed Rick a piece of paper to autograph. He didn't even look up. He just took the paper from my hand. Then I said, 'Sign it. It's a three-year contract.' I figured that would break him up. But then he looked at me and didn't even smile. That's when I knew time was running out."

Before he signed with the Oaks, Barry visited Warrior teammate Nate Thurmond. Thurmond had already agreed to a long-term contract with a salary and benefits that would add up to about $90,000. "There is no way," Barry said later, "that I could have turned that down if Mr. Mieuli had offered it to me. If Franklin had come up with the right money the whole thing could have been averted. I never went to Mr. Mieuli and said, 'Franklin, the ABA wants to pay me this much,' and then go back to the ABA and say, 'He is going to give me this much, what are you going to come up with?' I've never done that—yet people brand me as a money-hungry person who jumps here and there to make an extra buck."

For Barry, the greater irony is that Mieuli had always assured both his stars that they would be paid virtually the same. Not only that, but it was Barry, before he caught the ABA fever, who urged Mieuli to go high for Thurmond so that the ABA would not tempt him. At one point, Barry even told Mieuli, 'Franklin, since I make all that money on the side and Nate (being black) will never get it, don't ever worry about paying him a higher salary than I get. That's only fair."

And in the spring of 1966, when Barry and Mieuli met to discuss terms of his second pro contract, Mieuli told Barry, "Rick, you're special to me and to San Francisco. We're lucky. You came at the right time and the right place. Timing is luck, and you have it. I don't ever want to dicker with you. The special ones—Mays, DiMaggio—nobody ever dickers with them because they're above it. That's the way it should always be with us." The next year, when Mieuli offered $40,000 (plus 5 per cent of any increase over the previous season's gate) Barry was hurt, although he didn't complain. He simply started listening to the ABA.

"I never told Franklin how disappointed I was," Barry said, "because if I had and then come back I would be pressuring him into a bidding contest. When I went there the main thing I wanted was to find out exactly what he thought of me, and I sure found out, didn't I? For me to have made $75,000 (under Mieuli's original offer) the gate would have had to go over a million, and only the Lakers and the Knicks had ever done that."

The day he signed with the Oaks, Mieuli showed Barry a $75,000 base-salary contract which he said had been prepared while Mieuli was in Europe, but it was too late. "I had no idea he would sign with the ABA without first consulting me," Mieuli said.

Mieuli's dream of making the Warriors a dynasty was shattered. His strategy had backfired. Some said

it was the most mishandled business maneuver of
Mieuli's spectacular business career.

"Rick has this great desire to be a movie actor," he
told newsmen after Rick had left his office. "I could
promise him money, but I couldn't promise him that
sort of future."

Rick, although he admitted to be interested in the
movies, never admitted that Boone's Hollywood influence had been a serious factor in his decision.

Reaction to Barry's decision in the NBA was imme-
diate. Owners began preparing for other ABA raids
and players, many of them among the lowest paid
athletes in major league sports, saw a great opportunity ahead.

In August, 1967, a month after Barry's jump, a
large group of NBA players held a secret meeting in
Detroit because of their feelings against Mieuli's suit.
At that meeting, many players agreed to play out
their options. Now, at long last, the NBA option
clause had been forced out from hiding and the players could avail themselves of the benefits it could offer. They watched the Barry case closely.

Barry had become a pioneer, and professional basketball salaries would never be quite the same.

Chapter Six

Eleven basketball teams with players who were either slightly too short, a little too old, lacked experience, were underrated or had been discarded, went into strange gymnasiums and became the American Basketball Association. It was October, 1967. "Gentlemen," Commissioner George Mikan announced, "the game is on."

The ABA opened its first season with teams in Dallas, New York, New Jersey, Louisville, Anaheim, California, Indianapolis, Denver, New Orleans, Houston, Pittsburgh, Minneapolis (site of the league office and Mikan's home) and Oakland. It was called "the colorful league" by ABA friends, "the Mickey Mouse League" by its NBA enemies.

The ABA was different. It used a red, white and blue basketball, the idea of George Mikan. It used a 30-second time limit on shooting instead of the 24-second rule the NBA had pioneered, and it borrowed an old 3-point basketball rule (for shots from 25 feet) from the ill-fated American Basketball League, which had died almost at birth five years earlier.

It was a bright new show. Referees came out dressed in white trousers, blue belts, blue shoes and scarlet shirts with their names in block letters across the back.

It offered some strange heroes. Les Selvage, for instance. You don't remember Les Selvage? After the first quarter of the ABA season, Selvage was making more 3-point baskets than any team in the league for the Anaheim Amigos. The Amigos found him working as a shipping clerk at Douglas Aircraft and playing with the Phi Beta Sigs of the Interfraternity Negro League. He was out of Kirksville, Mo., State, where he had broken all of Harry Gallatin's records. After 17 games, Selvage had hit on 47 of 107 3-point baskets.

The New Orleans Buccanneers offered Doug Moe, a 6-5 do-it-all kind of player who was extracted from exile in Italy, and then signed Larry Brown, who stood 5 feet 10 inches tall. That got a lot of laughs at NBA meetings.

The NBA, in fact, was having a lot of laughs. Concerning the 3-point rule, Eddie Gottlieb, an NBA rules committeeman, said, "What is it but an admission that you are dealing with inferior players who can't do anything but throw up long shots? Is length the only criterion for excellence? I would say that out of every 40 or 50 shots, at least 20 are more difficult than a simple long shot. If it is worth 3 points to make a standard long jump shot, well then, a twisting, driving hook, going full speed to take the pass, curving between two big defenders—why that must be worth 6 points. You encourage mediocrity when you give extra credit to this sort of thing."

But the ABA discovered that the fans enjoyed the 3-point basket, when the games went down to the very last seconds and the team with the ball was down 3 points. Mel Nowell of the New Jersey Americans tied such a game early that year against New Orleans with a 30-footer. The game went into overtime and the Americans won an eventual victory.

The longest 3-pointer was made when Jerry Harkness of Indiana banked in a 92-foot throw at the buzzer to beat Dallas, 119-118. This won Harkness a Sharpshooter's medal from the Indianapolis Marine Reserves and broke what was probably the pro distance record, set by Bill Sharman in the 1957 NBA All-Star Game in Boston. Sharman's shot had been an intended pass to Bob Cousy, but swished the nets from 80 feet instead.

While the first ABA season was being played, Barry jogged the hills of San Francisco, kept his shooting eye sharp by playing with a radio-station team of disc jockeys, took acting lessons under Vince Chase at Universal Studios in Universal City, and moved to a plush new apartment in Lake Merritt, about 30 minutes from the Oakland Coliseum. Rick found the off year to be "less difficult than I had expected."

He was wearing English walking jackets, alpaca sweaters "you know, like Andy Williams," driving his new Porsche and hanging around with show-business types.

"He is image conscious, Hollywood conscious," wrote Arnold Hano, a California writer, "where the reflection of a thing is more important than the thing itself."

Meanwhile, many sportswriters around the country had unleashed the most righteous indignation since they had tried to hound Muhammad Ali out of boxing. They treated the Barry move (and all his subsequent moves) not as a legal or monetary issue, but as a moral one. Rick questioned whether the newsmen were villifying him in an effort to maintain certain standards of purity in professional sports.

"The writers who knocked me would be quick enough to jump to a newspaper that offered them more money and a better spot without any deep feeling of guilt," Barry said. "The San Francisco fans who felt I betrayed them include people who had left the bosses who gave them their first jobs because the guy in the next town made them a better offer."

Without Barry, Oakland finished in last place in the ABA's Western Division, winning only 22 games and losing 56, 26 games behind division-winning New Orleans, which went on to the championship final and lost to Pittsburgh, 4 games to 0.

The Oaks averaged only 2,539 fans a game and lost $750,000. No ABA team made money and the champion Pittsburgh Pipers drew so poorly they moved to Minneapolis the next year, where the old Minneapolis team had lost $400,000 and moved to Miami. Only Indiana and Kentucky drew well. But most of the owners took their losses with seeming equanamity and talked hopefully of "next year when we have Rick Barry."

The Warriors, meanwhile, had dropped to third place in their NBA division without Barry, with a 43-39 record and the Warriors' owner, Franklin Mieuli, moped around like a heartsick lover. Mieuli, a man who wears a guru beard, embroidered shirts, turtle neck sweaters, denim jackets and jeans and throws lavish parties on his yacht, told newsmen:

"There is just the chance, I guess, just the slim chance that Rick could come back and say he was sorry, say he knows now his head was turned, that he made a mistake, that he really didn't leave his heart in San Francisco. Maybe then he would rehabilitate his image and we could catch that lightning in a bottle all over again."

Mieuli vowed to let his beard grow until Barry returned to the Warriors. He hung Barry's No. 24 uniform on his office wall, prayed for Barry's return and moaned.

"Where did I go wrong," he would ask, pacing the rugs of his lawyer's office. "My father—he was a florist—always told me, 'Don't ever worry about the other guy's store. Just mind your own.' The Warriors had everything. It never occurred to me that Rick was boxing me clever. How could I know that suddenly, like that, the strange and wonderful world of Franklin Mieuli would come cascading down over my ears?"

The strange and wonderful world of Franklin Mieuli includes light-weight sailing, ocean yachting, motorcycle riding, shrewd business maneuvers, high finance, a good-luck deerstalker's hat and, his critics say, the guiding hand of Lady Luck. His office, on Golden Gate Street, has the comfortable look—messy desk, a green barber's chair and a short wooden chair carved in the shape of a hand. On the walls are pictures of athletic teams, Albert Einstein, Rudolph Valentino and Rick Barry.

In the stodgy business of professional sports, Mieuli is what is known as a maverick and his success has always been muted by insinuations of luck and happenstance. In short, people are jealous of him.

"That lucky eccentric," his business associates sometimes call him when he isn't around. "He's going to get his someday."

Mieuli's "luck" started back in 1953 when he was working as the head of advertising for a San Francisco brewery for $12,000 a year. Through advertising contacts, he was offered 10 percent of the San Francisco 49ers fooball team for $60,000. He bought the stock, with the help of his father and banks, and the 10 per cent is now worth about $1.5-million. Mieuli later bought a share of the San Francisco Giants baseball team when it moved west, stock which he still owns.

Eventually Mieuli left the brewery and went into business for himself, producing radio and television sports shows in San Francisco. When the Philadelphia Warriors moved west in 1962, Mieuli put together a group of nearly 40 Bay Area residents and purchased 66-⅔ interest in the Warrior franchise.

In their first season in San Francisco, the Warriors

lost $250,000 and when Mieuli went around to collect the debt, the owners were in a near uproar.

Mieuli became upset and offered to purchase the stock of any dissatsfied stockholder. Twenty took him up on the deal and in short time Mieuli owned 94 per cent of the club.

The professional sports fraternity looks upon Mieuli with suspicion, sometimes, for he wears love beads and silver necklaces and, once, he drove his motorcycle to a Warriors' game and parked it in the center jump circle. He once drafted a female basketball player. And signed her.

Once he was asked how he thought he was perceived by other NBA owners and he replied, "I'm the gifted eccentric—except when they have a $28-million television contract to negotiate with CBS so they can dump ABC. Then I can do business."

But all his luck and business expertise couldn't get Rick Barry back from the ABA in 1967. Mieuli's legal bill soared beyond $100,000 as he waged a court battle to keep Barry from playing in the new league. Meanwhile, his Warrior franchise started a downhill run that would, by the end of the 1969-70 season, record the second-worse record in the NBA—30 victories and average attendance of about 2,000.

Mieuli was successful in keeping Barry sidelined through the 1967 season, but then Judge Walter Carpenti ruled that Barry was free to join Oakland for the 1968-69 campaign.

Mieuli's love for Barry never wavered during their long separation. They talked on the telephone often and visited from time to time.

"I know there are a lot of people around who think Rick's some cavalier," he would say later. "He made a mistake at 23 and he made it out in front of God and everybody, not in private like everyone makes theirs. He's been paying and paying for it. He's been a very unhappy man. I remember one day when I was talking to him on the phone I told him we had signed this girl, Denise Long, I said, 'She's a girl Rick Barry,' and Rick said, 'Poor girl.'"

By the time the 1968 season rolled around, Barry's father-in-law, Bruce Hale, had given up the Oaks' coaching job in favor of Alex Hannum, one of Barry's favorite people. Hale, after his disastrous first season, had stepped quietly into the front office and left matters to Hannum and his wife, who watched the budget.

"We're elated," Hannum said when Barry's court victory was announced. "We expect to build a strong franchise and a strong league. And now, we expect some sellout crowds."

Hannum, who had coached championship teams in the NBA at Syracuse and Philadelphia, had signed an eight-year contract with the Oaks as coach and executive vice president and had been assured by Pat Boone and Kenneth Davidson, another Oakland owner, that they planned to "see this thing through to the end." Hannum had been dismissed as the head coach at Philadelphia in the NBA and he abandoned his construction business in Southern California to take the Oakland position.

"I remember Alex telling me in Oakland," Barry recalls, "that we would have the best team in the world someday. 'I don't know if it will take three years or 10 to build it, but it can be done and we will do it someday.'"

Barry had not missed a basketball season since he learned to walk and dribble at approximately the same time in Elizabeth, N.J. "It hardly feels like it has been a year," he said when he reported to the Oaks' first practice session. "I can remember the last play of the 1967 season. It was the sixth game of the final series and we were down one point and . . ."

Barry had missed his last shot trying to shoot over the omnipresent form of Wilt Chamberlain. But there was no Chamberlain to shoot over in the ABA, no intimidating Bill Russell, no Nate Thurmond to stare down at him.

There were some skeptics who were afraid that a Rick Barry turned loose in a new league could only lead to one of two things: He could dominate it so completely as to underline, for a long time to come, the inferiority of the rest of the product; or he could fail to dominate it, and thereby raise unjustified but inescapable questions about the new league's integrity.

The pressure was squarely on Barry, the young NBA scoring champion, the most prominent player to switch leagues.

"It's a different start and different challenge," Barry said at the time. "With the Warriors I had Nate Thurmond back there, so I could concentrate on other things like running and shooting. Now I'm going to have to play more defense. We're building a new team and my role will be entirely different."

Hannum, who had coached Rick as a rookie with the Warriors and had coached against him with the Philadelphia 76ers during the 1966-67 season, said Barry was "a symbol to the Oaks, to the city and, at the moment, more important than anyone to any team anywhere. As far as the technical phases of basketball are concerned, the layoff won't hurt him. Rick would have been a little farther ahead technically had he played last season, and he's bound to improve each year with experience," Hannum said.

Bruce Hale quietly predicted his son-in-law would average 45 to 47 points in the new league.

The Oaks' season opener in 1968-69 was at Indianapolis and a crowd of 9,000, double the usual crowd, had gathered at the Fairgrounds to see the controversial and talented Barry in his ABA debut.

With faint strains of band music drifting in from the court below, Barry sat with his teammates in the dingy old locker room, sweat beading on his forehead. He was wearing a green and gold uniform and he drummed his fingers while listening to Hannum go over his bench signals, which Barry had heard many times before when they were together with the Warriors.

Then it was time to move down into the arena. The players stood just off the court in the dark as each one was introduced in turn, the spotlight following each man to center court. With the proper sense of the dramatic, Barry was saved for last. Only an hour or so before, on his way to the game, Barry had kidded teammate Doug Moe, who had a massive fear of airplanes.

"You might be the first player in the NBA to lose 25 pounds from fear," Barry had said.

"This is the ABA, Rick," Moe had replied softly, smiling.

"This," Barry said to himself as he waited in the darkness, "is a whole new ballgame."

The next-to-last Oak was introduced and ran on the court and now Barry stood alone with Hannum in the dark. "Maybe I should trip and fall," he said.

Hannum grinned. Then the public address announcer called out, "Rick Barry," and the 6-7 superstar was off, never looking back, loping along in the spotlight that followed him across the court, enjoying his fame. At last, he was back to doing what he did best.

The next night in Louisville, 13,067 people nearly filled the huge Exposition Center and that was an ABA record. In two games the Oaks drew 21,956 fans; in the previous season they hadn't passed the 20,000 level in attendance until their 14th game.

Barry's accomplishments against Indiana and Kentucky were equally prodigious as the Oaks, already schooled in the finest Hannum tradition, slaughtered the opposition, 144-133, in Indiana, and 134-113 in Kentucky. Barry scored 36 the first night and 46 the next, making 31 of 54 shots and all 20 of his free throws. He picked up 23 rebounds, leading both teams in the Kentucky game with 14, and he passed off for 12 assists, second only to the total Larry Brown (currently the coach of the Denver Nuggets), who had been among the league leaders the previous season.

In fact, during "garbage time"—late in one-sided games when players often pad their scoring averages—Barry became even more intent on assists, as if that kind of action offered a greater challenge. Most of this Barry appeared to manage with the ease of a man falling out of bed. On the occasions when Hannum called a play like his "two-down" (clearing a side for Barry), Rick scored with such ridiculous ease that it seemed as if basketball itself was defeated, not just Indiana or Kentucky.

But when Barry and the Oaks went home to the Bay Area, they drew only 6,000 for the opening game against New Orleans and dropped to an average of 3,-000 for the first five home games, not much better than the previous season. The drop was curious. Oakland had been a doormat the previous year, losing its last 17 games, and small crowds had been expected. But now the Oaks were the class of the league, winning 12 of their first 14 games, and Rick Barry was leading the league in scoring with a 35-point average.

As the season progressed, Barry continued to pile up points, but he didn't win many friends with the league's management. In his outspoken manner, he became critical of the ABA.

Barry said that the only ABA players good enough to start in the NBA were Roger Brown of Indiana and Connie Hawkins of Pittsburgh (he modestly omitted himself). He also complained to the press about the level of competition and that the Oakland management had not lived up to the financial promises made him.

There were other disappointments. Because of a

knee injury, Barry's first major injury in athletics, he played in only 35 games and missed the playoffs.

But his short season was a sensational one. He won the league scoring title with a 34-point average (he hit 23 consecutive foul shots in one game), Oakland led the league in offense with a 126-point average and the Oaks swept the ABA championship, achieving a 60-18 regular-season record, 14 games ahead of New Orleans. Oakland marched past Denver, 4 games to 3, then New Orleans by 4 games to none and finally the Eastern Division champion Indiana Pacers, 4 games to 1, for the ABA championship. But at the gate, Oakland was a failure.

"We finally got a big crowd in Oakland," Barry tells the story today, "something like 7,000 for a championship playoff game. George Mikan, the league commissioner, was there. He strolled out to center court and announced over the loudspeaker, 'It sure is a pleasure for me to be here in Oklahoma.' "

After the season, Barry got one of the biggest shocks of his career one day when the telephone rang. A friend had called to tell him that the Oaks had been sold and that the people from Washington wanted to talk to him.

"What?" Barry said, obviously stunned. "Washington? What people from Washington?"

There had been some mild rumors that the team might be sold, but Barry had called Pat Boone to ask about it. "He told me it wasn't true," said Barry. "He told me that the Oaks would never leave Oakland. I never heard from him when the Oaks moved on to Washington."

The Washington people turned out to be Earl Foreman, a District of Columbia attorney who had bailed Boone and Davidson out of debt and who had grandiose plans of his own—back in Washington.

When the new owner announced that the franchise would be moved to Washington for the 1969-70 season, Rick balked.

"I felt honestly and truthfully that I had this verbal commitment," Barry said, "that I would never have to leave Oakland. Unfortunately, I didn't have it written in the contract."

Rick also began to find out some other things about his ABA contract. He hadn't been aware, for instance, that he was liable for $750,000 if he walked out on the Oaks.

"I was advised to sign," he said later. "I had no idea. I should have had a lawyer the whole time. It wouldn't have happened if I had had a lawyer with me."

Barry argued that his contract was with the Oakland Oaks, and not with the Washington Capitals. Since the Oaks no longer existed, he felt he was free to negotiate a new contract. Across the Bay, Franklin Mieuli was waiting with open arms to welcome him back to the San Francisco Warriors. Barry signed a five-year $1-million contract, but the courts stepped in once more and ordered him to honor the ABA contract.

Barry began working out with the Warriors anyhow, but re-considered after a message from the Washington owner was carried by the national wire services: "When we open the season and begin prac-

ticing about Sept. 18," said Foreman, "I expect everyone with a contract to be there. Whatever rights we
have I intend to assert as far and as long and as force-
fully as I have to. If Barry breaks his contract with
the Oaks, we will avail ourselves to the full extent of
our legal remedies and rights. It is applicable to anyone who may have breached a contract."

Barry admits today that he tried to take advantage
of the fact that the Warriors wanted him back and
the market value had gone up considerably, "but I
wasn't trying to screw the Washington or Oakland
people," he said. "I was just trying to do what was
right. I wasn't playing one side against the other. I
have honored every contract I've ever had, even
though I may have had two agreements going at the
same time. But they were all predicated on what the
court would decide. What I was doing was not signing contracts to screw anybody, but only to protect
myself according to how the court would rule."

Barry went reluctantly to Washington to begin his
fourth and unhappiest pro season. The last month had
been an emotional time for Barry. He had realized
that he owned 15 per cent of a team with no assets,
that he was not an owner, after all. He had decided
to leave his family in Oakland and take an apartment
in Washington for the season. He was also worried
about his left knee, which had had the medial cartilage removed.

Despite a three-week layoff when he arrived in
Washington, he apparently found that he could play.
He went to the basket well, stopped sharply, cut
quickly, moved well in a crowd. He was shooting his

jump shot effortlessly and people who had seen him before said he wasn't favoring the knee.

Then, suddenly during a Caps' scrimmage a week before the 1969-70 season, he drove and came down wrong on his left leg, hurting the knee again. Now the lateral cartilage was messed up. He tried to play anyway, but the knee gave out a couple of weeks later in a game in Charlotte and Barry was really scared for the first time in his professional life.

"There I was in Washington," he said, "where I didn't want to be in the first place, and having a second operation on my knee, this one leaving me with no cartilage at all." After the operation Barry made all kinds of appearances for the Caps, did the color on television and tried in every way to help the franchise prosper. He also used the time to get mentally adjusted to the idea that he would be playing with no cartilage in his knee. He could not think of another pro basketball player who had played without cartilage. Was his career to be over this soon? He called his wife in California often during the long, cold winter in Washington, and prepared for his comeback on the court in January.

"The biggest problem was getting my body in shape after the layoff," he said. "I tired easily. There was no pain in the knee while I played, just a little unnerving clicking noise. I don't know what it is except I know it's not my cartilage," he said. "In a way, I would like pain, if it meant I could go out and still play the next game. It's been frustrating for me to sit around so much because of injuries when I had never been hurt in my life. Before I was hurt the first time,

I felt I was playing better than I ever had. That includes the 1966-67 season season when I won the NBA scoring title."

With the Warriors, Barry's main asset was his scoring. He could "cheat" a little on defense and others would make up for it. Now he had to play more defense. He passed and set up plays. He did more rebounding, something he hadn't had to worry about when Nate Thurmond was around. Ira Harge, the Caps' center, was a good man, but he was no Nate Thurmond.

Barry played in 52 games and averaged 27.7 points, which was second only to the 30-point average of Spencer Haywood, then playing for Denver, but now an All-Star forward with the Seattle SuperSonics of the NBA. Barry had a 54-point game that season, just one shy of the ABA record.

The Washington Caps, still a member of the Western Division, finished third with a 44-40 mark. They were eliminated in the semifinal round of the playoffs by the then Denver Rockets, 4 games to 3, and Rick averaged 40 points a game during that series.

But it had been a long, lonely season for Barry. The Caps had played 54 road games and their home court was the Uline Arena, old and dingy and in a bad section of Washington.

The Caps were a big bust. Fewer people came to see them play than had seen the Oaks in Oakland.

The game itself had been satisfying to Barry in the ABA, but playing before the small crowds hadn't been. Indiana was about the only team drawing good

crowds consistently, sometimes selling out. "But it is
not much fun playing in Washington before 1,200
Barry said, "and it totally destroys any home court
advantage."

Barry was clearly homesick for California and it
didn't help any when he learned that Earl Foreman
would take the Capitals out of Washington for the
1970-71 season and move them to Virginia. Barry's
fourth team in six seasons would be known as the Virginia Squires and they would play their home games
across the state in Norfolk, Roanoke, Richmond and
Hampton.

The move from city to city was based on the same
formula the Carolina Cougars had tried the season
before.

Once again Barry balked and appealed to the Warriors to help him, but once again he was forced to
stick to his ABA contract. At first, Barry tried to con-
vince Earl Foreman, who had suffered heavy losses in
Washington, to permit him to buy his way out of his
$75,000-a-year contract. After a lot of publicity, in
which Barry was supposed to have offered Foreman
$250,000, the Squires' owner said no reasonable amount
of money could get Barry out of Virginia.

"He can't buy his own contract for $500,000," Fore-
man said at the time. "Barry is more important to basketball, the ABA and Virginia than any reasonable
amount of money. Down in Virginia I'm telling
people we have Rick Barry, Charlie Scott and Doug
Moe and I'm saying they're getting a contender. How
can I say all that and then go out and take green
money for Rick Barry?"

But in an interview with Sports Illustrated magazine, Barry made some totally unexpected remarks that caused Foreman to reconsider. Said Barry, "My son Scooter is supposed to go to nursery school this year. I hate to think of the complications that'll cause in Virginia. I don't want him to go down there to school and learn to speak with a Southern accent. He'll come home from school saying, 'Hi y'all daaad.' I don't want that."

Barry also said, "I've been to Virginia once before to a basketball tournament in Portsmouth. It seemed all right then but I knew I'd be leaving right away. That gives you some idea how I feel about the place. I could say a lot worse things, but I won't ... yet."

Barry continued his assault in the newspapers: "Earl apparently thinks he can offer me enough money so that I'll be happy to go. I don't know if I'd be happier in Norfolk or wherever the hell it is even if he gave me a million dollars a year. I'm very lucky. I live better than all but a very small percentage of people in the country now. How much better can I live?"

The quotations caused a furor, exactly as Barry had hoped. Foreman and Barry were flooded with mail from irate Virginians. Now Foreman was faced with sending his superstar gate attraction into hostile country. Foreman tried to counter with kind words.

"Let me say this about Rick Barry right now," he said. "In my book he has to be one of the best kids I have ever had with me. He wasn't happy in Washington last year but he put out 100 per cent. He is an unusual piece of property and I can't set a value on him."

But the uproar in Virginia worsened and Foreman was advised, for the good of the Squires and the league, to make Barry happy. Foreman called Barry and told him the people around Roanoke did not ever want to see him wear a Squires uniform, and asked how he would like to be traded.

"That was nice of him, you know," said Barry later. "He didn't have to ask me. I told him if it came down to that, there's only one team—New York." Barry meant the Nets, of course.

The next day the Nets' owner, Roy Boe, contacted Barry, and a settlement was soon reached. The estimated price for Barry was $250,000 cash plus the Nets' No. 1 draft choice.

Barry agreed to play his two remaining ABA contract years with the Nets, then return, at last, to San Francisco. "I've always believed if you're going to be any place in sports and be successful, this is the place to be," Barry said at a New York news conference on signing day. "If I can't play for San Francisco, then there's no place I'd rather be."

Then he disclosed his ploy. "I have to apologize to the people in Virginia for using them," he said of his remarks about the state, "but it really helped my position. I doubt I'd do the same in New York. I'm not the type person to do that. A lot of people who know me were surprised when they read those things I said. Even my wife was upset. I have nothing against the South."

The timing seemed perfect for the ABA. The struggling new league, about to enter its fourth season, had begun to realize that in order to compete with the older NBA, and hopefully attain a national television contract, it needed a powerful New York franchise and a superstar for the New York press to write about.

Jack Dolph, a former television executive at CBS, had replaced George Mikan as commissioner and was elated by the Barry transfer.

"Barry is three times more important to us in New York than Virginia," Dolph said. With Barry generating news, it would be easier for Dolph to secure television sponsors, he reasoned.

As for living in New York, where he would pursue his television career, do some modeling and get top endorsements, Barry told friends it was "like having my cake and eating it, too."

As for his legal problems, Berry said he was "fed up" with being in the courtroom. He was also fed up with writers who had knocked his every move.

"People have formed an image of me," he said. "They've pre-judged me when they don't know any of the facts." He said his attorneys had advised him a number of times that he could have brought suit because of the libelous material that was printed, but Barry had had enough of the courtroom.

Although Barry's contract with the Warriors, which he had signed in 1969 trying to stay out of Washington, still had three years to go, Barry signed a three-year agreement with the Nets "just in case Mr. Boe can work something out with Mr. Mieuli," he said.

As for the season ahead, Barry told New York Net

fans, "I feel I'm better than I ever was—rebounding and ball handling as well as shooting, and it's my hope that I can help this team win a championship. My interest in basketball was at its lowest ebb at the prospect of playing in Virginia, but it has been rekindled now that the Nets have taken over my contract."

From the day he arrived in New York, Barry seemed to be a changed man. He took his wife and two sons to New York, rented a home on Long Island and settled down to the serious business of basketball. His new basketball home was the Island Garden in West Hempstead, L.I., where the Nets played while the new Nassau Coliseum in Uniondale, L.I., was being completed.

Lou Carnesecca, who had left St. John's University to take over the Net's coaching job, smiled when Barry arrived for his first workout. "He'll give us new life," he said, "the type of leadership we need."

New York fans loved him immediately. The acquisition of the superstar gave the Nets something they had never had—one of the game's great scoring punches. Carnesecca, starting a five-year contract, took seven holdovers to camp from a 1969-70 team that had reached the playoffs but was beaten, 4 games to 3, by Kentucky in the first round.

The closest thing to a star for the Nets had been now-forgotten LeVern Tart, who had led the team with a 24-point average. The Nets had finished fourth in the Eastern Division in the regular season with a record of 39 victories and 45 defeats.

Before that, the New Yorkers had finished last with a dismal 17-61 record (1968-69) and in 1967-68 they had tied for last place in their division with a 36-42 record (when they were known as the Jersey Americans.

As the Americans, the team had played in an armory in Teaneck, N.J., where the water pipes burst and caused the playing floor to buckle, where fans huddled in overcoats to keep warm during games and where the team attracted a gross gate of $106,000 for 42 home games. After that, the Americans became the Nets and moved to Commack, L.I., and played under conditions only slightly better, about 65 miles from New York City.

The Nets had drawn 154,678 fans at the Island Garden in their third year, almost four times their attendance record to that time, but the figure still was low. Rick Barry would change all that, everyone agreed.

Barry's new teammates were Manny Leaks, Sonny Dove, Joe Depre, Jeff Congdon, Ollie Taylor, Luther Green, Bill Bunting, Bill Melchionni and a promising freshman from St. John's named Billy Paultz. Barry, at 26, was the old man in the starting lineup.

Barry did change things. The Island Garden had been expanded to hold about 5,500 but the Nets had never filled it to capacity. Barry began filling sets, but the fans had to wait to see much of their new superstar. On Oct. 29, just as the 1970-71 season was getting under way, Barry, trying to play on a sore foot, broke it on the court and didn't get back into action until Dec. 9, the night before the Nets were scheduled to make their first appearance ever at

Madison Square Garden in part of an ABA double-header.

Injuries had become a major factor in his career. In the past three seasons he had played in only 89 games because of ailments or court orders. With the Nets, he got in 59 games that first year, scored 1,734 points and narrowly lost the ABA scoring title to Kentucky's Dan Issel. Issel finished with a 29.88 average, Barry 29.39.

Barry led the league with 451 foul shots made out of 507 attempts. What made him exceptional, though, was his uncanny ability to produce when it counted.

"When you have a player of Barry's ability," said Carnesecca, "you take full advantage of it. I rate Rick up there with Jerry West as the two players a coach would love to have take the final shot of the game."

Here is a thumbnail sketch of game highlights after Barry's return to the line-up during the 1971-72 season:

January 10. League-leading Virginia led by 3 points with less than five seconds remaining when Barry scored from 35 feet to tie it and send game into overtime. Nets lose, Barry scores 39.

January 15. Barry scores 53 against Pittsburgh in a bruising, fight-marred game, playing despite stiffening knee in the third period.

January 16. Nets trail Kentucky by 18 points early in the fourth quarter when Barry leads comeback. With two seconds left and the Nets behind by 1 point, Barry drives on former Net Walt Simon and his spinning, driving shot drops through to give the Nets victory. Barry finished with 39 points.

January 20. Barry scores 22 points in the last 15 minutes, including seven straight as the Nets beat Florida, 120-117.

January 23. All-Star Game: Barry leads East to a 126-122 victory, scoring 4 points in last 49 seconds.

January 27. Barry scores 9 of 11 points in overtime as Nets beat Utah, 108-107.

January 29. Barry's 44th and 45th points with 4 seconds left give the Nets a 132-131 victory over Pittsburgh.

His heroics showed at the cash register. The Nets, who had been largely ignored by the media, began to attract attention. He played to two capacity crowds, one of which he treated to a 53-point scoring performance.

In the growth of the Nets," said Coach Carnesecca, "no one player could have done as much for a franchise as has Rick. Dave Debusschere (of the Knicks) is a great forward, one coaches pray will come along, but for the Nets, a Barry is more important. When he came to New York, he brought us his outstanding playing ability and tremendous public relations value. He is controversial, much the Leo Durocher type when he managed the old Brooklyn Dodgers. Our older fans respect and enjoy his play and our younger fans idolize him."

One of the controversies surrounding Barry had to do with his running feud with Norm Drucker, an official the ABA recruited from the NBA. One night in Tampa Drucker hit him with three technical fouls, which cost Barry $350—$50 for the first, $100 and automatic disqualification for the second and $200 for the third. And if Barry hadn't been pulled bodily away by his teammates, he could have tried for a fourth technical, which would have cost him another $400. Of the six times Barry had been ousted from games, three times it was ordered by Drucker.

Barry's tantrums with officials and his court drama soon caused him to be labeled "cry baby" and "Mighty Mouth." The physical punishment he absorbed during each game—the welts, the scratches, the shoving, the hatchet jobs—loosened his tongue as never before and he soon led the league in technical fouls.

Barry defended himself. "People have told me about it," he said. "They tell me how it looks and how it disturbs people in the stands when I let go. But I think I'm fouled a lot more than I get to the line and if I don't let the ref know how I feel, it will just get out of hand."

Barry says that one of the first moves he would make, if he had the power, would be the assignment of a third referee in each game.

"Officiating is the most difficult job in basketball," he said, "and it's the one that becomes involved in the most controversy. Basketball has changed so much in the last 25 years that it can no longer keep the same concept of officiating it had 25 years ago. Basketball has become so fast the officials can no longer keep up. They can't stay ahead of the game, so they're bound to miss a few calls. With three officials, you'll always have someone under the basket on a fast break. Now, sometimes the official winds up trailing the play. The main thing that plagues officiating is inconsistency.

The extra man would help that problem. What the leagues should do is implement an intensive college recruiting program for officials, set up a school for them and pay them enough to make it a fulltime job.

"When I was in San Francisco in my second year of pro ball," he said, "I made it a point not saying anything to the officials. For seven games you didn't hear a word of protest out of me and you know what were the results? I went to the line a maximum of five times in those games when I had been averaging 12 or 13. If you're not hollering, letting them know what's going on, then the refs are going to figure everything's cool. I've just got to try and let them know in a nicer way maybe. That's all.

"I don't play the way I play to satisfy the fans or do anything special so that people will like me. But it doesn't mean that I don't want them to like me. I certainly do. My wife, Pam, gets very upset when she hears abuse from the stands. She wants everyone to like me, but it can't be. If I'm satisfied, then that's all that counts. I'm very very easy to love or hate."

Barry was especially disliked in Virginia, the state he had spurned. A few days into his first season with the Nets, the team traveled to Virginia to play the Squires, who were having a "Banner Night" promotion. The hosts asked Barry to be the judge. A big crowd had turned out to hiss and boo him and to insult him with its signs.

Barry chose this winning banner: "Great Scott, Who Needs Barry?" The sign referred to the Squires' super rookie, Charlie Scott.

If Barry was attracting attention, so was the ABA.

The league got its greatest exposure with the December 9 doubleheader at Madison Square Garden, the first ABA show there in its four seasons. A crowd of 12,552 was announced, many of them children who had been lured by the give-away of 6,000 red, white and blue basketballs, which critics said belonged on a beach or on the nose of a seal. The ball became a source of envy in some NBA quarters after the ABA had announced a sale of 2 million of them.

After the doubleheader, fans began comparing the two leagues more objectively. Leonard Koppett, in the New York Times, wrote:

"No one believes that a strong ABA team, like Indiana, would hold its own, night after night, with the strongest NBA clubs, like the Knicks or Milwaukee, or Los Angeles or Baltimore. But beyond that, the difference in ability narrows quickly. A big difference in style is that team defense is less aggressive and less well organized in the ABA and rebounding is less fierce. In short, the ABA is just about where the American Football League was in its fourth year with respect to the National Football League—and everyone is aware how quickly that gap closed.

"The biggest single difference is the presence of experienced, expert big men in the NBA. They not only make the NBA teams stronger by their own play, they create conditions for their teammates that make these teams stronger."

And as for Rick Barry, many were considering him the best pure shooter in the game, but Barry disagreed.

"I'm not a great shooter," he said. "I think I'm a

good scorer an I know how to get points, but don't think of myself as an outstanding shooter. A great shooter is someone who can stand outside all night and pop in better than 50 per cent of his shots. I can do that on a given evening, but not most of the time.

"My idea of a great shooter is Jerry West. If I had to have someone take an outside shot late in the game to win it, West would be my choice. I drive to the basket a lot and I get fouled a lot. I think you have to go to the foul line 10 or 12 times a game to be a big scorer, and I make the most of my scoring opportunities."

By the time Barry's first season with the Nets had ended, he was a happy 26-year-old New York celebrity whose handsome face filled the advertising pages of Long Island newspapers. He was beginning to have second thought about returning to San Francisco.

When he was asked about his plans after the Net contract expired, he said, "I really look at the situation as one in which I can't lose. We love the Bay Area and I would love playing with (Nate) Thurmond again and the rest of the Warriors. It's just that, like I keep saying, I've got things going in New York. They're all activities I expect to be involved in years after my playing days are over."

Barry launched the 1971-72 season in grand style, often scoring 30, 40, 50 points a game. In five games over an eight-day stretch he averaged 40.4 points. He began his outburst with 38 points against the Virginia Squires. Two nights later he scored 40 at Miami and followed that with a 41-point show the next night against Pittsburgh. Three days later he battered Pittsburgh again with 32 points and topped it off with a 51-point effort against the Carolina Cougars in Greensboro, N.C.

He almost single-handedly led the undermanned Nets to the final round of the ABA playoffs against the Indiana Pacers after helping New York to a third-place finish in the regular standings (44-40). The Nets staged a colossal upset in the first playoff round when they knocked off the Kentucky Colonels, winners of a record 68 games during the regular season. The Nets eliminated the Colonels in six games.

Though he had been hurting for weeks, Rick played magnificently and was the key figure, along with rookie guard John Roche, in steering the Nets to the final round against Indiana. With Rick Mount, George McGinnis, Freddie Lewis, Mel Daniels, Roger Brown and Billy Keller, the Pacers won in six games. But the Nets tied the series, 1-1, with a 117-115 second-game victory when Barry hit a basket and a free throw in the last 27 seconds. Barry scored 44 points in a third-game loss, then spearheaded a last-quarter rally as the Nets tied the series again, 2-2, before a record Playoff crowd of 15,890 at Nassau Coliseum.

The Pacers won the fifth game, 100-99, and the sixth, 108-105, and that's how close Barry and the Nets came to winning the ABA title in 1972.

For the year, Barry finished second to Virginia's Charlie Scott in league scoring, Scott averaging 34.58 points a game, Barry 31.47. Barry again led the league in free throws, making 641 shots in 730 attempts for an 87.8 percentage. In the playoffs, only

Julius Erving of Virginia had a better scoring average, 33.27 to 30.78.

At the end of the season, Barry made a decision to stay in New York. "There is nothing like my New York television deal available to me in San Francisco or Oakland," he explained. "I want to finish my career here." Barry was a sportscaster on Channel 7 Eyewitness News, he was making excellent money on endorsements and the Nets were on the verge of a championship.

Barry even threatened retirement if he could not stay with the Nets. The Warriors' contract which he had signed in 1969 "was just an agreement," he said. He filed suit to remain in New York.

Despite attempts by Nets' owner Roy Boe to keep him (one published report said Boe offered $600,000 for Barry and was refused, but Boe denied it), Barry lost. When the pretrial hearing came before Federal Judge Alphonso Zirpoli in June of 1972, Barry had resigned himself to another defeat.

"I've been going to court to settle one case or another ever since 1967," he said. "I cannot keep the cases straight anymore. I'm not sure which suits have been settled and which have not been. If they send me back, I pack my stuff and go back."

Judge Zirpoli ruled in favor of the Warriors on October 6, just a few days before the 1972-73 season was to open. An out-of-shape Barry packed and flew to San Francisco and back into the life of a happy Franklin Mieuli.

"Even when he said he'd retire," said Barry's roommate with the Nets, Bill Melchionni, "I knew he couldn't. You have to understand. Rick really wants to play basketball. Sitting out would have killed him."

Roy Boe, the Nets' owner, offered no regrets. "We knew when he came here we had him for just two years," he said. "We needed a great player and a great gate attraction and he was the answer. He has played in pain, led us to our best season in history and has made himself available to our fans and our public relations needs. I have released him from all his contracts with me. He's 28 years old. When I was 28, I changed my mind many times, too. I had hoped Rick would stay, but I wasn't really hurt. I think the team was hurt."

Coach Carnesecca said, "There's no resentment. There is sorrow. We're just the richer for having had him."

By the time Barry left New York, the Metropolitan press seemed to better understand him. "What he has done," wrote Jerry Izenberg, a syndicated columnist, "is make the best deals he can for himself and his family, and if you do not think that is important, try to visualize what happens to a fellow who is cheerful, loyal, obedient, etc., who breaks his leg, can't ever play again and waits for his loyal, cheerful employers to demonstrate how deep their alleged loyalty actually runs."

The year Barry rejoined the Warriors, the Naismith Memorial Basketball Hall of Fame in Springfield, Mass., accepted three items from the growing ABA: two red, white and blue basketballs and Rick Barry's No. 24 Nets uniform, the first ABA uniform ever put on display in the hall.

Chapter Seven

Simultaneous with Barry's return to the Warriors, Franklin Mieuli, the ecstatic owner, changed the team name to Golden State and moved into a new home in Oakland. He also shaved off the five-year-old beard, which he had vowed to wear until Barry returned to the Warriors. "My father called the day it happened," Mieuli said, "complimented me on sticking it out and then reminded me about the beard.

"Barry's return made us whole again," he said. "I used to pray Rick would return. I wanted him back so badly I could taste it. I knew that after all the bad things that had happened to us that something good was coming up."

Once Rick realized he was a Warrior again, he said he could not be more delighted. He was in Utopia, he said. He bestowed all the virtues upon the Bay Area that, a year earlier, he had said belonged solely to New York. He no longer brooded.

"I'm tired of doing all that stuff," he said of his itinerant past. "I'm settled down, finally enjoying myself and my family. The Bay Area still doesn't have the side things an athlete can get there (New York) and the people are still not as crazy for their basketball, but I've got the cake, maybe not the icing, but it's a good cake."

The Barry who returned to the NBA for the 1972-73 season was a much more mature player than the boy who had left in 1967. The immature Barry had been strictly offensive-minded. The mature Barry was a polished player, team-oriented. He had done everything he had set out to do except lead a team to an NBA title and that was the next item on his agenda.

The new Barry was best exemplified by his steady growth in the assist column. As a rookie he had 173 assists. In his first season back in the NBA, the number was 399. The next year it was 484, and then 492.

"Sure I'm a different player," Barry admitted. "I don't think I have to prove to people that I can score points. I've done that. I only want to show that I can play the game, not just shoot. I enjoyed my first season back because I felt more a part of the game. I think the time I spent in the ABA helped me become a complete player. I had to do things over there that I didn't have to do when I was with the Warriors. I think I was almost forced to develop myself as a complete player."

Jeff Mullins, Barry's teammate when the Warriors went to he NBA final in 1967, hailed Rick's return.

"Defenses have changed since 1967," he said. "Playing teams like the Knicks, Bulls, Lakers and others, requires intelligent defenses. Defenses try to jam you now, try to overplay you, double up, sag; do anything legal to change your pattern. The forwards are shorter, the game is faster. And Rick is ideal for today's game.

"He is also more polished offensively then he was in 1967. He doesn't go to the hoop as much because we have plenty of shooters, but he's a far better passer, and in fact, I don't know of any forward who passes as well on the give-and-go."

While Barry was playing in the ABA, Al Attles, his teammate in 1966, had become the Warriors coach. Attles, a 6-1 center from Weequaic High in Newark N.J., who had become one of pro basketball's finest guards, was developing into one of the league's finest coaches.

"He's our mother," Nate Thurmond said of Attles, "our father, our good friend. His is a very personal relationship with a team and he has the ability to unite the oddest mixture of people and circumstance and turn it into what seems to be a family atmosphere."

Attles had never attracted a lot of attention as a player except with his contemporaries, who called him "The Destroyer". He had uncanny leaping ability for his height, frequently came up with big plays and was a willing fighter in defense of his teammates.

Once, when he was a teammate of Barry's, Barry became involved in a heated dispute with an opponent who had been bumping him around and just as Barry started to take fistic action, Attles stepped in with a quick flurry that settled the issue.

Attles' greatest offensive performance, perhaps, went almost unnoticed. It happened on March 2, 1962 in Hershey, Pa., when he was a teammate of Wilt Chamberlain's with the Philadelphia Warriors. He shot eight times that night against the New York Knicks and made all eight—a perfect night. But that's the night that Chamberlain scored 100 points and Attle's performance was hardly mentioned.

Attles had been an admirer of Barry's when they were teammates and his admiration grew as he watched his star perform, from the bench during the 1972 season.

After watching Rick for the first two months of the season, Attles said, "For my money, he is the best forward in the league. There are guys who do things better, but there isn't anyone who can put it all together like Rick can. No forward in the league can do as many things as well. He changed his style when he came back and it was all his doing."

In Golden State's first encounter with the Knicks after Barry's return (with Barry's presence paying off in Golden State's biggest crowd in memory), Dave De-Busschere moved in to muscle Rick. Rick muscled back. The Knicks' tactic was to drive Barry outside, beyond his normal shooting range. Barry promptly sank the Warriors' first two shots—30 footers. When the Knicks ganged up on him, he fed passes to team-mates isolated under the basket or drove around the startled Knick defenders.

Rick made 12 of 20 shots and the Warriors won, 127-104. There was no doubt in the NBA after that. Barry had grown up.

The Warriors finished the season second to Los An-eles in the Pacific Division with a 47-35 record and were eliminated by the Lakers, 4 games to 1, in the Western Conference playoff, a disappointment. Barry's scoring average was his lowest as a pro, 22 points a game, but it led the Warriors. More important, Barry had become a better team man than at any time of his career.

He hauled in 728 rebounds, second highest in his career, led the team in assists with 399 and played in all 82 regular-season games for the first time in his pro career. His league-leading .902 free-throw per-centage (358 of 397) was one of the highest ever recorded. He scored 39 straight foul shots a the be-ginning of the season.

Barry had one of his super seasons the following year. Despite a nagging injury, he made the All-Star team and scored 40 or more points eight times in the final 41 games. He again led the team in assists with 484, in scoring with a 25.1 average, and he was the second-leading rebounder with 540.

Two weeks before the end of the 1973-74 season, the Warriors were in command in the Pacific Division when, incredibly, they couldn't win. While the sec-ond-place Lakers were bounding back to win four straight, the Warriors lost five in a row—and the division title.

Instead of playing in the playoffs, Barry became the color man on the NBA playoff telecasts and his outspoken manner delighted viewers and irritated players.

Although the year was a disappointment, Barry achieved one of his personal goals, a 60-point night. It came in March of 1974 against the Portland Trail Blazers. It should have been one of Rick's happiest moments in basketball, but two nights before the Warriors had been eliminated from the Division title by the Lakers and it had taken all the joy from a 64-point performance.

"I used to think it would be nice to score 60 points in a game some time," he said, "but the fact that I did it, what did it mean? The whole season was lost, so what did it mean?" Only such legends as Wilt Chamberlain and Elgin Baylor had scored more points in a game and only Chamberlain had made more than the 30 field goals Barry amassed in his awesome performance.

Barry turned 30 as the 1973-74 season ended and he announced that he would probably play only two or three more years. After nine years in the pros, he was still chasing the NBA championship and time was running out. "I have nothing left to prove individually," he said. "I just want to win."

Barry vowed to do whatever he had to do to win, the next season, be whatever he had to be. And if one factor could be considered responsible for the Warriors' 1975 NBA title, it would be Barry's infectuous spirit.

There were times during Barry's rise when he had been impatient, and lacked warmth. Perhaps he had shown a touch of greed, had been tactless or contradictory. But those were scars of learning. He had also shown great slices ot generosity, loyalty, honesty, kindness, unbending standards of quality, incredible dedication and sheer greatness. These were the virtues that had come to the fore in the mature Rick Barry. He had come a long way from Roselle Park High in New Jersey, where he had been a sometimes sad and lonely star waiting to blossom.

When the 1974-75 season started, everybody was together with Rick Barry and Rick Barry was together with the world.

Gone was Cazzie Russell. Gone was Nate Thurmond. Gone were Jim Barnett and Clyde Lee. It was a new family of teammates when he arrived for his first workout in September.

"You know," Barry told a friend one afternoon as he looked over the young, rag-tag Warrior team, "one of the priests I'm friendly with, Father Keegan, always tells me the best things come out of the worst. He said that from out of the mud grows the lotus."

This is the "Family" that Coach Attles turned in for the printers as game programs were prepared for the season opener:

No.	Name	Pos.	Hgt.	Wgt.	Age	College	Yrs. Pro
24	Rick Barry	F	6-7	220	30	Miami ('65)	9
21	Butch Beard	G	6-3	185	27	Louisville ('69)	4
22	Steve Bracey	G	6-1	175	24	Tulsa ('72)	2
40	Derrick Dickey	F	6-7	218	23	Cincinnati ('73)	1
34	Frank Kendrick	F	6-6	198	22	Purdue ('74)	0
10	Charles Johnson	G	6-0	170	25	California ('71)	2
15	Charles Dudley	G	6-2	180	24	Washington ('72)	1
52	George Johnson	C	6-11	220	25	Dillard ('70)	2
23	Jeff Mullins	G	6-4	200	32	Duke ('64)	10
44	Clifford Ray	C	6-9	235	25	Oklahoma ('71)	3
20	Phil Smith	G	6-4	187	22	San Francisco ('74)	0
41	Keith Wilkes	F	6-6½	190	21	UCLA ('74)	0

Bill Bridges, who had been in playoffs 10 different years with St. Louis and Atlanta, didn't join the team until late in the season when the Warriors were looking for playoff help. He played in only 15 regular-season games before the playoffs.

The Warriors opened with a 105-90 loss to Los Angeles, but then quickly took command in their division. After the first quarter of the season, Golden State had won 17 of its first 24 games and Rick Barry was leading all candidates nationwide on the All-Star ballot.

"There's a strange chemistry sparking on this team," Coach Attles kept telling his friends, "like something good is about to happen."

The underdog Warriors survived a mid-season slump, won the Pacific Division championship and gained momentum as they marched through the playoffs.

"This is a Cinderella team," said Bill Bridges, the old man of the club at age 36, as the Warriors prepared to meet the highly favored Washington Bullets in the 1975 championship final. "It's never going to take the glass slipper off. Sometimes the clock never strikes 12."

It never did.

When Captain Barry and his family of no-name Warriors went out and swept four straight games from the Bullets in one of the greatest storybook finishes in sports history, the last Barry critic had been answered. He went to the dressing room, sat down with his face in his hands and cried.

The controversy and the criticism are behind Barry

now and he doesn't have to explain anything to anybody, or prove anything. He can just go out and play his game. The only questions that remain deal not with his past, but with his future. What will drive him now that his goals have been reached?

"You know what I want now," he says, "what I dream about? It's playing the perfect game ... shutting my man off with nothing ... not missing a single shot or a single free throw ... not making a single turnover ... the perfect game."

"Beyond the ingredients themselves, eating the traditional Mediterranean way is a philosophy in itself: Life is for savoring, and food is a glorious and beautiful expression of life."

—from *The Mediterranean Diet*

LOSE WEIGHT AND BE HEALTHY— INDULGE IN THE LUSCIOUS TASTES OF THE MEDITERRANEAN

- Thick, dark, whole grain breads . . .
- Wild greens, zucchini, spinach, peas, tomatoes, mushrooms—the freshest vegetables . . .
- Tasty pasta, from Italian spaghetti to Moroccan couscous and polenta; whole grains, including risotto and pilaf . . .
- Protein-rich legumes: lentils; chickpeas; fava, white haricot, and cranberry beans
- Succulent fruits: peaches, cantaloupe, watermelon, figs, grapes . . .
- Savory seasonings: garlic, onion, basil, oregano, parsley, cilantro, olive oil . . .

AND MUCH MORE!

Bon appétit!

THE
Mediterranean
DIET

Newly Revised and Updated

Marissa Cloutier, MS, RD
and Eve Adamson

Recipes by Eve Adamson

Produced by Amaranth

HARPER

An Imprint of HarperCollinsPublishers

THE MEDITERRANEAN DIET is not a substitute for sound medical advice. The ideas, procedures, and suggestions in this book are intended to supplement, not replace the medical advice of a trained medical professional. All matters regarding your health require medical supervision. Consult your physician before adopting any suggestions in this book, as well as about any condition that may require diagnosis or medical attention. The authors, publisher, and book producer disclaim any liability arising directly or indirectly from the use of this book.

HARPER

An Imprint of HarperCollins*Publishers*
10 East 53rd Street
New York, New York 10022-5299

First Harper paperback printing: September 2006
First Avon Books paperback printing: February 2004

Avon Trademark Reg. U.S. Pat. Off. and in Other Countries, Marca Registrada, Hecho en U.S.A.
HarperCollins® and **HARPER**® are registered trademarks of HarperCollins Publishers.

Printed in the U.S.A.

Visit Harper paperbacks on the World Wide Web at
www.harpercollins.com

20

This book is dedicated to Michael and Sophie.
Wishing you both good health and a long, happy life.

—M. C.

To my children, Angus and Emmett,
that they may learn to eat well, live well,
and take their health into their own hands.

—E. A.

Acknowledgments

I would like to thank Normand J. Cloutier, Ph.D.; Michael D. Cloutier; Gail Zyla, M.S., R.D.; Mary Thang; and Sharon Lee Asta for their support and inspiration.

—M. C.

Thanks to my parents, my most appreciative taste testers for the past fifteen years.

—E. A.

Contents

Contents

Introduction

If you grew up with a television set, you've probably seen the familiar scenario: a family gathered around the breakfast table, their plates piled high with eggs, bacon, sausage, maybe even a breakfast steak and a formidable stack of pancakes made with that ubiquitous box of handy biscuit mix. A bottle of maple-flavored syrup and a stick of butter (or tub of margarine) adorned the center of the table. A large glass of whole milk and a small glass of orange juice stood sentinel in front of every plate. A mother, coiffed and smiling, urged the family to finish the "nutritious" breakfast, that "most important meal of the day!"

One has to wonder how Americans got the idea that bacon and pancakes for breakfast made for a healthy meal. And what about dinner? America's "ideal" dinner in the 1950s and 1960s consisted of a large hunk of meat and a baked potato with butter and sour cream, along with a stack of packaged white bread and butter and possibly a small bowl of iceberg lettuce and a few carrot shreds on the side, or a few spoonfuls of overcooked, heavily salted, buttered vegetables. We all thought this sort of "home cooking" made us strong and healthy, didn't we? Not to mention, we got pretty accustomed to that comfort-food taste.

So why on earth would we want to switch to unadorned, whole-grain cereal and fruit for breakfast, or salads and vegetable soups for dinner, with (the horror!) no cream and butter to help them go down? Why would we want to eat whole-grain bread when the neat white stuff is so cheap and readily available (and presliced!)? And why would we give up that big dish of ice cream, slab of cake, or wedge of apple pie à la mode for dessert in favor of a bowl of fruit?

Then again, why would we want to eat in a manner that has made America one of the leading countries in the number of heart attacks per year? Surely Mom's home cooking hasn't been killing us off—or has it?

The irony of the situation is that while 1950s Americans were happily downing forkfuls of high-fat, highly refined fare in enjoyment of their prosperity, at the same time in history, the people living around the Mediterranean Sea, in regions less wealthy and with food budgets far lower, were eating what scientists and researchers have recently discovered is one of the healthiest ways to eat in the world. Today, as Americans struggle to retain or regain their coronary health, they are turning to the latest, cutting-edge research for guidance, and that research is pointing with increased frequency toward the traditional cuisines of the working class in the Mediterranean region as seen during the 1950s and 1960s and before. Sometimes, progress means looking backward—and, in this case, to another continent.

The problem is, Americans love their food, and aren't quick to adopt any program, guideline, or advice that takes them away from their beloved burgers and fries. But let's give the traditional Mediterranean diet a second look. What is so special about the traditional Mediterranean diet? Why, for the past forty years or so, have researchers been excited about the traditional dietary habits of the people around the Mediterranean Sea? Aren't eating habits from so many years ago outmoded today, when so many cutting-edge food products line our supermarket shelves? Isn't progress the name of the game? Those frozen dinners don't taste too bad . . .

First, let's look at how Americans have developed their ideas about nutrition and what makes for a healthy meal. Without an understanding of how our own preconceptions developed, a change in diet probably won't be effective. Why do we eat what we eat? And how do we know what to eat now? What does the research say?

⊘ THE GOLDEN AGE OF NUTRITION

In the early part of the twentieth century, nutrition science was in its infancy but growing fast. Many exciting and significant advances in nutritional knowledge were made between 1910 and 1960, particularly the discovery of specific nutrients and their biochemical relationship to human health. What was required to maintain health and support growth and reproduction? And what would happen when certain nutrients were missing? These were the questions that concerned nutrition scientists of the day.

During this period, scientists learned that without vitamin C, people develop scurvy; without vitamin A, night blindness. Vitamin D deficiencies lead to rickets in children, thiamin deficiencies to beriberi, niacin deficiencies to pellagra, and calcium deficiencies to stunted growth in children and osteoporosis later in life. Iron deficiencies lead to anemia, iodine deficiencies to goiter, and zinc deficiencies to growth failure in children. These conditions are classics in nutrition science today, and have all led to an understanding that a certain nutrient profile is necessary for health. The emphasis of research was on what might be missing from our diets that could compromise our health.

One significant example of this research emphasis was the work of several British investigators, including Corey Mann and Boyd Orr. In the first half of the twentieth century, these two researchers attempted to remedy the problem of why the working classes in northern England and Scotland—the groups reproducing at a higher rate than the aristocracy—seemed to be getting shorter and thinner. The government of Great Britain was concerned. Prominent was the notion that the "lower" classes were simply genetically inferior, but how could Britain compete in an increasingly global world as a colonial power if their very genetic stock was degenerating? Was there anything they could do to restore the working class? Was the answer within the realm of human control?

Mann and Orr embarked on an investigation to determine whether anything could be done to induce growth in short children. Sure enough, the results of feeding studies using short children as subjects revealed that feeding butter and sugar induced weight gain but no height increase; children fed milk or meat supplements, on the other hand, grew taller. The British working class wasn't genetically lacking—it was malnourished! Public policy began to evolve in conjunction with farmers and social activists to provide milk in schools, milk and orange juice to pregnant and nursing mothers, and, once World War II began, milk and meat rations equally to all classes. Food production became a major priority for many nations, not just Great Britain. "Avoid deficiencies" was the battle cry.

Once the war hit and the possibility arose that the enemy might be able to prohibit the importation of food, food production and rationing took on an even greater importance. Great Britain's agricultural policy shifted to emphasize the production of milk and meat to ensure the welfare of children, the "nation's future." Agricultural autonomy became a matter of national survival as well as national pride. Unfortunately, this meant that much of the farmland that was used to grow crops such as oats, flax, and winter wheat were cleared to support the increasing meat and dairy industry.

✐ POSTWAR NUTRITIONAL PRIORITIES

Since World War II, efficient food production has been the order of the day for developed countries all over the world. Science applied to farming methods in the form of pesticides, fertilizers, growth regulators, and genetic selection has resulted in higher yields from crops, more efficient production of livestock and dairy herds, and agricultural policies that distinguish farmers from all other business industries. Farming became big business—ultra-efficient and a major money-maker, too.

The second major development since the war was in the area of food processing. Processed food—in cans, in dried form, and otherwise packaged for our convenience—is a relatively new phenomenon. Packaged food, often enriched, seemed to be a cheap and efficient way to feed the masses. Because the current climate emphasized the need for calories and the inclusion of all the required micronutrients (to prevent stunted growth, for example, or a range of other health problems), the food industry's invention and production of ready-made foods seemed to represent a revolution in nutrition. As long as these products had sufficient calories and micronutrients, little thought was given to what else they might contain: high saturated fat and sugar content, preservatives, highly refined ingredients, and so on. These products were easily distributed, lasted a long time, and seemed to represent an efficient way to meet the energy requirements of a large population. Most nutritionists of the day were in favor of this new trend.

Even today, politicians, physicians, and the food industry believe that deficiency prevention should be the primary nutritional objective. Of course, preventing nutritional deficiencies is still important. If micronutrients are lacking in the diet, health problems will still occur. However, the previous approach, which emphasized sufficient calories and micronutrient deficiency prevention, has led to problems the policymakers before World War II could hardly have foreseen. Our technologically advanced and vastly automated society has a lower need for calories, or energy, than it once did in a more labor-intensive climate. (Even farming, once a very hard and active lifestyle, has, on the whole, become largely machine-driven.) Less physical activity translates to fewer calorie needs. Also, we are discovering that highly processed and packaged food sometimes contains additional undesirable elements—too many calories, too much sugar, too much saturated fat or chemically altered trans fats, or artificial preservatives, for example—and may also lack components such as phytochemicals and fiber not previously factored into nutritional requirements.

⊛ THE MEDITERRANEAN DIET: BEYOND ADEQUATE

But what does all this have to do with the Mediterranean diet? As America and Great Britain shifted their focus toward meat and milk as well as toward the efficient feeding of large numbers of people, those living in the Mediterranean region after World War II continued to eat much the way they had eaten for centuries, their diet peacefully undiscovered. With diets consisting primarily of plant foods instead of foods from animal sources, people in the Mediterranean region were enjoying exceptionally low levels of coronary heart disease and other chronic diseases, such as certain forms of cancer.

The first major study to examine the diet of people living in the Mediterranean was a comprehensive and astonishingly thorough examination of the diets of the people living on the island of Crete in 1948. The Greek government, in an attempt to improve the postwar conditions of its country, turned to the industrialized nations for advice. In response, the Rockefeller Foundation assigned epidemiologist Leland Allbaugh to the case.

Whether or not everyone assumed the animal protein–based diet of the industrialized nations would be superior to the plant-based diet of underdeveloped Crete, the results of the Rockefeller Foundation study were surprising. Far from presenting a bleak health picture of poverty, malnourishment, starvation, and ill health, the Cretan diet, according to the foundation researchers, was "surprisingly good." Deriving approximately 61 percent of its calories from plant foods, only 7 percent from animal foods, and a full 38 percent of total calories from fat (similar to the percentage of fat in the United States food supply of the late 1940s, but primarily from olive oil and olives rather than from animal fats), the diet was indeed more than "surprisingly good." It was very conducive to health, specifically heart health.

Ironically, however, Allbaugh's final analysis included a recommendation that the Cretan diet could be improved with more foods of animal origin, primarily because study respondents generally expressed a wish for more meat, rice, fish, pasta, butter, and cheese (in that order) in their diets. A full 72 percent of people in the survey named meat as their favorite food. In contemporary Crete, foods of animal origin make up a greater percentage of the diet than they once did. One recent study of the urban population of Crete found increased intake of animal products and a decreased intake of bread, fruit, potatoes, and olive oil compared to the 1960s diet. Similar changes in other Mediterranean countries are also evident, and scientists have also observed an increase in the rate of coronary heart disease, diabetes, and several types of cancers in the Mediterranean region today.

The Rockefeller Foundation study was the first major study to examine the diets of those living in the Mediterranean. Since then, researchers have studied why people living in these areas were living longer lives and enjoying far lower rates of coronary heart disease and other chronic diseases than those living in more industrialized countries. Study after study examining the traditional diets of the

Mediterranean region has supported the notion that a primarily plant-based diet may indeed be at the heart of longer life and better health.

⊘ RECENT TRENDS

The message is still prevalent in the minds of people living in the Western world: Eat animal protein and lots of it. One unfortunate result of this dictum has been an overemphasis on foods that contain a high amount of saturated fat. This also results in a deemphasis on plant foods, which scientists are discovering contain a wide array of health-promoting compounds such as fiber, antioxidants, and phytochemicals.

As public health issues change and nutritional science advances, it pays to be aware of a few past misconceptions. People tend to overlook the fact that the studies advocating the feeding of animal protein supplements were conducted on children whose growth was stunted due to malnutrition. Milk and meat are certainly beneficial in the diets of children. For full-grown adults, milk (especially low fat or nonfat) can support the maintenance of bone structure. However, in general, the average, healthy adult American (not including pregnant or breastfeeding mothers, or others with special nutritional needs) tends to consume far above the baseline protein need. Especially considering the influence of fad "protein diets," as a culture we don't tend to be protein-deficient!

The link between saturated-fat consumption and heart disease did not go unnoticed. Around 1970, the beef industry and the dairy industry both began to produce lower-fat products. The word in the media was that fat was bad—saturated fat in particular, but in general, all fat. Other food-industry sectors responded as well. Hundreds of low-fat and nonfat versions of our favorite foods appeared on supermarket shelves and were purchased with enthusiasm. The

Mediterranean diet, already proclaimed by the media as a healthful alternative to the standard American diet, became known as just another low–fat eating plan.

In the early 1990s, research began to illuminate the differences between types of fats. Scientists Frank Sacks and Walter Willett, among others, recognized that high levels of a certain type of blood cholesterol—HDL, or what has become known as "good cholesterol"—could actually be just as important for coronary heart disease prevention as low levels of total blood cholesterol, or of "bad" (LDL) blood cholesterol. Because diets low in saturated fats and high in monounsaturated fats appear to be promoters of HDL cholesterol, the Mediterranean diet again became a topic of interest. Olive oil, the principal fat in the Mediterranean diet, is a rich source of monounsaturated fat. This, surmised scientists, could be an important contributor to the lower levels of coronary heart disease in the Mediterranean region.

In addition, research began to reveal that hydrogenated vegetable fats (the notorious "trans fats" so often in health news today), such as those used to create margarine and vegetable shortening, may actually contribute to heart disease risk. Fat in the diet was no longer simply a matter of percentage. Fat in the Mediterranean diet, researchers began to realize, was distinctly different from fat in the standard American diet, even if the percentages of total calories from fat were similar.

In recent years, refined-carbohydrates foods, such as white breads and processed snack foods, also have been under investigation. It appears that large consumption of such items, coupled with a large intake of sugar from soft drinks, candy, and other processed foods, can overtax the body, resulting in an increased production of insulin. This puts the body at risk for developing heart disease, diabetes, and obesity.

Carbohydrates in the traditional Mediterranean diet are in their natural, whole state. Whole-grain breads, pastas, and rice were omnipresent. Whole grains, unlike refined grains, are digested at a much slower rate, resulting in a more easily manageable level of blood glucose. They also contain healthy doses of fiber. As for dessert, the daily sweet treat was provided from whole fruits, not from heavily sweetened, processed snack items or store-bought baked goods.

⊛ THE FUTURE OF NUTRITION

As nutrition science evolves, consumers and scientists alike may still find it difficult to get past the basic mantra of deficiency prevention. Once again, deficiency prevention is an essential part of a complete nutritional profile. Many of the "traditional" vitamins and minerals scientists have known about for many decades remain an important part of the fight against heart disease and cancer, especially vitamin E, folacin, and selenium. The Mediterranean diet, with its emphasis on vegetables, fruits, and whole grains, is an excellent and complete diet that will not result in nutrient deficiencies and is compatible with good health.

However, a new movement is taking place in the area of nutrition. This new way of thinking, called the "second Golden Age of Nutrition" by Mark Messina, Ph.D., a soy foods expert and former researcher with the National Cancer Institute's Diet and Cancer Branch, concerns itself with what we include in our diets—specifically, the wide array of compounds in plant foods called phytochemicals—rather than what is missing. Phytochemicals are chemical compounds in plants. These include the well-known vitamins C and E and the oft-touted beta-carotene. They also include thousands of other nutrients not formerly a part of the layman's nutrition vocabulary: lycopene, the substance that makes tomatoes and red peppers red; and allium, the compound that gives garlic its unique aroma, just to name a few.

The latest research into phytochemicals is promising, and

according to scientists studying phytochemicals, these plant compounds may support our health in more ways than we can imagine, from slowing the aging process and strengthening our immune systems against disease to preventing or even reversing chronic conditions such as cancer and heart disease.

The traditional Mediterranean diet's emphasis on plant foods (including olive oil) makes it a rich source of phytochemicals, as well as HDL-boosting monounsaturated fats. Truly a diet for the new millennium, the traditional Mediterranean diet is the best of paradoxes: an ancient eating tradition with cutting-edge health benefits that is both simple to prepare and perfectly delicious.

And so we come to the purpose of this book: to explore the traditional Mediterranean diet in terms of how it can improve the health, well-being, longevity, and quality of life for those of us living half a century later and thousands of miles away. How can we adjust our own diets, lifestyles, activity levels, even attitudes, for better health, à la the Mediterranean? Can we improve on the traditional Mediterranean diet to make it more compatible with our contemporary lifestyles and preferences? Is creating health for ourselves as simple as indulging in simple, fragrant, gratifying meals? These are the questions this book will address. We hope you will join us on our sun-drenched, cypress-lined, color-soaked, flavor-rich, and irresistible journey through the Mediterranean in search of greater longevity, healthier hearts, and a better quality of life. It is sure to be a magnificent vacation, and one that can last all year round. Bon voyage and *au revoir,* steak and potatoes! Shall we set sail?

PART I

The Benefits of Eating Mediterranean

1: *Mediterranean Magic*

Imagine yourself sitting in a sun-drenched outdoor café on the banks of the Greek Mediterranean shore. The vast turquoise sea meets the brilliant blue sky, and everything around you seems influenced by sea and sky, from the aquamarine-painted tables and chairs of the café to the foamy-white buildings and small shops jutting out over the seawall where the Mediterranean laps and splashes. The warm sun on your shoulders and the cool sea breeze on your face enhance the spectacular view, as the fragrance of white flowers scaling a peach-colored trellis above your table mingles with the smells of salt and sea.

You feel yourself relaxing into your chair as you are gently serenaded by the musical dialect around you. You recall your morning trek across the vast white beaches, and images of ancient Greece envelop you. You can almost envision Socrates walking along the shoreline with tall Greek ships sailing in the far distance, the ruins whole, the early blossoming of Western civilization. Poseidon, that great god of the sea, is smiling at you, amused to see how easily the stresses of daily life have suddenly melted away.

Ah, the magical Mediterranean. With all its glorious old-worldliness, you feel connected with history. You feel completely at peace. And just when you think it couldn't get any better, you are awakened from your relaxed bliss by a waiter who brings you a bowl of fragrant, lemony soup the color of the sun, followed by a steaming plate of sea bass infused with oregano, olive oil, and lemon, surrounded by colorful roasted vegetables grown on the rolling hills just behind you.

With each bite you are catapulted further into the heaven that surrounds you. You cannot help but savor every mouthful. You've never tasted food so fresh, so wholesome. You feel renewed, even healed, down to your very soul.

Who can deny the sensual power of the Mediterranean? Anyone who has traveled to this area cannot forget its beauty, its history, and its charm. Sun and sea, relaxed lifestyle, and miraculous food—these things draw people to the shores of the Mediterranean from every corner of the globe.

Yet the seductive Mediterranean climate, cuisine, and way of life aren't the only reasons to focus on this region's approach to eating. Study after study have revealed that people eating a traditional Mediterranean diet are generally healthier, are longer-lived, and have a lower incidence of chronic diseases—particularly coronary artery disease—than people in other parts of the world.

The potential health benefits inherent in eating and living in the traditional Mediterranean way are the impetus for writing this book. Is it really possible to eat so well, savoring and relishing delicious food, and at the same time increase our wellness? In fact, it is both possible and surprisingly easy to accomplish. We need only look to the Mediterranean lands of Greece, Italy, France, Spain, Turkey, North Africa, and the Middle East.

✆ THE MEDITERRANEAN REGION

The Mediterranean region encompasses all the countries bordering the Mediterranean Sea, from the Strait of Gibraltar separating the rocky cliffs and crags of southern Spain and the seaport of Tangier in mountainous northern Morocco, to the Mediterranean's far western reaches along the shores of the Middle East. Between these extremes lies a broad sampling of European, Middle Eastern, and African countries, all Mediterranean, yet each unique in culture and character: pastoral southern France with its orange groves, vineyards, and rolling hills; scenic Italy with its snowy peaks and sultry beaches; the former Yugoslavia with its dramatic coastline; the tiny yet sensationally mountainous Albania; historical Greece with its hazy, sea-infused ambience and its scattering of islands; geologically volatile Turkey; the Middle Eastern countries of Syria, Lebanon, and Israel, with their coastal planes backed by a sudden rise of mountains; and then, returning east, the northern ends of Egypt, Libya, Tunisia, Algeria, and back to Morocco, an African panoply of cliffs, peaks, ports, plateaus, and scorching sands.

Surely such a vast array of countries and cultures must dine on an equally vast assortment of foods. Although each country bordering the Mediterranean Sea does indeed have its unique culinary characteristics, the region maintains many common, and many more mutually influenced ingredients, recipes, and cooking techniques. Pasta may come in the form of ziti in Italy and couscous in Morocco, and of course the ubiquitous olive oil, sea salt, durum wheat, and the most vibrantly fresh and irresistible vegetables and fruits characterize the entire Mediterranean with their unique, striking flavors. Not insignificantly, Mediterranean countries also share an attitude toward food and how it should be eaten.

✿ THE EVOLUTION OF A SHARED CUISINE

The magnificent diet of the Mediterranean region has been evolving for thousands of years. The history of the region, coupled with its distinct (though widely various) climate and the pervasive influence of the sea, has shaped the choice of foods and the types of cooking so characteristic of traditional Mediterranean culture. Bread, olive oil, and wine—which continue to play a significant role in the Mediterranean diet today—accompanied meals in ancient times. The cultivated vegetables and other plant-based foods so central to the diet date back to Neolithic times. According to archeological evidence and depictions and descriptions of food and meals in the art and literature of ancient Greek and Roman civilizations, ancient populations probably relied primarily on plant foods, with only occasional indulgence in meat and seafood.

More recent studies of the Mediterranean diet, from the 1950s and 1960s, reveal eating habits and preferences similar to the ancient diet: a primarily plant food–based diet that included minimal processing, whole grains, olive oil as the primary fat source, and animal products (with the exception of cheese in some areas and yogurt in some areas) consumed only a few times per month. The groundbreaking Rockefeller Foundation study of the Cretan diet around 1950 stated that "olives, cereal grains, pulses, wild greens and herbs, and fruits, together with limited quantities of goat meat and milk, game, and fish have remained the basic Cretan foods for forty centuries . . . no meal was complete without bread . . . [and] Olives and olive oil contributed heavily to the energy intake." This study, originally undertaken to determine how the people of Greece could improve their diets after World War II, concluded that the diet couldn't get much better.

While the Mediterranean diet today strays from its original roots somewhat (due to the "McDonald's invasion" and other nutritionally tragic "modern" influences, such as the growing popularity of heavily processed convenience foods), the Mediterranean diet in the first half of the twentieth century, with appropriate modifications to make it more suitable and convenient for contemporary eating, lives at the heart of this book.

⊘ TO EAT À LA MEDITERRANEAN

Let's look more closely at this traditional diet and its various common components. Eating the traditional Mediterranean way is largely a seasonal and regional affair. While each country has its unique customs, every country produces foods locally or regionally and serves them soon after harvest. In spring, the freshest new vegetables are harvested and eaten, often within a few miles of where they were picked—wild greens, thin zucchini, green beans, spinach, spring peas, finocchi, cherries, and wild mushrooms. Summer marks the arrival of an abundance of tomatoes, eggplant, peaches, cantaloupe, watermelon, figs, peppers, and onions. Outdoor markets offer the freshest fruits and vegetables. The pale, bland produce so often available in American supermarkets would be virtually unrecognizable next to the vibrantly colored and succulent array of regionally produced plant foods. The perfect dessert? Fresh fruit, of course. Throughout the summer, most Mediterranean countries enjoy an overflow of the best garlic, onions, and tomatoes.

At the end of the summer, the grape harvest and wine pressing begin. Persimmons and pomegranates follow, and then olives are harvested and pressed to yield the oil so essential to Mediterranean cuisine—and, as we'll discuss later, an important component of the heart-healthy, traditional Mediterranean diet.

Beyond the magnificent year-round harvest of fruits and vegetables and the reliance on olive oil as the principal source of fat, the Mediterranean people shared other dietary similarities. Meat was more luxury than staple, and although many Mediterranean dishes are flavored with meat, those that feature it are usually reserved for special occasions. Lamb and veal are more common than beef because grazing land is scarce in the Mediterranean, and chicken or seafood are more likely to feature prominently in main courses when meat is featured at all.

Bread has always been a staple, even in Italy, where that more famous Italian starch, pasta, is consumed so readily. Traditional Mediterranean bread, especially in rural areas, is dark, heavy (some loaves could weigh almost five pounds!), and full of whole grains, unlike the soft, refined white bread neatly sliced and conveniently bagged for American consumers. Whole grains are consumed in abundance outside the obligatory loaf of bread—rice in the form of paella, risotto, and pilaf; pasta in its many incarnations, from Italian spaghetti to Moroccan couscous; and the versatile cornmeal mixture called polenta. Legumes are another staple—inexpensive and high in protein, they were an essential part of the traditional Mediterranean diet. White haricot beans, small red cranberry beans, lentils, chickpeas, and fava beans remain popular options today. Another common Mediterranean theme is wine, although it was traditionally consumed primarily by men and always with meals, never recreationally. A small piece of cheese to begin or end a meal was common, but food was never smothered in cheese the way it sometimes is in Americanized Italian dishes. Many Mediterranean dishes share a similar flavor and character due to a few popular flavoring ingredients: garlic, onion, lemons, olive oil, basil, oregano, Italian parsley, and often a few small pieces of pancetta (an unsmoked bacon).

Beyond the ingredients themselves, eating the traditional Mediterranean way is a philosophy in itself: Life is for savoring, and food is a glorious and beautiful expression of life. Meals are gatherings of family and friends—genuine events, not inconvenient chores. Food sustains life, and the quality of the food we eat, not to mention the manner and spirit in which it is prepared, is a reflection of the quality of our lives.

In traditional Mediterranean culture, food was both more and less significant than it is in the United States today. Food was less important because it wasn't the source of anxiety we often make it today. Neither was it a commodity, continually reinvented to be faster, cheaper, lower in fat (in other words, tapping the latest buzzwords to make it a more profitable industry). Yet, in the Mediterranean, food was and arguably still is far more important than in the United States. Handled and consumed with reverence for its life-sustaining capabilities, food celebrated the beautiful, the simple, the healthful. Food means vitality, a ritual to share with loved ones, an integral part of life itself.

⊕ THE MAGIC DISCOVERED

In the early 1950s, the great American researcher Ancel Keys and his wife, Margaret, traveled to the southern Italian shores, not just to escape the cold and dark skies of Oxford, England, where Keys was spending a year sabbatical as a visiting professor at Magdalen College, but to explore the curious notion that heart disease was apparently almost nonexistent in this area. At a time when Americans, particularly those in their forties and fifties, were subject to an unusually high rate of heart disease in the United States, Keys was intrigued by reports that the then-new American epidemic was almost unheard of in southern Italy. Heart disease appeared to occur with any significance only within a small upper-class subculture.

Also intriguing were reports of the diet of this region, which was described as nutritionally wholesome but containing very little food from animal products. The diet was low in total fat, with minimal amounts of saturated fat, and consisted primarily of plant foods such as vegetables, fruits, and whole grains.

Remember, this was 1950—a time when Americans in general believed large steak dinners, baked potatoes, and refined white bread rolls slathered in butter, along with a hefty glass of whole milk, made a nutritious dinner. How could such a meager, plant-based diet result in such heart-healthy citizens? It seems obvious to us now, but at the time, Keys felt compelled to investigate.

Ancel Keys helped to define the link between nutrition and health as we understand it today. Before Keys, awareness of the connection between diet and health was tenuous at best. Keys suspected the link to be more than incidental, and we can credit him with the discovery of the relationship of diet to coronary heart disease. From as early as the 1940s, his clinical work at the University of Minnesota as well as epidemiological observations showed how blood cholesterol was an indicator of heart disease, and that diet—particularly the type of fat consumed—affected blood cholesterol levels. His interest in the relationship of prolonged dietary habits to coronary heart disease rates led him to spearhead one of the greatest and most influential epidemiological studies of our time, the Seven Countries Study.

Keys began his research in Naples, Italy, where he and his wife, Margaret, along with local medical colleagues, studied the blood cholesterol levels and heart disease rates of the local working men. Serum measurements from the initial study subjects revealed extraordinarily low blood cholesterol levels. The male subjects in their forties were especially impressive, with blood cholesterol averaging 165 compared with about 230 from blood samples of males of the same age living in Minnesota. As Keys must have suspected, heart disease and low cholesterol levels rarely coincide.

In his subsequent book *How to Eat Well and Stay Well the Mediterranean Way,* Keys described his results: "What these men told us about their eating habits confirmed dietary studies in the area that reported only about 20 per cent of calories from fats compared with around 40 in Minnesota. According to the doctors who helped us, the hospitals caring for the general populace rarely had coronary heart patients; such patients were found to be only in private clinics caring for the rich."

Even considering that the rich were more able to afford hospitalization at this time and in this area, evidence suggested that deaths attributable to heart attack among the working classes were far lower than those among the richer classes. According to Keys, the diet of the Neapolitan working class was of a quite different composition than the diet consumed by the upper classes, who consumed meat daily, as opposed to once every week or two. The diet of the working class sounds both simple and irresistible, as Keys describes it:

> *The ordinary food of the common Neapolitans consisted of homemade minestrone/vegetable soup, pasta in endless variety, always freshly cooked, served with tomato sauce and a sprinkle of cheese, only occasionally enriched with some bits of meat, or served with a little local seafood without any cheese; a hearty dish of beans and short lengths of macaroni (pasta e fagioli); lots of whole grain bread never more than a few hours from the oven and never served with any kind of spread; great quantities of fresh vegetables; a modest portion of meat or fish perhaps twice a week; (red) wine; always fresh fruit for dessert.*

Keys states in his book that, when asked years later to formulate a diet that might serve as a preventive against coronary heart disease, he could come up with nothing more suited for this purpose than the traditional working-class diet of early 1950s Naples.

☀ FROM ITALY TO SPAIN AND BEYOND

After their foray into Italy, the Keyses moved on to Spain. The Spanish government was conducting a nutrition survey in Madrid and enlisted Keys and a team of doctors to take and analyze blood samples from a sample of the population in a working-class district called Vallecas. Compared to Naples, Vallecas was a more impoverished region, and the typical diet was even lower in fat, meat, and dairy products than the diets of the Neapolitans. Once again, the incidence of coronary heart disease was exceptionally low, except among the upper class, whose diets were higher in fat from animal sources.

Keys's observations continued. In wealthier Bologna in northern Italy, where the diet is said to be the richest in all of Italy—heavier in cream, butter, and eggs than anywhere else in the country—sure enough, coronary heart disease rates were higher than in Naples (but still far below the rates of coronary heart disease in Boston or Minneapolis). The link emerged with increasing clarity. In Keys's words: "[saturated] diet fat to blood cholesterol to heart attacks."

Keys continued his explorations, moving on to South Africa, Japan, Hawaii, California, and Finland (the hands-down winner for sky-high cholesterol levels—for more on Finland, see Chapter Three).

The purpose of these investigations was to determine whether an even larger-scale study was warranted, and the results suggested such a study could prove illuminating. The resulting Seven Countries Study was, in fact, not only illuminating, but eventually became one of the most famous and significant of epidemiological studies.

✱ THE SEVEN COUNTRIES STUDY

The plan for the Seven Countries Study was to identify coronary heart disease risk factors and disease rates. In 1958, Keys and his cohorts began examining nearly 13,000 men between the ages of forty and fifty-nine over a five-year period in Greece, Italy, Croatia and Serbia (at the time, both part of Yugoslavia), Japan, Finland, the Netherlands, and the United States. Rather than obtaining data through question-and-answer forms, dietitians were actually stationed in the homes of study subjects, measuring everything eaten and collecting samples to send back to Minnesota for chemical analysis. This type of hands-on data collection resulted in a dietary picture of the study subjects that was probably far more accurate than could ever be obtained via a questionnaire. The extensive study included a follow-up period of an additional ten years on more than 10,000 men and examined a range of lifestyle factors in addition to diet and coronary heart disease rates.

The results of the now famous Seven Countries Study provided strong epidemiological evidence that, indeed, the percentage of calories from saturated fat is linked to increased blood cholesterol levels that result in an increased risk of coronary heart disease. Those countries with the highest consumption of saturated fat, such as the United States and Finland, had the highest rates of heart disease. The American men participating in the study, as well as the Finnish and Dutch men, had heart disease rates that were twice that of Italian men, and four times that of Greek, Japanese, and Yugoslav men (saturated-fat intake was, and still is, comparatively low in Greece, Japan, and Yugoslavia). Furthermore, the study determined that the rates of all-causes, age-specific death rates were among the lowest in the Mediterranean regions.

The Seven Countries Study also identified other key factors that appeared correlated with heart disease. These factors were age, blood pressure, and cigarette smoking. These factors, along with blood cholesterol, came to be known as "universal risk factors" for heart disease. Study after study continued to show that as these factors increased, so did the risk of heart disease. Of all of the identified risk factors, however, blood cholesterol appeared to have the strongest correlation to heart disease.

Although a high saturated-fat diet (which appears to lead to high blood cholesterol levels) may not be, and probably isn't, the sole factor in lower rates of coronary heart disease in the Mediterranean compared with the United States, Keys succinctly states, "The Mediterranean diet is certainly compatible with superior health."

✸ THE INVESTIGATION CONTINUES

Over the past few decades, research study after research study has confirmed the results of the Seven Countries Study: that a diet rich in fruits, vegetables, and whole grains, with low saturated fat, and monounsaturated fat as the primary fat, has been shown repeatedly to be beneficial to health and to decrease the risk of coronary heart disease and other chronic adult diseases such as diabetes and certain types of cancer. A study conducted in Lyon, France, led by Michael De Lorgeril, M.D., tested whether a Mediterranean-type diet high in omega-3 fatty acids might reduce the risk of a second heart attack in people who had had a previous heart attack.

The study, which came to be known as the Lyon Diet Heart Study, divided about six hundred patients who had recently had a heart attack, were under the age of seventy years old, and suffered no other medical or social ailments, into two groups. The first group, called the experimental group, was placed on a Mediterranean-type diet featuring fish, fruit, cereals, and beans, with about 30 percent of calories from fat. The main source of fat was canola oil, a good source of monounsaturated fat similar to olive oil. Only 8 percent of the calories in this diet were from saturated fat. The diet included about 200 milligrams of cholesterol.

The experimental group was given dietary and lifestyle counseling from health care professionals to ensure compliance. The other group, the control group, were given general low-fat diet instructions by their physicians to follow.

The study was originally scheduled to run for five years, but after a little over two years, the study was stopped. It appeared that the experimental group, the group consuming the Mediterranean-type diet, had far fewer cardiovascular complications than the control group. Therefore, it was deemed unethical to keep the highly beneficial Mediterranean diet a secret from the control group.

One of the most striking things about this study was that, after the researchers continued to track about 425 of the original study participants for another nineteen months, the original Mediterranean-diet group continued to eat a diet inspired by Mediterranean elements. They liked it that much! And their cardiac health status continued to be much more favorable than that of those who were not following a Mediterranean-type diet. Patient compliance is often a difficult factor to obtain, so the fact that the experimental group kept eating the prescribed diet even after the study's termination speaks volumes about both the health benefits and, presumably, the enjoyable nature and palatability of a traditional Mediterranean diet.

Research refining the health benefits of various aspects of the Mediterranean diet has been plentiful. The nature of different types of fats has been discovered. For instance, transfatty acids—which are found in processed foods containing hydrogenated or partially hydrogenated vegetable oils such as margarine—have been shown to increase heart disease risk. Omega-3 fatty acids, available in fish and from certain vegetable sources like flaxseed, have been shown to decrease the blood's tendency to clot, thereby decreasing heart attack risk. Monounsaturated fats, of which olive oil and canola oil are rich sources, have been shown to lower "bad" LDL cholesterol, and promote "good" HDL cholesterol. (For more on fat, see Chapter Three.)

Fat isn't the only component of the Mediterranean diet that seems to be so compatible with good health. The discovery of phytochemicals, the wide array of chemical compounds in plant foods, has prompted a new revolution in nutrition science. The benefits of fiber, antioxidants, and other treasures available to the body through the consumption of plant foods continually interest nutrition science

Recently, there has been a lot of focus on refined carbohydrates as being promoters of heart disease, as well as diabetes and obesity. Researchers are pointing out that the body metabolizes sources of refined grains—white bread, sugary cereals, and processed snack items, for example—the same way it processes sugar, by causing a rapid rise in blood sugar, or blood glucose. Unless a person burns off the sugar present in his or her system through activity, insulin is released by the body to take the glucose out of the blood stream and into fat cells for storage. If the body keeps getting flooded with refined carbohydrates and sugar, its sugar-removal system begins to break down, resulting in more and more insulin production. This puts the body at risk for developing diabetes, obesity, and heart disease.

Our bodies metabolize whole-grain products (whole-grain bread, pastas, and cereals) differently, digesting them more slowly so that blood glucose levels rise more slowly. This is a more natural way to get energy and is less extreme, or more "gentle" on the system.

In the traditional Mediterranean diet, as observed by Ancel Keys and others, refined grain products were virtually nonexistent because the technology simply was not there to process whole grains into refined grain products. Sweetness in the traditional Mediterranean diet came from succulent fruits, not from processed sugars.

Of course, no one nutrient or even a single food group holds the secret to perfect health. Instead, a combination of factors, from fresher and more abundant produce to whole grains and a lower intake of fat from animal sources, to a change in attitude, lifestyle, and activity level, seem to contribute to greater heart health, lower cancer risk, healthy long-term weight control, and longer life.

The particular "magic" of the traditional Mediterranean diet is just such a combination of factors. Not just monounsaturated fats such as olive oil. Not just whole grains instead of refined. Not just a lower intake of animal products and a higher intake of legumes, nuts, and seeds. Not just fish. Not just the small daily dose of wine with dinner. Instead, all these factors together, resulting in a low overall fat intake with a specific saturated-to-monounsaturated fat ratio, a higher fiber intake, and what amounts to a wide array of phytochemical benefits from daily plant foods, create a nutritional plan that can improve anyone's health.

⊛ MEDITERRANEAN STYLE: A PHILOSOPHY OF FOOD AND LIFE

Any good scientist knows that research subjects don't exist in a vacuum, and every study runs the risk of producing results influenced by unknown factors. Scientists do their best to minimize the effects of other factors on results, but this isn't always completely possible.

One obvious consideration in examining the lower heart attack rates of people from 1950s and 1960s Mediterranean countries is lifestyle. Today, the effect of the mind on the body is widely publicized and studied (with varying degrees of scientific rigor). Even if a diet is good for health, could the lifestyle, the stress levels, even the mindset of the people in the Mediterranean contribute to their low coronary disease rates? And what about levels of physical activity? Was exercise a part of life in the Mediterranean?

The Mediterranean lifestyle seems to be as heart-healthy as the Mediterranean diet. We will explore the lifestyle and activity level of the people in the Mediterranean during the 1950s, 1960s, and before. During the postwar era, much of the Mediterranean region was impoverished and didn't advance technologically as the United States did. The area remained largely untouched by technology and all its accompanying developments, relying instead on traditional methods for everything, from farming to cooking. This translated to a lot more daily physical activity, a greater reliance on family and friends, and a closer daily communion with the natural world. People worked vigorously throughout the day, getting plenty of fresh air and cardiovascular, as well as muscle-strengthening, exercise. Even the Mediterranean sun may have certain health benefits. A study reported in the *Tufts University Health & Nutrition Newsletter* revealed that women who live in sunny places were 30 to 40 percent less likely to get breast cancer than women who live in northern areas or those who usually stay inside during the day.

The emphasis on family and a strong support system of friends in small communities probably contributed to lower stress levels, as did a slower pace of living, an appreciation of nature, and, not insignificantly, a reverence for the food on the table. Food is an essential component of everyday life in the Mediterranean, not something to grab on the go, not something that comes in a freezer box or a microwaveable packet, but something grown by hand, then picked, and, within hours, eaten. Food is cooked according to long tradition and savored as the life-giving force it is.

Assessing the benefit of attitudes about life, nature, and food on coronary health is difficult from a scientific point of view. These factors are harder to isolate than dietary components. However, common sense can come into play once again when considering the lifestyle of the people in the Mediterranean. To live well, at a slower pace; to love well and rely on family and friends; to appreciate the natural world by living in it, working it, and harvesting its bounty; and to relish the food on the table each day—this kind of life must certainly be conducive to a long, healthy existence.

⊛ LIVING THE GUIDELINES

The traditional Mediterranean diet may sound pretty good right about now, but how does it compare to every other diet you've recently heard touted on a talk show or in the columns of your favorite health magazine or local newspaper? A steaming plate of pasta laden with fresh vegetables and a fragrant hunk of whole-grain bread for supper tonight sounds great, but how does this compare with the guidelines proposed by the American Heart Association and the American Dietetic Association? Will you be satisfied without a hunk of meat on top? And what about all those carbs?

In the next chapter, we will examine in more detail the breakdown of components in the traditional Mediterranean diet, as well as the components of the traditionally recommended American Heart Association diet and several other widely available eating systems recommended by different organizations, from vegetarian to low-carb protein diets. We won't send you off to the dinner table without a little more knowledge under your belt.

⊘ QUESTIONS AND ANSWERS

❀ *Can the Mediterranean diet help with weight loss?*

Certainly! The traditional Mediterranean diet features the consumption of low calorie, high fiber foods that are compatible with good health and the maintenance of normal body weight. Many weight-loss plans advocate increased consumption of vegetables, fruit, and whole grains, with a decreased consumption of high calorie, high saturated fat foods. Design your meals to feature fresh produce and whole grains. Use high-fat animal products only occasionally, deriving daily protein from beans, low-fat dairy products (or preferably low-fat soy products, such as low-fat soy milk), moderate amounts of nuts, and small amounts of low-fat meat for flavoring. Stick to single portions, and add to that a more active lifestyle. You should be able to lose weight, if you are overweight, with relative ease, and at a sensible rate (1 to 2 pounds per week). Also, if you are trying to lose weight, you may be better off forgoing that Mediterranean glass of wine with dinner. Alcohol can stimulate the appetite and add extra calories. Contact a registered dietitian to help determine your individual caloric and nutrient needs. Also, see Chapter Nine for more on how to lose weight the Mediterranean way.

❀ *How does one switch over to a more Mediterranean-style diet without changing eating habits too drastically?*

Moving to a more Mediterranean-influenced diet is an easy and delicious experience. Gradually replace butter and margarine with olive oil in dishes—to sauté vegetables, to add to soup for flavoring, or to keep pasta from sticking. Olive oil even works for baking. The distinctive olive oil flavor disappears during the baking process (or, if you find olive oil undesirable for baking, try the milder-tasting canola oil). Then stock up on whole grains, legumes, pasta, canned tomatoes, and in-season produce, when available. Have fun with meal planning, and keep a few guidelines in mind: Feature fresh fruits, seasonal vegetables, and wholesome whole grains like rice, cornmeal, and bread at every meal, but keep the butter or margarine off the table.

Get in the habit of using meat for flavoring only, and not at every meal. Many delicious Mediterranean dishes don't use meat at all, and are, consequently, economical as well as delicious. Remember that legumes, nuts, and seeds are excellent sources of protein. If you eat a lot of meat, slowly decrease portion sizes. Don't eliminate it entirely, or all at once, or the change will be too difficult.

Visit farmer's markets, produce stands, or the produce department at your local grocery store to find the best, freshest seasonal fruits and vegetables available. Remember, to eat Mediterranean is largely a matter of eating what's in season. Jettison the dessert course. If you are in the habit of finishing with something sweet, choose the best, ripest, freshest fruit when available, or dried fruit such as sweet, plump dried figs, dates, or a handful of raisins to satisfy your sweet tooth. Even canned fruit, in its own juice, is preferable to high-fat, high-sugar fare. Although certain Mediterranean desserts may be famous worldwide (baklava from Greece or canoli from Italy, for example), such extravagance is traditionally reserved for special occasions.

Last, if you drink alcohol, try drinking wine, but only with meals and in small amounts. (More on this later.)

Remember the Mediterranean rules: Quality, not quantity. Fresh and whole, not processed and preserved. And most important, relish the experience of eating. Savor every bite.

 ❧ *What studies have been done on the diets of some of the other Mediterranean countries besides Greece, France, and Italy?*

One study published in the British journal *Lancet* examined the life expectancy in Albania. Albania is considered the most impoverished European country, with one of the highest infant mortality rates in Europe. Yet Albanian adults have a life expectancy about equal to that of adults in other central and eastern European countries, and male deaths from coronary heart disease are about the same level as those in Italy. Mortality rates were lowest in southwest Albania, along its Mediterranean shore, where people consumed the greatest quantities of olive oil, fruits, and vegetables, and the lowest levels of meat and dairy products. The study concluded that diet was the most likely explanation for Albania's surprisingly low mortality rates, even though reliable dietary information on Albania wasn't available.

 ❧ *What ingredients and dishes compatible with a healthy diet are characteristic of Mediterranean countries whose cuisines are less well known than those of Spain, France, Italy, and Greece?*

The cuisine of Morocco is distinctive and delicious, including such traditional dishes as tagine (stew), couscous (steamed cracked durum wheat semolina), and kesra (an anise-scented bread). Fresh produce favorites include pumpkin, zucchini, eggplant, potatoes, tangerines, strawberries, Medjool dates, green beans, and bananas. Moroccan cuisine also relies heavily on seafood, sometimes marinated with charmoula, a stimulating combination of cumin, paprika, fresh herbs, and lemon juice. Spices characteristic of Moroccan dishes include cumin, paprika, turmeric, Spanish saffron, cinnamon, and ginger. Meals are typically very low in fat and high in fiber, consisting primarily of grains, beans, and fresh vegetables and fruits (dried fruits are sometimes used in stews). Meat, seafood, and poultry are special-occasion ingredients. Meals often end with fruit salad, and dessert usually consists of mint tea made with fresh spearmint, Morocco's national drink.

Algerian food is notoriously spicy with lots of sauces and fish dishes. Meals often start with soup or salad, then feature roast meat as a main course and fruit for dessert. Couscous is an Algerian staple, and French bread covered in spicy sauce as well as meat on skewers are available in many food stalls. Alcohol is expensive, and although Algeria produces some wines, they are generally not served in the country itself due to the Muslim prohibition of alcohol.

Tunisian cuisine has recently become popular. Tunisians are big fans of hot peppers. Common ingredients in the simple, healthful meals include nuts; olives; fish; olive oil; spiced octopus, squid, and shrimp; shredded greens; carrots; pumpkins; and zucchini. Vegetables and seafood are often blended or served separately with hot peppers, spices, lemon juice, and olive oil. Meals almost always begin with a salad of tomato, lettuce, onion, spices, and olives. Coriander, anise, cumin, and cinnamon are popular spices. Couscous is another mainstay. A fried pastry snack called brik is popular but not a daily part of the traditional diet. Other popular Tunisian specialties include chorba, a peppery soup; chakchouka, a ratatouille with chickpeas, tomatoes, peppers, garlic, and onions served with an egg; and tagine, a thick stew.

Libyan cuisine is much like the cuisines of Algeria and Tunisia. Couscous is a mainstay. Spiced rice with meat and vegetables is a common meal. Libya is a Muslim country as well, and alcohol was banned by the government in 1969.

Egyptian cuisine is influenced by the cuisines of Greece, Turkey, Lebanon, Palestine, and Syria. Common dishes include vegetable stews, rice and pasta, salads, and bread.

Some traditional dishes include fried eggplant, mixed or grilled salads often including grilled eggplant, beetroot, potato, mushrooms, chickpeas, black-eyed peas, cauliflower, tahini (sesame butter), artichokes, onions, spinach, and tomatoes; soups made with onion, tomato, yellow lentils, and other vegetables, and a variety of dried bean dishes; mixed dishes of ground meat, rice and lentils with tomato sauce, garlic and potatoes; stuffed grape leaves, walnut sauce, and a variety of breads.

The cuisine of Lebanon has had an incredible influence on the world, considering the country's small size. It is also in line with the components of the traditional Mediterranean diet: whole grains, fruits, vegetables, and seafood. Although chicken and lamb are the most common meats, animal products make up a small portion of the diet. Garlic and olive oil are the primary flavorings, and butter and cream are rarely used. Raw, cooked, and pickled vegetables make up a major part of most meals. Lebanon's national dish is kibbeh, a fresh lamb-and-bulgur wheat paste similar to pâté, and sometimes served with yogurt sauce. Bread is a mainstay, present at every meal, often seasoned with olive oil. Several excellent Lebanese wines are available, but alcohol is always served with food. Like the tapas of Spain and the antipasti of Italy, mezze is a Lebanese collection of appetizers often including pickled vegetables, bread, seafood, and salads, both cooked and raw. Baklava, of Greek origin, is a popular Lebanese dessert. Coffee is served throughout the day, often flavored with cardamom and heavily sweetened. Traditional Lebanese dishes include tabbouleh, a salad of bulgur wheat, parsley, and mint; fattoush, a toasted bread salad; hummus tahini, a paste of chickpeas, sesame butter, olive oil, lemon juice, and parsley; and baba ghanouj, a roasted eggplant puree.

Traditional Turkish food includes many yogurt-based dishes, fish in olive oil, a variety of salads and stuffed vegetables including vine leaves, and the syrupy phyllo-pastry desserts also popular in Greece and other Middle Eastern countries. The Turkish diet is still mostly in conformance with the traditional Mediterranean diet. Turkish vineyards produce wine grapes and yellow sultana raisins. Lamb and chicken are the most popular meats. Fresh ingredients are of primary importance, and produce is typically served seasonally. Bread is a primary part of the Turkish diet. Popular local produce items include eggplants, olives, figs, pistachios, peaches, apricots, and several types of nuts, including pistachios and hazelnuts. Shish kebab and flatbread are two classic Turkish dishes. Popular seasonings include mint, parsley, cinnamon, dill, garlic, pepper flakes, and sumac. Turkish meals often include a zeytinagli, or olive oil course, in which various foods are prepared with olive oil. Minced meat dishes and seafood specialties are well known, and fruit is the most common dessert. Although Turkish coffee is famous worldwide, tea is a popular drink. Other traditional Turkish dishes include ashure, a cereal pudding with dried and fresh fruit and nuts; a yogurt drink called ayran; borek, a stuffed pastry; dolma, the term for any stuffed vegetable but most often referring to stuffed grape leaves; manti, a small, ravioli-like, meat-stuffed pastry; sis kofte, or shish kebab; and yufka, a flatbread.

✤ How much wine is typically included in the traditional Mediterranean diet?

Keep in mind that a serving of wine is only about 4 ounces. Many wineglasses available today hold twice that much or more! In Greece, the subject of much research and considered by many the standard against which all Mediterranean diets should be measured, men traditionally drank two or three glasses of wine each day. That comes to only 8 to 12 ounces. Women consumed less, and sometimes none at all. Considering the research that suggests alcohol consumption, even in moderation, could increase breast cancer risk, women should proceed with caution when considering whether to include wine as a part of their diets. Also remember that in general, research has revealed that moderate alcohol consumption is often found to reduce the risk of cardiovascular disease, but at the same time, it increases the risk of some cancers, and also increases the risk of accidents, including motor vehicle accidents.

2: A Recipe for Wellness

Have you noticed that almost every time you turn on your television, some authority on something is proclaiming that what we eat, or don't eat, is negatively impacting our health? From local news broadcasts to tabloid news shows, nutrition is big news these days. What to eat, what not to eat, how much of this or that, eat nothing but this, never ever eat that . . . how did eating ever become so complicated?

Ever since scientists discovered that diet can indeed impact health, people have been excited that they can exercise a measure of control over how well they feel, not to mention their chances of developing chronic disease. In response to this excitement, a profusion of "diets of the week" has arisen. Fad diets proclaiming to be a panacea for health problems, weight problems, low energy, inability to concentrate, and on and on, have saturated the media for years. Some stem from sensible principles, while others can be downright dangerous for your health. Is the Mediterranean diet just one more fad? Or does it make good sense in terms of the nutritional guidelines familiar to Americans for decades?

Exotic as it sounds, with its suggestions of romantic France, dramatic Spain, effusive Italy, and sun-drenched Crete, the traditional Mediterranean diet is more than practical and easy to follow. It fits right in with our contemporary way of eating, and the nutritional "laws" we have been taught to follow. Sure, a traditional Mediterranean diet has its unique qualities—olive oil instead of butter, its own characteristic combinations of herbal flavorings, and recipes combining foods in ways many Americans haven't previously considered. Yet, taken at its core principles, the Mediterranean diet sounds pretty familiar to anyone listening to nutritional advice offered by influential health-related organizations such as the United States Department of Agriculture (USDA), the American Heart Association, and the American Cancer Society. These organizations, and others, have proposed nutritional guidelines and/or food pyramids in the hopes of improving the health of the general population. To get a perspective on where the traditional Mediterranean diet fits in relation to the systems proposed by others, let's examine some of the major nutritional guidelines commonly available. The following describes nutritional advice from some of the more influential of these organizations. As you will see, the Mediterranean diet fits nicely into the parameters of most of these recommendations.

⊘ THE AMERICAN HEART ASSOCIATION

The American Heart Association actively promotes a heart-healthy diet, from the publication of their popular cookbook first issued in the early 1970s to an extensive, user-friendly web site (http://www.americanheart.org). Back in 1957, the AHA proposed that a reduction in dietary fat intake would result in a reduction of coronary heart disease, which was already the leading cause of disability and death in the United States and in other developed countries as well.

The AHA continues to issue policy statements relating to the link between diet and coronary heart disease, modifying and updating their position as necessary in response to the latest research. The AHA's position remains consistent, however, when it comes to fat consumption: too much fat, especially saturated fat, increases the risk of coronary heart disease.

In an attempt to help Americans prevent heart and blood vessel disease, the American Heart Association has issued dietary guidelines to promote heart-healthy nutrition. In October 2000, the AHA released the following Eating Plan for Healthy Americans, which focuses on reducing the three risk factors for heart attack or stroke: high blood cholesterol, high blood pressure, and excess body weight.

- Eat a variety of fruits and vegetables. Choose five or more servings per day.
- Eat a variety of grain products, including whole grains. Choose six or more servings per day.
- Eat fish at least twice a week, particularly fatty fish.
- Include fat-free and low-fat milk products, legumes (beans), skinless poultry, and lean meats.
- Choose fats and oils with 2 grams or less saturated fat per tablespoon, such as liquid and tub margarines, canola, corn, safflower, soy bean, and olive oils.
- Limit your intake of foods high in calories or low in nutrition. This includes foods with a lot of added sugar like soft drinks and candy.
- Limit foods high in saturated fat, trans fat and/or cholesterol, such as full-fat milk products, fatty meats, tropical oils, partially hydrogenated vegetable oils, and egg yolks. Instead choose foods low in saturated fat, trans fat and cholesterol from the first four points above. (Trans fat comes from adding hydrogen to vegetable oil, which partially hydrogenates it. It tends to increase blood cholesterol levels.)

- Eat less than 6 grams of salt (sodium chloride) per day. That's equal to about 1 teaspoon of salt, or a daily sodium intake of less than 2,400 milligrams.
- If you drink alcohol, have no more than one drink per day for a woman or two per day for a man. "One drink" means it has no more than ½ ounce of pure alcohol. Examples of one drink are 12 ounces of beer, 4 ounces of wine, 1½ ounces of 80-proof spirits or 1 ounce of 100-proof spirits.
- Balance the number of calories you eat with the number you use each day. To find that number, multiply your body weight in pounds by 15 (if you're active). This means if you weigh 200 pounds, you expend about 3,000 calories (200 × 15) calories in an average day. If you're sedentary, multiply your weight by 13 to find the calories you expend.
- Get enough physical activity to keep fit, and balance the calories you burn with the calories you eat. Walk or do other activities for at least thirty minutes on most or all days. To lose weight, do enough activity to use up more calories than you eat every day.

As you can see, the Mediterranean diet is almost perfectly compatible with the above guidelines. It is almost as if the American Heart Association guidelines are simply describing the Mediterranean diet!

⚕ THE AMERICAN CANCER SOCIETY

According to the American Cancer Society (ACS), about 1,334,100 people will die from cancer in the United States in 2003, and an estimated one-third of these deaths are due to dietary factors. (Another third can be attributed to cigarette smoking.) It is only natural, then, that the American Cancer Society would publish its own set of nutritional guidelines. If behavioral factors like diet have a significant influence on cancer risk, that's good news! Behavioral factors, unlike genetic factors, are largely within our control. A healthy diet, coupled with physical activity and other lifestyle changes, can go a long way toward reducing cancer risk.

Not surprisingly, the ACS's dietary guidelines are also in line with the traditional Mediterranean diet. They include a high proportion of plant foods in the diet, limited consumption of high-fat foods, and a sensible balance of caloric intake and physical activity. The specific ACS dietary guidelines, as formulated by the ACS Advisory Committee on Diet, Nutrition, and Cancer Prevention in 1996 (and reaffirmed by the ACS Advisory Group on Diet, Physical Activity, and Cancer in 1998), are as follows:

1. Choose most of the foods you eat from plant sources.
   - Eat five or more servings of fruits and vegetables each day.
   - Eat other foods from plant sources, such as breads, cereals, grain products, rice, pasta, or beans several times each day.
2. Limit your intake of high-fat foods, particularly from animal sources.
   - Choose foods low in fat.
   - Limit consumption of meats, especially high-fat meats.
3. Be physically active: Achieve and maintain a healthy weight.
   - Be at least moderately active for thirty minutes or more on most days of the week.
   - Stay within your healthy weight range.
4. Limit consumption of alcoholic beverages, if you drink at all.

⊛ THE UNITED STATES DEPARTMENT OF AGRICULTURE

The United States Department of Agriculture (USDA) formulated the Dietary Guidelines for Americans in 1995, which were most recently revised in 2000. Many organizations, such as the American Dietetic Association, endorse these guidelines as a healthful way to eat and a proactive approach to chronic disease prevention.

We've summarized the Dietary Guidelines for Americans 2000 below. They, too, are quite compatible with the traditional Mediterranean diet:

- Aim for fitness, for a healthy weight, and for moderate physical activity of at least thirty minutes on most days.
- Build a healthy base by making smart food choices, such as a variety of whole grains, fruits, and vegetables each day, aiming for variety while attempting to avoid foodborne illness.
- Make sensible food choices by eating foods low in saturated fat and moderate in total fat, choosing beverages and foods with low sugar content, choosing and preparing foods with less salt, and drinking alcohol in moderation.

In 1992, the USDA also formulated the Food Guide Pyramid, which has been widely distributed and printed on the packaging of many ready-to-eat foods, such as cereal boxes and bread bags. The pyramid consists of nutritional advice and replaces the four food groups the government had previously espoused. In conjunction with the Department of Health and Human Services, the USDA developed its Food Guide Pyramid to be a visual representation of how much of what types of foods should be eaten, on average, each day. The

Food Guide Pyramid

A Guide to Daily Food Choices

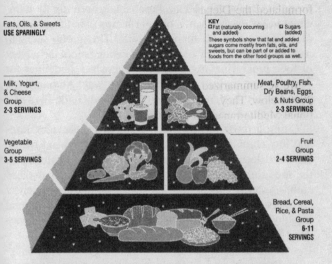

SOURCE: *U.S. Department of Agriculture/U.S. Department of Health and Human Services.*

pyramid shape was chosen because it clearly depicts the foods that should be eaten in greatest quantity each day at the widest part of the pyramid, working up to foods that should be eaten only sparingly at the apex.

The pyramid has met with praise as well as criticism, and is currently under review. Any changes to the current pyramid will most likely correspond directly with the Mediterranean model of eating. In recent years, one of the biggest critics of the current USDA's Food Guide Pyramid has been the Oldways Preservation and Exchange Trust.

☻ EATING THE "OLDWAYS" WAY

The Oldways Preservation and Exchange Trust may not be familiar to the public, but this nonprofit organization based in Cambridge, Massachusetts, has been highly influential in the dissemination of information about the benefits of the traditional Mediterranean diet. This group seeks to resurrect many of the "old ways" of eating before the advent of food processing, and they have published guidelines for eating in the traditional Mediterranean way. Among these guidelines is their own version of the Food Guide Pyramid, the Mediterranean Food Guide Pyramid.

Citing a recognition of high adult life expectancy rates and low chronic disease rates in the Mediterranean region around 1960, knowledge of food typically consumed in the area during this time, and the compatibility of these eating patterns with current knowledge of nutrition science, Oldways developed a list of "Characteristics of Traditional Healthy Mediterranean Diets" that make the diet sound anything but unusual:

- A diet centered on foods from plant sources: vegetables, fruits, whole grains, bread, pasta, nuts, and seeds.
- Focus on foods that are locally grown and minimally processed.
- Olive oil as the primary source of fat.
- Total fat consumption between 25 percent to over 35 percent of calories, with no more than 7 to 8 percent of calories from saturated fat.
- Daily consumption of low to moderate amounts of cheese and/or yogurt (preferably low-fat or nonfat).
- Weekly consumption of low to moderate amounts of fish and poultry (with an emphasis on fish).
- No more than four eggs per week, including those used in cooking and baking.

The Traditional Healthy
Mediterranean Diet Pyramid

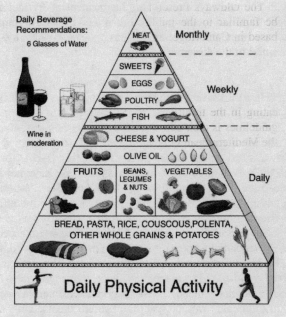

© 2000 Oldways Preservation and Exchange Trust, Cambridge, Mass., http://oldwayspt.org.

- Fresh fruit as a typical dessert; high-sugar and/or high-fat desserts no more than a few times per week.
- Red meat only a few times per month (no more than 12 to 16 ounces or 340 to 450 grams per month).
- Regular physical activity to promote a healthy weight and overall fitness.
- Moderate wine consumption with meals (although Oldways now emphasizes this as an optional component, not appropriate for everyone).

These guidelines give a simple overview of trends in the general Mediterranean diet. According to Oldways, the widely circulated United States Department of Agriculture (USDA) dietary guidelines and their Food Guide Pyramid have not made enough of an impact on the public health profile in the United States.

⊘ THE PYRAMID SCHEME

The USDA Food Guide Pyramid may be the most widely circulated of the pyramids, but other organizations, such as Oldways and the American Heart Association (AHA), publish their own versions of food pyramids. (We have not included the AHA pyramid in this book because it is not as widely distributed as the USDA pyramid.) These pyramids are similar, but certain important differences exist as well. And because all these pyramids have their important aspects but also include elements we believe could be improved, we will add our own pyramid to the mix, the Mediterranean Diet Pyramid. While we feel the advice contained within the other guidelines and pyramids is good, sensible, and conducive to health, we find that the pyramids themselves—the visual representations of the guidelines—tend to be less than user-friendly, sometimes vague, sometimes complicated, and not necessarily updated to reflect the latest research. Our Mediterranean Diet Pyramid includes what we feel is missing from the others, including helpful information based on the most cutting-edge research findings on the Mediterranean diet. This pyramid is simply a guideline, not meant to be taken as dietary dogma. It represents a modernized approach to the traditional Mediterranean diet that we believe is user-friendly and compatible with the tastes, habits, and food availability in the United States today. We hope you will find it a useful guide as you begin to alter your dietary patterns to reflect the Mediterranean way.

Our Mediterranean Diet Food Guide Pyramid

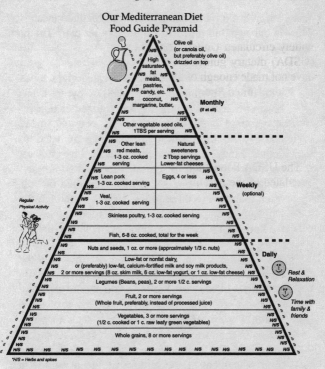

The Mediterranean Diet Pyramid is intended to show general guidelines. Those with special nutrient needs, such as children, pregnant or lactating women, or those with special dietary requirements, should seek the guidance of a registered dietitian or other qualified health care provider for their individual nutrient requirements.

At first glance, the three pyramids may look similar. However, as mentioned before, we felt the other pyramids to be less than user-friendly as guides to the traditional Mediterranean diet. Our pyramid is a general guideline to help modern Amer-

icans eat in a more healthful, traditional Mediterranean way.
How is our pyramid different from the other two? The highlights of our pyramid are as follows:

- The Mediterranean Diet Pyramid categorizes foods
  with clearer distinctions. The USDA pyramid has
  been criticized for lumping foods together that really should be distinguished. For example, meat,
  poultry, fish, dry beans, eggs, and nuts are listed together. Many of these options are healthy choices,
  but others are high in saturated fat, and so are less
  desirable options that should be consumed far less
  often than two to three times per day. Although the
  Oldways pyramid provides more food categories,
  we hope that we have provided even clearer distinctions.
- The Mediterranean Diet Pyramid lists not only the
  recommended number of servings to be eaten daily
  within each category, but how you should structure
  your diet over the course of a day, a week, and a
  month. For example, within the daily section, whole
  grains in the form of whole grain breads, pasta, cereals, and so on should be eaten the most (hence
  their placement at the bottom of the pyramid) in
  eight or more servings daily. How much you eat in
  total depends on your individual caloric needs. Consultation with a registered dietitian or other qualified
  health care provider would be helpful in determining your unique caloric and nutrient needs.
- The daily food section of the Mediterranean Diet
  Pyramid highlights those plant foods that have been
  found to be beneficial to health, and in what proportions they can be consumed. As mentioned above,
  whole grains in the form of breads, cereals, pasta,
  and so on should be eaten the most in a traditional

Mediterranean diet (as also recommended by Old-ways and the USDA). You should aim for at least eight servings or more per day. Next, vegetables should be consumed in at least three daily servings. Two or more servings of fruit should also be included daily. An additional cup or more of legumes, as well as 1 ounce or more of nuts and/or seeds should be enjoyed daily. All of these foods contain ample amounts of health-promoting fiber, phyto-chemicals, vitamins, and minerals.

- For adequate daily intake of calcium and protein, without undesirable excess saturated fat, we suggest a daily intake of low-fat, calcium-fortified, or soy milk or soy milk products, or low-fat or nonfat dairy foods. Although soy is not a traditional food item of the traditional Mediterranean diet, it can and should be enjoyed in the Mediterranean spirit of healthy plant food, low-saturated-fat eating. Soy milk and soy milk products are low in saturated fats, and an excellent source of protein and phytochemicals. Soy is technically a legume, but we placed soy milk in this category to highlight soy milk as a healthy and delicious alternative to cow's milk. Notice that some cheeses that are not classified as low-fat, yet are not overly high in fat, such as mozzarella made from part-skim milk, were placed in the weekly section to be consumed in moderate amounts (up to 3 ounces total for the week—see Chapter Seven for more on dairy foods), which is still compatible with heart health and in keeping with the traditional Mediter-ranean spirit.

- The Mediterranean Diet Pyramid separates protein foods in more distinct categories. As mentioned, legumes primarily, followed by soy milk products (or low-fat or nonfat dairy foods), and then nuts and seeds should be your daily protein providers. Animal meats should be considered as weekly meal enhancers, rather than the main daily protein source.

- The Mediterranean Diet Pyramid further categorizes different animal meats according to their general saturated fat content. Fish, which contains the lowest amount of saturated fat among animal meats, should be eaten the most frequently, up to 6 to 8 cooked ounces total for the week. This more frequent inclusion is also because some fish, particularly the fattier fish like salmon, mackerel, and herring, contain omega-3 fatty acids (more on the health benefits of the omega-3s later). It is best to consume fish that were raised in their natural habitats, such as the deep ocean—instead of being raised on farms, due to the risk of contamination from pollutants.

Next on the upward climb on the pyramid is skinless poultry, followed by veal, lean pork, and then lean red meat (such as extra-lean ground beef, tenderloin, and sirloin). High-fat red meat (such as regular ground beef or prime rib) sits at the top of the pyramid and should be consumed only once a month, if at all. Eggs sit on the periphery of the weekly animal list. Moderate intake of eggs (four or fewer per week) is in keeping with the heart-healthy Mediterranean-inspired eating plan.

Of course, consuming all of the "weekly" animal food sources within a week's time is not likely nor our aim. We give you options, and you choose, from week to week and month to month, which choices suit you. In addition to fish, one or two of the other animal meats can be included in a week's meal plan, if at all. Certainly, a week without animal meat is also fine and in the spirit of the traditional Mediterranean diet. Just be sure to include plenty of plant protein sources, and you're in for a heart-healthy week.

- The Mediterranean Diet Pyramid also separates fats and oils in more distinct categories than the other pyramids. Olive oil, the Mediterranean culinary star, should be the principal source of fat, followed by canola oil. These oils are high in monounsaturated fats and appear to promote heart health. Butter (high in saturated fat), margarine (which can be high in trans-fatty acids), and other vegetable oils should be used on a monthly basis in a truly Mediterranean-inspired diet. Note that olive and canola oil are "drizzled" over the top, not poured. This is because all oils and fats are high in calories, and how much you drizzle depends on your individual caloric needs.

- The Mediterranean Diet Pyramid places highly re-fined and processed desserts and pastries, which contain large amounts of saturated fat and calories, at the top to show that there is little room for these foods in a traditional Mediterranean eating plan. Candy is another food that lacks nutrients and should be reserved for monthly treats. (Dried fruit makes for a delicious and in many ways a more sat-isfying daily sweet treat. In fact, fruit should serve as the basis of the majority of desserts and sweets consumed.) To be realistic and in keeping with the American love for sweets, however, we placed "nat-ural sweeteners" such as raw sugar, honey, pure maple syrup, and molasses in the weekly section to be enjoyed on a moderate basis, if at all (they cer-tainly aren't required!).

- Herbs and spices, designated in the pyramid as H/S, are "sprinkled" throughout the Mediterranean Diet Pyramid to emphasize their importance in our rec-ommended eating plan. After all, herbs and spices are plant-derived foodstuffs, and they also contain beneficial phytochemicals. (Even though only small amounts of herbs and spices are usually used at one time, if you use them often enough, the benefits are there.) Indeed, a plant-based Mediterranean-style diet would not be the same without using these items. Who needs a lot of excess salt when using herbs and spices, preferably organic and fresh from your own or a local garden, such as oregano, parsley, thyme, rosemary, and black pepper? Likewise, who needs a lot of excess sugar when cinnamon, cardamom, nutmeg, and vanilla add their natural flavor?

- Outside of the Mediterranean Diet Pyramid, we've listed important lifestyle indicators to remind our readers of the important role of regular physical activity (Oldways also indicates this in their pyramid), rest and relaxation, as well as social interaction (especially at mealtime) for overall health. All these lifestyle attributes, in addition to diet, most likely contributed to the healthier hearts seen in those living in the traditional Mediterranean regions.

- Unlike the Oldways Mediterranean Pyramid, we did not highlight wine in our pyramid. We've chosen not to include wine, as we feel it is an optional component. We feel that the foods emphasized in our pyramid are so beneficial to health that if wine were omitted, it would not be missed, and because benefits to women, or possible cancer-promoting side effects, are not well understood. Women especially can feel confident following our alcohol-free Mediterranean plan.

In the following chapters, we will discuss all the different Mediterranean Diet Pyramid food categories in more detail.

In the Mediterranean Diet Pyramid, the best elements of both the USDA and Oldways pyramids have been combined, along with other elements to make it even more user-friendly, such as serving sizes and more food groups, to fully distinguish between foods within certain groups in terms of nutritional value and recommended frequency of consumption.

That does not mean, of course, that you must, or even should, follow it precisely, or all the time. This pyramid is only a general guideline meant to promote a varied, low-saturated-fat, whole-food diet compatible with good health. We hope it will remind you that many, many healthy foods exist out there from which you can choose and still be within the Mediterranean spirit of eating. With all the conflicting nutritional information available, it is easy to become confused. In the simple and down-to-earth spirit of traditional Mediterranean culture, however, we suggest that common sense may be the best indicator of action. Choose a diet that tastes great, is low in saturated fat, is high in fiber, includes ample amounts of nutrients, and makes you feel fantastic. We've found that the traditional Mediterranean diet, with sensible modifications, fits the bill perfectly. And what better reminder of just how healthy, diverse, delicious, and easy this diet can be than the visual representation provided by the Mediterranean Diet Pyramid?

☞ QUESTIONS AND ANSWERS

☞ *In general, what counts as a serving?*

The Mediterranean Diet Pyramid lists serving sizes in each of its food categories. The USDA also publishes a list of serving sizes for a variety of food groups. In general, however, one serving from the grain group equals one slice of bread. Note that by "slice of bread," we are referring to the standard 70-calorie portion size. If your whole-grain bread contains more calories per slice, adjust accordingly. For example, some prepackaged whole-grain breads contain

110 calories per slice, which would equal 1½ Mediterranean Diet grain servings. A serving is also equal to 1 ounce of ready-to-eat cereal or ½ cup of cooked grains, including whole-grain rice, pasta, or cooked cereal. This serving is fairly small. Drop ½ cup of pasta on a plate and you'll see what we mean. The small serving size (by American standards, where we have become accustomed to "supersizing" our meals) puts the USDA's six to eleven serving recommendation from the grain group in perspective. For the carb-concerned, six to eleven servings sounds out of control, and even eight servings sounds like a lot, but eat a cup of whole-grain, sugar-free cereal for breakfast (like hot oatmeal), one sandwich on two slices of whole-grain bread for lunch, and a cup of whole-grain pasta for dinner and you're there. In general, whole-grain foods will not promote wide fluctuations in insulin levels. (For more on carbs and protein, see Chapter Nine on how to lose weight the Mediterranean way).

For the vegetable group, 1 cup of raw leafy vegetables or ½ cup of chopped or cooked other vegetables or ¾ cup of vegetable juice equals a serving. One medium piece of fruit or ½ cup of chopped or cooked fruit, or ½ to ¾ cup of most fruit juices equals a fruit serving. In the dairy category, 1 cup of milk or yogurt or 1½ ounces of cheese equals a serving, and in the protein group, 2 to 3 ounces of cooked lean meat equals a serving (that's not very big, so take note). Note: One egg, 2 tablespoons of peanut butter, ⅓ cup of most nuts, or ½ cup of cooked lentils equals an ounce of meat.

℘ *Does the Mediterranean diet provide enough daily protein for the average adult?*

Yes! The Recommended Daily Allowance (RDA) for protein for the average adult male (age twenty-five and up) is 63 grams. For the average adult female (age twenty-five and up and who is not pregnant or lactating), the RDA for protein is 50 grams. If you eat the minimum daily Mediterranean Diet recommendation of 1 cup of legumes (such as chickpeas and red kidney beans) per day, you'll be eating roughly 14 grams of protein. Add in $\frac{1}{3}$ cup of nuts (such as walnuts) and you'll be consuming 7 grams more. Consume at least three servings of vegetables (such as green beans and carrots), and you are adding about 3 more grams of protein. Two cups of low-fat soy milk equals roughly 16 grams of protein. Eat at least eight servings of whole grains (such as whole-grain bread and couscous), and you are adding about 24 grams of protein. This already puts us up to 63 grams of protein, and we haven't even left the minimum recommendations of the daily food section of the Mediterranean Diet Pyramid. Toss in an ounce of fish (such as tuna) and you'll be getting about 7 more grams of protein.

✛ Can a vegetarian eat a Mediterranean diet?

The traditional Mediterranean diet is almost a lacto-ovo vegetarian diet. While both Mediterranean diet pyramids list meat, poultry, and fish to be consumed anywhere from weekly to a few times per month, these items are not, by any means, required. The traditional Mediterranean diet centers around plant foods, with small amounts of cheese and yo-gurt (depending on the country of a recipe's origin). Many people living in the Mediterranean during the 1950s and 1960s probably were vegetarian by necessity.

Even a vegan (someone who consumes no animal prod-ucts at all) can follow the traditional Mediterranean diet. Al-though cheese, yogurt, and milk, can be added in moderation to a heart-healthy eating plan, they aren't required. Soy cheeses and milks make delicious substitutes, or try almond milk. Vegans must be careful to eat food from a wide variety of sources, to ensure that all the nutritional bases are covered. Vegans might also consider taking supplements, particularly of vitamin B_{12}, which is most available from animal sources. We strongly recommend that anyone planning to eliminate an entire food group from his or her diet should seek the counsel of a registered dietitian to ensure that the proportions of food eaten are sufficient to meet all nutrient and caloric needs.

⅌ Is the Mediterranean Diet Pyramid appropriate for children? What about pregnant or breastfeeding women? What about teenagers?

Yes to all! The Mediterranean diet, when eaten in correct proportions and sufficient amounts, is nutritionally adequate for anyone. Again, however, we recommend that you contact a registered dietitian if you have any special nutritional and/or caloric needs such as those of a growing child or a pregnant or breastfeeding woman.

⅌ Can someone with a chronic disease such as diabetes or kidney disease safely eat a Mediterranean diet?

People with chronic diseases have unique nutritional and/or caloric needs, so again, we recommend contacting a registered dietitian about the diet that is right for the individual. Certain food items or groups may be prohibited for you. Although you may have to customize certain elements according to your needs, in general, a Mediterranean diet is a healthy, nutrient-dense diet appropriate for anyone able to eat it.

❧ *Are vitamin, mineral, or other dietary supplements necessary or beneficial while following the traditional Mediterranean diet?*

No, the nutrient-dense Mediterranean diet provides all essential nutrients when eaten in sufficient quantities (as depicted in the Mediterranean Diet Pyramid). If you suspect you aren't deriving adequate nutrition from your diet or if you have special nutritional needs, seek the advice of a registered dietitian.

❧ *Why does the American Heart Association recommend averaging percentages, such as the 30-percent-of-calories-from-fat rule, over a few days or a week rather than on a daily basis?*

This concept works for both the AHA-recommended diet and the Mediterranean diet. In the words of the AHA, "Applying the 30 percent standard to single foods greatly limits the variety of foods in the diet and can be misleading. The only way to maintain balance, variety and enjoyment of the AHA eating plan is to interpret the guideline with emphasis on the words 'total calories.'" In other words, occasionally it makes sense to have a day where calories from fat will exceed 30 percent. If days like this are balanced with days where total calories from fat fall below 30 percent, this is more conducive to a varied (and interesting) diet.

❧ *Can flaxseed be consumed on a Mediterranean diet?*

Absolutely! There has been a lot of exciting news surrounding flaxseed and flaxseed products. Flaxseed is an excellent source of health-promoting omega-3 fatty acids, as well as phytochemicals. Although not traditionally a part of the Mediterranean diet, it can definitely be incorporated in a healthy Mediterranean style of eating. Several whole-food manufacturers have started incorporating flaxseed in wonderful breads and ready-to-eat cereals. You, too, can incorporate flaxseed, or flaxseed meal (which is similar to wheat germ, and can be purchased in most whole foods markets) as part of your daily nut or seed consumption. Sprinkle flaxseed meal in your cereal, yogurt, quick bread and muffin mixtures, and so forth. Another source of flaxseed is flaxseed oil, which can be quite expensive and, like all oils, high in calories. You can try using flaxseed oil as a substitute for olive or canola oil in cooking from time to time, or drizzle a little on a salad. Keep flaxseed oil in the refrigerator.

✸ Which dairy products besides nonfat or low-fat milk are a sensible addition to a low-saturated-fat diet?

Try some of the many low-fat and nonfat plain yogurts. Stir in some fresh fruit for sweetness. Also, while some cheeses contain a lot of fat, others are relatively low in fat. Check the labels, or look for cheeses made from skim milk (such as mozzarella made with part-skim milk). Pretty much all the cheeses come in reduced or nonfat versions. Cottage cheese, ricotta, feta, gouda, Cheddar—the list seems endless—are now offered in reduced-fat or nonfat varieties. We recommend organic cheeses, or cheese imported from the Mediterranean region. They may cost a little more, but the taste is so intensely delicious that a little goes a long way.

✸ Where does high-fat cheese fit into the Mediterranean Diet Pyramid?

High-fat cheeses (such as Gruyère, muenster, blue) are full of flavor, so as we mention above, a little goes a long way. Although a dairy product, high-fat cheese is more appropriately located with high-fat meats as a high-fat protein source. If you like them, consume high-fat cheese only every month or so and in small amounts.

℘ *Canned beans are much easier to prepare than dried beans. Are they just as healthy?*

Yes. For those who are salt-sensitive, however, be careful about the excess sodium. Rinse canned beans in a colander to wash away the salt. Rinsing will also wash away some of the starchy liquid, making your dishes more attractive, as well as reducing the likelihood of developing intestinal gas after bean consumption. If the recipe in which you are using canned beans calls for added salt (not often the case with traditional Mediterranean recipes), you might consider adjusting the added salt accordingly.

℘ *Are certain nuts and seeds better than others?*

From a nutritional point of view, all nuts and seeds are nutrient-dense plant foods. Some are lower in fat than others, however, and consequently lower in calories, so these nuts and seeds might be more appropriate for people who are attempting to control their weight. Chestnuts are actually a low-fat food. A 1-ounce serving of roasted (European) chestnuts (about three and a half nuts) contains less than 1 gram of fat, all unsaturated, and about 70 calories. On the opposite end of the scale, 1 ounce of dry-roasted cashews contains about 13 grams of fat and 163 calories, and 1 ounce of toasted or roasted sesame seeds contains about 14 grams of fat and 160 calories. The key is to get a variety of nuts and seeds to benefit most from the varied nutrients and phytochemicals (more on this later). The more variety, the healthier the diet really is. Of course, eating that variety in moderation is important, too.

Coconuts are a rare exception to the heart-healthy plant food rule. Coconuts are high in saturated fat and are best avoided most of the time.

❦ The Mediterranean Diet Pyramid lists "four or fewer" eggs at the "weekly" level. Is it okay to eat more eggs if only the whites are consumed?

Yes, by all means. Egg whites do not contain cholesterol, which is found only in the yolks. They are a good source of protein and can be used to cut fat in egg dishes and baked dishes as well. Also, research supports the notion that consumption of saturated fat, not dietary cholesterol (sometimes called preformed cholesterol), has the most impact on blood cholesterol levels. While some people are very sensitive to dietary cholesterol and should limit egg consumption, the general population need not be overly concerned about dietary cholesterol. The "four or fewer per week" egg rule is just a general guideline for a Mediterranean-inspired (or any nutritionally sound) eating program, due to the saturated fat element in whole eggs.

❦ How can someone lose weight putting olive oil on everything?

We certainly don't recommend putting olive oil on everything! Olive oil is fat, and fat in excess contributes to obesity, which in turn contributes to many health problems. One common misconception about the Mediterranean diet is that adding olive oil to an already high-fat diet will "fix" the fat problem. On the contrary, olive oil should substitute for other types of fat, not be added to them. Overall fat intake from all sources, including olive oil, should be lower than is typical for Americans. This is why we recommend "drizzling" olive oil, not pouring it, over our visual representation of a healthy Mediterranean-inspired diet. A little goes a long way.

✌ Are some vegetables better choices than others? What about fruits?

All fruits and vegetables (in fact, all plant foods, with the exception of coconut and palm oils—more on these in Chapter Three) have their "star" qualities. Also, every type of plant food has a unique combination of nutrients and phytochemicals. That's why a variety of plant foods is more important than choosing a few "right" plant foods and eating only those. The more variety in your diet, the more nutritionally complete your diet will be.

✌ What about table sugar? Is sugar an acceptable addition to a healthy, Mediterranean diet?

The sugar controversy rages on. Some people proclaim refined sugar as among the worst possible additions to your diet. Others say that, as long as a person maintains a healthy weight and consumes sufficient nutrients, sugar is fine. The truth probably lies somewhere in the middle. Whenever you eat a high-sugar product, you are filling up with empty calories when you could have eaten something more nutrient-dense instead. If you are getting enough to eat but add sugar, you may have trouble maintaining that ideal weight. But, if consumed occasionally in moderation, as part of a healthy diet, sugar is probably just fine—and pretty hard to avoid these days.

✤ What about coffee and tea?

Although not listed on either Mediterranean food pyramid, coffee and/or tea are both integral—albeit nonnutritive—parts of the diets in many Mediterranean countries. In fact, it would be difficult to discuss the Mediterranean region without mentioning the infamous Italian espresso, not to mention the thick, sweet, sludgy concoction known as Turkish coffee. Tea is also widely consumed in many Mediterranean countries. However, we suggest that if you enjoy coffee and/or tea, you consume them in moderation like anything else, and not at the expense of more nutritionally complete foods. Recent research has linked green and even black tea with cancer prevention, as teas contain antioxidants and other phytochemicals that could bolster the body's immune system and fight cancer-causing free radicals. Of course, caffeine-free herbal teas are a great way to relax with a hot beverage free of caffeine. If you are caffeine-sensitive, we recommend discussing the use of caffeine with your physician.

✤ Is canola oil just as good as olive oil?

Canola oil is, by necessity, more processed than olive oil. Therefore, it loses many of the vital phytochemical components still present in extra virgin olive oil. However, it is a good source of monounsaturated fat and it is generally cheaper than olive oil. For more information on fat in general and olive and canola oil in particular, see Chapter Three.

✤ Can the Mediterranean Diet Pyramid be used as a guide for non-Mediterranean types of cuisine?

Yes! The idea is to apply the Mediterranean concept, not necessarily the particular food ingredients, to all your food choices. You need not limit yourself to pasta primavera, for example. Instead, base your diet around plant foods, focusing on vegetables, whole grains, fruit, primarily beans for protein, fish, and animal meat in moderation. This goal works for just about any cuisine. In fact, bar-and-grill-type American restaurants often have grilled vegetable entrées. Most restaurants have salads with small amounts of meat such as grilled chicken or salmon on top. Ask for olive oil and vinegar as a dressing and you've got a great Mediterranean-inspired meal!

Asian cuisine is right in line with the principles of traditional Mediterranean cuisine. Many foods unique to this cuisine have distinctive health benefits, such as soy foods like tofu. Rice and vegetables with protein from small amounts of meat or tofu or nuts and seeds (peanut sauce, walnuts, almonds, cashews, and peanuts are common Asian additions) make an exceptionally healthy meal.

Even an American home barbecue can fit in with the Mediterranean concept if you fill up on green salad, baked beans, coleslaw made with vinaigrette instead of mayonnaise, grilled or raw vegetables, and fruit such as watermelon and fresh fruit salad. You probably won't even miss the burger and hot dogs!

ℂ The Mediterranean Diet Pyramid seems to require a lot of food be consumed, especially in the daily food section. Will I gain weight?

No, not very likely, especially if you incorporate daily activity into your schedule. If you consume the minimum requirement of each of the recommended daily food groups, you will be consuming about 1,385 calories. Add in a tablespoon of olive oil, and you are still talking about only (roughly) 1,500 calories. Factor in a 3-ounce cooked portion of fish, such as salmon, and you're adding around 200 calories, for a total of 1,700 calories for the day. The average adult can easily maintain weight on such a diet. In fact, many people will lose weight on any diet below 1,800 calories, especially those who are moderately active.

The Mediterranean diet really should not be about numbers. Rather, the culinary spirit of the traditional Mediterranean region should be celebrated and enjoyed for the many benefits it possesses. Again, if your health requires you to gain or lose weight, you should seek the guidance of a registered dietitian or other qualified health care provider for your individual needs. Our pyramid should act only as a general guide to shape your eating habits to closely resemble the healthy traditional Mediterranean diet.

3: *Olive Oil and Other Fats: What You Need to Know*

Fat. Does the word make you cringe? Fat is bad, bad, bad . . . isn't it? Eating fat makes us overweight, gives us heart attacks, causes cancer, wrecks our health . . . doesn't it? If it says "fat free," it must be healthy . . . isn't that true?

Yet, if fat is so bad, how is it that in certain Mediterranean regions such as the Greek island of Crete during the 1950s, where heart disease and other chronic disease rates were startlingly low, fat consumption was about equal to fat consumption in America? Cretans during this time in history were among the longest-lived people in the world. Yet their diet was full of fat.

According to researcher Ancel Keys, Cretans consumed 3 to 4 ounces (or about ½ cup) of olive oil per day, per person. That's a lot of fat! Keys reported that the people of Crete drenched their salads in it, dunked their bread in it, poured it on their potatoes. Some Cretan farmers even drank a wineglass full of the stuff for breakfast! Why weren't the people on this tiny island suffering from the same health problems as Americans during the 1950s and 1960s, those health problems we've been told had (and still have) everything to do with too much fat in our diets?

Perhaps Crete is an anomaly? Yet studies from other countries reveal similarly striking results. Heart disease rates in the southern, or rather the Mediterranean, regions of Italy, Spain, and France were also remarkably low, even though percentage of fat calories varied greatly around the region.

Yet not every country could get away with fat consumption to the degree enjoyed in the Mediterranean. Keys's studies of fat consumption and diet also included Finland, the country with the most coronary heart disease and the shortest life spans in Europe. Keys examined middle-aged men in Finland to determine why coronary heart disease was so common in this country, even among men who were thinner and more physically fit than many of the overweight, less fit American men in Keys's studies. Blood cholesterol levels of the Finnish men proved to exceed average levels in American men.

Subsequent dietary surveys revealed that the typical diet in Finland was extremely high in saturated fat. According to Keys, meals included "great mounds of butter," and it was not unusual to see "grown men down a couple of glasses of rich milk." Keys also relates watching Finnish loggers take "slabs of cheese the size of slices of sandwich bread, smear them a quarter of an inch deep with butter and eat them with a beer as an after-sauna snack."

Other studies conducted by Keys revealed that among patients with very high blood cholesterol levels, diets very low in fat produced dramatic drops in cholesterol levels within one week, and studies examining the effects of different types of fatty acids—saturated, monounsaturated, and polyunsaturated—on blood cholesterol levels revealed that saturated fatty acids tended to raise blood cholesterol levels the most.

It would seem, then, that the type of dietary fat, not just

fat in general, is specifically related to the risk of developing coronary heart disease and other chronic diseases. Does this mean some fat is "good" and some fat is "bad"? That we should eat all of one and none of the other?

Actually, the fat issue is a complex one, and not simply a matter of "bad" and "good," as the media often imply. For instance, just because the Cretans drowned their food in olive oil doesn't mean we can do the same and remain slim with unclogged arteries. The residents of rural Crete had far more active lifestyles than most Americans today. Also, scientists now know that fat per se isn't bad. On the contrary, fat is beneficial and even necessary to a healthy, fully functioning body. However, certain types of fat in differing proportions do apparently tend to be more or less beneficial to health.

Americans eat a lot of saturated fat, mostly from animal sources. The residents of Crete during the days of Ancel Keys's research were eating almost all their fat from plant sources, namely olive oil. What's the difference? While oil of any type is 100 percent fat and has the same number of calories as any other oil, each oil or fat type has a different composition—its own ratio of saturated to monounsaturated to polyunsaturated fatty acids. And the fatty acid makeup of an oil appears to make all the difference. The fatty acid composition in, say, a cheeseburger, is far different from the fatty acid composition of a calorie-equivalent portion of olive oil.

Let's look back at Greece. According to Keys, at the time of his research, the general Greek population received approximately 20 percent of their calories from olive oil alone, with total fat intake ranging around 35 percent. (People living on the island of Crete had total fat intakes exceeding 40 percent of daily calories, again, mostly in the form of olive oil, as reported in the *American Journal of Clinical Nutrition*.) Keys describes the rural Greeks, who were accustomed to traditional eating habits and who couldn't afford richer foods, as "remarkably healthy." The wealthier population of Athens, on the other hand, tended to eat food more inspired by the French school of cooking (more prevalent in non-Mediterranean, northern France), which is relatively heavy on butter and cream compared to olive oil. Although no study has proven a direct correlation between these varied diets in Greece and heart disease, Keys could not "help but mention" that Athens had no shortage of wealthy coronary heart disease patients. Keys's observations significantly complicate the simplified message Americans have been accustomed to hearing over the past fifteen years or so: that fat is bad and we should eat less of it. Fat is not "bad." We need fat to function. The trick is how to consume it in a way that maximizes our health and gives us the best possible protection against chronic diseases like coronary heart disease and cancer.

⊘ WHY WE CRAVE FAT

Long ago, when humans were hunters and gatherers, before we learned to cultivate the land and raise our own food, we relied on our stores of fat to get us through long periods when food was not readily available. To survive, our bodies had to become adept at storing fat. Without it, we would not have survived to today.

Life was hard. Humans had to battle the elements without the luxuries of heating, electricity, and manufactured clothing. We had to hunt for our food instead of buying it at the supermarket. We had to build fires if we wanted to cook our food, and we certainly couldn't drive anywhere. We walked, or ran for our lives, or chased, or climbed, or swam. If we were lucky, once in a while, we ate to satiety. Life was physically formidable.

Times have changed, of course. In America, food is plentiful for most and automation has largely eliminated the need for physical labor. Although some Americans still squeeze exercise into their days, perhaps a running or jogging session a few times a week or a thrice-weekly workout at a health club or gym, such a degree of exercise is minimal compared to what humans once were forced to practice. And many Americans don't exercise much at all, spending their days in front of computers or behind counters or in comfortable office chairs.

Yet no one has informed our bodies that food is now far more accessible than it once was, and that survival requires far fewer calories than it once did. Still lagging behind our rapidly changing industrialized society, our bodies remain genetically engineered to handle prolonged periods without food. We aren't designed for high caloric intakes coupled with low physical activity, yet this scenario describes a way of life for many Americans. The result? An epidemic of obesity, and a high rate of chronic disease. Humans may not die from confrontations with large predatory animals very often anymore, but our lifestyles have evolved in such a way that we are confronted with other perils—heart disease, cancer, diabetes, high blood pressure, and cognitive decline, to name a few.

Our ancient origins also explain why women are more likely to put on excess fat stores during pregnancy, especially during the last trimester. Although women still require extra stores of fat for lactation, our bodies may overzealously prepare, in case of a famine. Long ago, to preserve the survival of the species, women had to be able to provide milk, whether food was roasting on a spit over the fire or not.

Because our bodies remain so proficient at fat storage, to maintain good health and a healthy weight, we must adapt our eating habits to match our twenty-first-century activity levels. Our "anti-famine" programming tends to convert dietary fat readily into body fat. On the other hand, many researchers believe that carbohydrates are much less readily converted to fat, and are used more easily as ready energy.

Further complicating the picture is the most recent weight-loss fad: the high-protein, low-carbohydrate (sometimes called "carbohydrate-controlled") diet. According to proponents of these "protein diets" or "low-carb diets," it is the carbohydrate, not the fat, that is to blame for excess gain. Because so much of the food in the standard American diet consists of processed, refined carbohydrates (white bread, refined pasta, crackers, cookies, and sugar, sugar, sugar), these are indeed an excessive source of calories. Often, refined carbohydrates combine with saturated fat or worse, hydrogenated fat, to form "convenience foods" that bear scant resemblance to foods in their natural form, as they first grew on or ambled across the earth.

We'll talk more about the carb/fat/protein connection in later chapters, but for now, suffice it to say that all excess calories will eventually be converted to body fat. You can still gain weight eating carbohydrates without fat, and you can still gain weight eating fat without carbohydrates. Controlled caloric intake is the key to weight loss (see Chapter Nine for more on how to lose weight the Mediterranean way).

Back to fat and heart disease: Some researchers, such as Dr. Dean Ornish, a medical doctor who has studied the effects of low-fat eating to prevent, control, and even reverse heart disease, believe that almost all fat should be eliminated from the diet, and that only about 10 percent of calories in the diet should come from fat sources. Studies Dr. Ornish has conducted reveal dramatic results in heart disease patients put on a very low-fat diet. However, other researchers believe such a level of dietary fat is too low, especially for those who do not have heart disease. Again, proponents of some low-carb diets believe that fat intake needn't be monitored at all when carb intake remains minimal. A more mainstream trend, and more heart-healthful approach, we believe, has been to substitute more healthful monounsaturated fats for saturated fats. Keep consumption of all food items (carbohydrates, proteins, and fats) within the ranges displayed by the Mediterranean Diet Pyramid. This will help promote achieving and maintaining ideal body weight. Such a diet may also be easier to follow, since Americans are so accustomed to a diet higher in fat than Ornish's recommended 10 percent, and many Americans are loath to give up bread, pasta, and other favorite (and healthy!) carbohydrates.

One study, "Dietary Oils, Serum Lipoproteins, and Coronary Heart Disease," reported in the *American Journal of Clinical Nutrition*, examined the effects of replacing hard fats in the diet with unsaturated fats such as olive oil, versus the effects of replacing hard fats with carbohydrates. Hard fats are fats that are relatively solid at room temperature and are high in saturated fatty acids (such as those prevalent in butter) or trans-fatty acids (such as those prevalent in margarine or other food items listing "hydrogenated" or "partially hydrogenated" vegetable oils on the label). Replacing hard fats with liquid fats resulted in a more favorable blood cholesterol profile than replacing hard fats with carbohydrates, but only if body weight was kept constant. (The study recognized the danger of obesity from excessive fat consumption.)

But fighting this preprogrammed desire for fat is a challenge. If you are craving a hot fudge sundae or a bag of potato chips, chances are you won't feel satisfied with a bowl of carrot sticks. Fat cravings often diminish when you get out of the high-fat habit. Once you've become accustomed to the taste of fresh foods unadorned by excess fat—tender vegetables, juicy fruit, wholesome whole grains, and crisp salads like those so celebrated in the traditional Mediterranean cuisines—the taste of too much fat can become unappealing. And when you just have to have that "fat fix," for satiety and culinary satisfaction, consider dipping those carrot sticks, broccoli florets, and red pepper strips into a shallow dish of green olive oil topped with a little pepper. Your low-cal snack just got more interesting!

⊛ FAT TALK

Americans tend to consume about 34 percent of their calories from fat, even though most dietary recommendations suggest we limit fat intake to 30 percent of calories or fewer. More specific recommendations by the American Heart Association (AHA) suggest that fewer than 10 percent of total calories come from saturated fats, 10 to 15 percent from monounsaturated fats (the kinds of fats prevalent in olive oil and canola oil), and about 10 percent from polyunsaturated fats (the main kind of fat in vegetable oils like corn oil and soybean oil). While the average overall fat intake common to the traditional Mediterranean diet is approximately the same as that recommended by the AHA and others, the combinations and proportions of food in the Mediterranean diet suggest that an even lower percentage of saturated fats and a higher percentage of monounsaturated fats might be an even more preferable balance.

In either case, fat is a nutrient required by your body to stay alive. Many experts such as the World Health Organization suggest that at least 15 to 20 percent of the total calories you consume should come from fat to keep your body functioning properly.

Fat is a challenge for the weight-conscious, however. Consider that over half of all adult Americans are technically overweight, and close to 25 percent are medically classified as "obese," according to the National Institute of Diabetes and Digestive and Kidney Diseases (NIDDK), a branch of the National Institutes of Health. With obesity a national epidemic, don't we have to be extra careful about the fat we eat, no matter what kind it is? Certainly, with 9 calories per gram (compared to only 4 calories per gram in both carbohydrates and protein), fat packs a caloric punch, and keeping caloric intake under control is important for health. According to the NIDDK, obesity not only increases the risk of many chronic diseases, including heart disease, diabetes, high blood pressure (which further increases the risk of heart disease), and even some cancers, but increases death risk by 50 to 100 percent!

Yet nutritionists know that the solution to obesity isn't to cut out all fat. As much as our current culture looks askance at body fat, fat provides stored energy, available for when we need it most. Too much is harmful, but we all need some, and too little fat in the diet can be harmful, too, especially for children and women trying to become pregnant, and according to some researchers, an extremely low-fat diet is dangerous for everyone!

Your body needs fat for more than energy. Fat helps to keep your skin and hair supple and healthy, helps children to grow properly, insulates your body from temperature extremes, and even protects your internal organs. Your cell membranes are composed largely of fat. Without fat, your body cannot absorb and deliver vitamins A, D, E, and K. And while your body makes certain fats, it must derive some from your diet. Two of these are essential: linoleic acid and linolenic acid. (These fats are called "acids" because fatty acids are what make fat.) Eating a variety of foods makes getting enough essential fat in your diet an easy task.

Fat takes longer to digest than other food types, so a meal with a sufficient fat content will generally satisfy your hunger longer than a low-fat meal, making fat (in moderation) an important weapon in the dieter's arsenal. It can also make food taste better by adding flavor and texture. Have you noticed that nonfat versions of your favorite foods tend to be less satisfying than the "real thing," even though many low-fat or nonfat foods dramatically boost the sugar content to make up for the lack of "fat flavor"?

Consequently, many low-fat and nonfat foods (such as a fat-free fig cookie) are as high or even higher in calories than the original higher fat version (such as a regular fig cookie). However, as we've mentioned before, engaging in a fat free-for-all makes it difficult to remain healthy and at an ideal weight. The point is that fat is necessary, but too much fat can compromise good health. A healthy portion of fat know-how will help you to include fat in your diet in a way that is beneficial, not destructive, to your health.

⌘ FAT IN THE BODY

We know fat in the diet has been linked to an increased risk of heart disease, some cancers, and other chronic diseases. Too much dietary fat can also contribute to obesity, a risk factor in itself for a slew of health problems, including coronary heart disease and certain cancers. To understand why too much fat in the diet is dangerous to good health, let's look at what excessive amounts of fat can do in the human body.

A high-fat diet featuring foods from animal sources may result in an overconsumption of a particular kind of fat called saturated fat. Too much saturated fat can cause blood cholesterol levels to rise, increasing the risk of coronary heart disease. (Blood, or serum, cholesterol refers to the cholesterol in your bloodstream.) Foods high in saturated fatty acids include many types of meat, whole milk, lard, and butter, and a few plant foods such as coconut, palm, and palm kernel oil. Saturated fatty acids may soften at room temperature but still remain relatively firm instead of turning to liquid (like a stick of butter left on the counter—more spreadable but still a solid, not a liquid).

Polyunsaturated fatty acids include vegetable oils like corn oil, soybean oil, sunflower oil, and safflower oil, and the fat in most seafood. Polyunsaturated fatty acids are liquid or very soft at room temperature. Some research suggests that excessive amounts of polyunsaturated fatty acids from these vegetable oils are linked to increased risk of cancer, but more research is required to confirm this. In the meantime, polyunsaturated fatty acids in moderate amounts may help to keep blood cholesterol levels low because they lower LDL, or "bad," cholesterol levels. They also lower HDL, or "good," cholesterol levels, however, making mono-unsaturated fatty acids an even better choice.

Monounsaturated fat is the fat type that dominates the traditional Mediterranean diet. Foods rich in monounsaturated fatty acids include olive oil, canola oil, and most nuts and seeds. Liquid at room temperature, monounsaturated fatty acids in the diet have also been shown to lower LDL ("bad") cholesterol levels, but not HDL ("good") cholesterol levels in the blood, making it the fat of choice for a heart-healthy diet.

In other words, what you eat affects the amount of cholesterol in your blood. How much is too much? A serum cholesterol level above 240 mg/dl is considered high, and is associated with an increased risk of coronary heart disease. Between 200 and 239 mg/dl is considered borderline high, and below 200 mg/dl is considered desirable.

Cholesterol levels in the Mediterranean region during the 1960s were generally below 200 mg/dl. Although some of the diets in the traditional Mediterranean region were considered high in fat (especially on the isle of Crete), the saturated fat component was low. Because olive oil was the primary source of fat and the use of animal foods was not high, saturated fat intakes were kept in check. Furthermore, with saturated fats low, the heart-healthy monounsaturated fats take center stage.

✒ BLOOD CHOLESTEROL: THE PLAYERS

Your blood cholesterol level can be determined through a simple blood test. Some cholesterol tests give you an overall cholesterol level, and the best tests break down your total cholesterol into LDL and HDL categories. (Those free or low-cost cholesterol screenings you sometimes see at shopping malls tend to give you only overall cholesterol level, while tests performed through your physician are usually more accurate and may give more specific information, making it worth the extra bucks if cholesterol concerns you.)

In general, according to levels set by the National Heart, Lung, and Blood Institute, your total cholesterol level should be under 200 mg/dl, although some researchers, such as Dr. Dean Ornish, feel that a level of 150 mg/dl is more desirable to effectively prevent heart disease. A cholesterol level in the 200 to 239 mg/dl range could be a red flag alerting you to be careful and take steps to lower your blood cholesterol, although a cholesterol level in this range might be better than it seems if good cholesterol levels are high and bad cholesterol levels are low. A blood cholesterol level of 240 mg/dl and above puts you at a high risk for heart disease, but again, keep in mind the HDL/LDL numbers separately.

Generally, strive to keep your "good" or HDL cholesterol level above 35 mg/dl and your "bad" or LDL cholesterol level below 130 mg/dl. If you haven't had a blood cholesterol test, or if you haven't had one recently, you should be able to schedule a physical exam with your primary care doctor and request a test to determine your blood cholesterol level. Or, if you see one of those free or low-cost tests at your local mall, why not check your blood cholesterol level while it's convenient? If your reading is high, give your physician a call to schedule a more complete test. Blood cholesterol should be screened every five years.

What do the results of a more complete test really mean, and why is "good" cholesterol good and "bad" cholesterol bad? HDL (high-density-lipoprotein) cholesterol is called the "good" cholesterol because this type of cholesterol moves through the body, picks up excess cholesterol, and delivers it to the liver, where it can be eliminated. High levels of HDL cholesterol have been linked to a decreased risk of coronary heart disease. Monounsaturated fats like olive oil have been shown to be promoters of HDL cholesterol.

Consuming a diet rich in monounsaturated fats has also been shown to make LDL cholesterol less prone to oxidation—a process that leads to atherosclerosis, or hardening of the arteries, that can lead to heart attack or stroke. For this reason, monounsaturated fats are recommended to make up the greatest proportion of fats in the diet (as they do in the traditional Mediterranean diet).

LDL (low-density-lipoprotein) cholesterol, the so-called bad cholesterol, has been linked to an increased risk of heart disease. LDL cholesterol takes cholesterol from the liver to be deposited throughout the body. (The body needs cholesterol for a variety of purposes, such as making hormones.) Unfortunately, LDL is highly prone to oxidation (more on oxidation later). Oxidized LDL (or o-LDL) is believed to cause damage to the walls of the arteries. Once damaged, fatty deposits (or plaque) can accumulate, which causes the artery walls to harden. Once plaque begins to form, blood is unable to flow as freely. Sometimes so much plaque accumulates that there is a complete occlusion of blood flow. The result is either a heart attack or a stroke.

There has been some recent research that shows oxidized LDL particles arise primarily from the ingestion of a certain type of polyunsaturated fat found mostly in corn oil, safflower oil, and other oils used widely in processed foods. LDL particles arising from monounsaturated fat metabolism, however, appear to be resistant to oxidation and, therefore, less available for incorporation into atherosclerotic plaques, which slows or halts the progression of atherosclerosis.

Once again, saturated fat in the diet has been shown to increase LDL cholesterol levels. Polyunsaturated fats have been shown to lower LDL cholesterol levels, but can also lower HDL cholesterol levels. Best of all, monounsaturated fats like olive oil have been shown not only to lower LDL cholesterol levels, but also to make any LDL cholesterol present less prone to the damaging oxidation process.

Keeping LDL blood cholesterol levels low will help to keep our arteries clear, flexible, and healthy, and dietary alterations are among the most effective ways to keep LDL levels in a healthy range.

⊛ EATING LESS FAT

Like so many other nutritional concepts, the fat picture isn't as simple as it often may sound in the latest news story or web site. Will you solve a cholesterol problem by completely eliminating animal products in your diet without changing anything else? Maybe, but maybe not. Will you develop a chronic disease if you eat too much polyunsaturated fat? Probably not, but nutritionists don't have a definitive answer to this question, either. Will you live to be one hundred years old if your fat intake comes primarily from monounsaturated fats? Again, maybe, and maybe not. Nobody exists in a vacuum, and even the Mediterranean diet is bigger than what kind of fat it includes. Common sense, and the traditional Mediterranean diet, dictate that moderation in all dietary aspects makes the most sense: small amounts of meat and dairy, with an emphasis on monounsaturated fats.

One of the best ways to cut saturated fat is to minimize your consumption of animal products like high-fat meat and dairy products, and maximize your consumption of plant foods. This is the crux of the traditional Mediterranean diet, and is easy to visualize with the Mediterranean Diet Pyramid. If plant foods make up the bulk of your diet, you'll need to do little else to keep your saturated fat intake under control. That's not to say you shouldn't eat any meat or dairy products. Lean meat, low-fat or nonfat dairy, and small amounts of richer animal products can flavor and enhance a plant-based diet. But when you eat in the Mediterranean way, these animal products embellish rather than dominate the dinner plate.

Center your meals around delicious whole-grain foods and bean dishes, with plenty of vegetables and fruit. Meats and cheeses make delicious and occasional condiments for flavoring. When you fill up on whole grains, vegetables, and fruits, you will not have much room left for high-fat foods.

When you do add fat to your diet, choose a fat rich in monounsaturated fatty acids, like olive oil or canola oil, as often as possible. The alternatives are far less appealing, healthwise. The major sources of saturated fat include butter, shortening, lard, and cocoa butter. Consume these fats on rare occasions. Try substituting olive and canola oil in baking and as a dip for bread. There are many ways to avoid the use of saturated fats in traditional American recipes and still produce an excellent dish. Contact the American Dietetic Association (see the Resources section of this book) for recommended cookbooks including such recipes. Coconut, palm, and palm kernel oils are perhaps the most notorious of the plant oils because they are among the few that contain a large proportion of saturated fat (take a deep breath and check the labels of your favorite processed foods).

If most of the fat in your diet comes from monounsaturated fat sources like olive oil and canola oil instead of the many sources of saturated and trans-fatty acids fat, you'll find you can indeed eat fat and maintain a healthy heart, as long as you eat fat in moderation, keep your weight at a healthy level, and eat a diet based on plant foods. Remember the Mediterranean Diet Pyramid when choosing foods and planning meals. Olive oil is best, but you only need a drizzle.

⊘ TRANS-FATTY ACIDS AND HYDROGENATION

Trans-fatty acids are made from the hydrogenation of unsaturated fats. Recent research has suggested that trans-fatty acid, which is found in most margarines and many processed baked goods, may be even more hazardous to our heart health than saturated fats! Confused? Isn't margarine supposed to be better for us than that saturated-fat villain known as butter? Nutritionists today say absolutely not!

Trans-fatty acids occur when unsaturated fat, such as polyunsaturated corn oil, is processed with hydrogen to form a solid fat (making for a better "spread" substitute for butter) and a product that has a longer shelf life. The drawback? Adding a hydrogen artificially to an otherwise naturally unhydrogenated oil creates a strange chemical formation called "trans." Research has indicated that high levels of these trans-fatty acids may increase LDL cholesterol ("bad" cholesterol) levels as much as saturated fat. Studies have also linked trans-fatty acids to increased rates of certain cancers.

Hydrogenated and partially hydrogenated fats have become a staple in many, many processed foods Americans know and love. Sources of trans-fatty acids include prepackaged, processed foods, even most of the "low-fat" varieties. Items such as crackers, cookies, chips, granola bars, candy bars, packaged baked goods, even some ready-to-eat cereals and breads and sweetened drinks contain trans-fatty acids. Trans-fatty acids are almost a hidden ingredient, buried in the long ingredient lists of prepackaged foods. The only way to know if an item has trans-fatty acids is to read the label and look for the words "hydrogenated" or "partially hydrogenated." Those words mean the food contains trans-fatty acids. The Food and Drug Administration is in the process of mandating that the amount of trans-fatty acids be listed on a food product's Nutrition Facts label.

So what is a Mediterranean-inspired person to do? Because these trans-fatty acids were never a part of traditional diets, why eat them? Choose natural whole foods (fruit, whole grains, fresh vegetables, and so on) over processed, preserved foods. Use olive oil as your principal form of fat, and if you can't decide between butter and margarine, why use either? Dip your bread in a bit of olive oil instead.

Fortunately, there are many prepackaged goods that do not contain any trans-fatty acids (or hydrogenated or partially hydrogenated oils), but again, read the labels to find which ones are available in your local grocery or health food store.

⌘ FAT IN THE MEDITERRANEAN

We've already introduced you to the notion that the entire Mediterranean region is olive country and that the primary fat in the Mediterranean diet is olive oil. Olive trees with their fruits burgeoning with oil virtually rim the Mediterranean Sea. When ripe, the olives are mashed into a paste and pressed between mats, squeezing the cherished oils into vats below. The process is simple, and the first pressing of the olives yields the olive oil that is the most pure, the most nutrient-rich, and the most flavorful: extra virgin olive oil. Extra virgin olive oil is the least processed olive oil.

Depending on the region where the olives were grown, olive oil varies in color, from gold to green. According to Nancy Harmon Jenkins in her *Mediterranean Diet Cookbook*:

> *[The] strong-flavored, green-tasting Tuscan oils are very different themselves from the lighter, rounder, fatter oils from Apulia in Italy's South. Which again are distinctive from the oils of Catalonia with their hints of almond and the richer, full-bodied oils from Greece and farther east in Lebanon and the bland, sweet oils from North Africa.*

Although strongly (and deliciously) flavored, olive oil is more versatile than some strongly flavored oils because its strong flavor diminishes or disappears when heated. It can, therefore, be used with great success in baking. Lesser grades of olive oil are progressively more processed and refined. Their slightly cheaper prices are not worth the loss of flavor and the benefits of other substances in the oil, not to mention the added undesirable effects of processing. (Keep olive oil out of the light and refrigerate any oil you won't use in one month.)

Although not a component in traditional Mediterranean cuisine, a good olive oil substitute is canola oil, another rich source of monounsaturated fatty acids. Canola oil, sometimes called rapeseed oil, contains a large proportion of monounsaturated fatty acids, like olive oil, as well as vitamin E and omega-3 fatty acids. Although it costs less than its Mediterranean cousin, it is also far more refined, less flavorful, and less widely consumed, historically. Canola oil is also devoid of phytochemicals (nonnutritive substances in plants that appear to offer protective health effects), those extra "goodies" available in olive oil that has been cold pressed. In terms of a heart-healthy choice, however, it still ranks just below olive oil.

During the time when Ancel Keys was conducting his research, some Mediterranean countries consumed greater or lesser amounts of olive oil. Remember how Cretans were found by Keys to be the olive oil heavyweights, consuming an average of about a half cup of olive oil per day per person? A full one-third of the calories in the Cretan diet came from olive oil. The Greek population in general received about one-fifth of its calories from olive oil. Elsewhere throughout the Mediterranean, olive oil consumption was not quite up to Cretan standards, but still far exceeded consumption in the United States. According to Keys, average olive oil consumption throughout the Mediterranean region equaled about 15 to 20 percent of total calories, "except in the most northerly part of Italy and the non-Mediterranean parts of France and Spain."

Coronary heart disease rates in these countries, as we have mentioned before, were (and still are, although not as dramatically) lower than in the United States, and although olive oil is not the only factor, researchers have narrowed the field enough to surmise that a high proportion of monounsaturated fatty acids in the diet is likely a significant factor in lower coronary heart disease rates.

But olive oil is healthy for more reasons than the monounsaturated fatty acids that lower the risk of coronary heart disease. As mentioned, olive oil contains phytochemicals, more specifically carotenoids, that give vegetables and their oils color, and the antioxidant vitamin E. Antioxidants inhibit the formation of free radicals, elements produced in the body by pollutants and human metabolism that appear to damage the immune system and may contribute to chronic disease. Remember how oxidized LDL leads to hardened and clogged arteries? Vitamin E helps to further prevent LDL from oxidizing (antioxidants are explained in more detail in the next chapter).

Again, when it comes to fat, moderation is the key. Focus on consuming a healthy proportion of monounsaturated fats compared to saturated and polyunsaturated fats. Use the Mediterranean Diet Pyramid to help change your diet to reflect the eating patterns and fat consumption of the traditional Mediterranean diet. Overall, fat consumption was moderate, and olive oil was certainly the fat of choice. Olive oil infused the cuisine of the Mediterranean with its rich aroma and its health-bestowing properties. It was (and still is) a culinary star—but not the only star in a richly varied, heart-healthy, Mediterranean-inspired diet.

⑦ **QUESTIONS AND ANSWERS**

∽ *How many Americans have high blood cholesterol levels?*

Too many! Approximately half of all Americans have high or borderline-high total blood cholesterol levels. Since blood cholesterol is, in many cases, controllable through dietary changes, you needn't be one of those 50 percent. Try to follow the guidelines of the Mediterranean Diet Pyramid to help keep your diet heart-friendly.

∽ *Can blood cholesterol levels be controlled through other methods besides diet?*

Yes. One of the most effective ways to keep total blood cholesterol levels down, as well as increasing "good" or HDL cholesterol levels, is to include lots of physical activity in your life. Exercise can help keep your blood cholesterol profile, as well as your muscles and heart, in great shape. Traditionally, the people in the Mediterranean had highly active lifestyles, probably a contributing factor to their excellent heart health.

Smoking has also been linked to increased blood cholesterol levels, so quitting the tobacco habit is an obvious way to help control blood cholesterol levels. Also, obesity tends to raise blood cholesterol, so achieving and maintaining a healthy weight is an effective way for many people to keep blood cholesterol levels in check.

∽ *How many Americans die from coronary heart disease?*

Too many again. Heart disease is the number one cause of death in America for both men and women. About 25 percent of the 275 million people in America suffer from cardiovascular disease, and over 42 percent of the deaths each year in the United States are due to cardiovascular disease. This includes heart attacks and strokes, both the result of blockages to the blood vessels.

✀ How much fat should I include in my diet?

Your total food choices over the course of a few days should average about 30 percent of calories from fat. But, more importantly, only 10 percent (one-third or less of the fat calories) should be from saturated fat. Foods that are high in saturated fat, such as fatty meats, need to be limited as much as possible. Eating in a pattern as described by the Mediterranean Diet Pyramid will help to keep saturated fat, as well as total fat and trans-fatty acids, within desired levels.

Most packaged food items have the amount of fat and saturated fat grams per serving, as well as fat calories per serving, on the Nutrition Facts label. If you want to know the percentage of calories from fat and/or saturated fat on any individual food item, you can make the following calculation:

1. Multiply the number of fat or saturated fat grams in a serving by 9 to get the number of calories from fat or saturated fat. (Eliminate this step if you already know the fat calories per serving.)
2. Divide the number of calories from fat or saturated fat by the total number of calories per serving.
3. The resulting number is the percentage of calories from fat or saturated fat per serving.

For example, if you want to eat a cup of plain, low-fat yogurt that has 230 calories and 2 grams of fat, multiply 2 grams of fat by 9 to get 18 calories from fat. Then divide 18 by 230 to get approximately .08, or a total of about 8 percent of calories from fat. To find the amount of saturated fat in the yogurt, look for the grams of saturated fat beneath the total fat grams. If 1 gram of saturated fat is listed, multiply 1 by 9 to get 9 calories from saturated fat. Then, divide by 230 to get approximately .04, or 4 percent of calories from saturated fat—a good choice, especially if you mix in some fresh fruit.

If you wish to calculate the amount of total and saturated fat you eat for any given day, use the following example as a guide. Let's say you require 2,000 calories per day. Then 30 percent of that number is 600 calories; 10 percent is 200 calories. Again, fat has 9 calories per gram, so 600 divided by 9 equals 67 grams from total fat, and 200 divided by 9 equals 22 grams from saturated fat. Remember, it may be more realistic to think of your fat intake over the course of a few days rather than on a day-to-day basis. You may eat more fat on one day and less on the next, which is fine and in keeping with heart-healthy guidelines.

✤ What about "fat-free" or "low-fat" foods? How do they fit in with a Mediterranean-inspired eating pattern?

Most prepackaged "fat-free" or "low-fat" foods are often high in sugar and/or artificial ingredients, fillers, gums, and other ingredients meant to simulate the taste and texture fat would have provided. These products are often high in calories, expensive, and devoid of nutrients. In addition, many prepackaged low-fat foods are deceiving because they contain trans-fatty acids. To eat in a true traditional Mediterranean way, limit the use of these foods as much as possible and opt for foods closer to their natural state. Dried fruit, nuts and seeds, and whole-grain crackers (those without partially hydrogenated oils—read the ingredients) are as convenient to grab on the go as prepackaged snacks. The Mediterranean way of eating is focused on whole, fresh foods.

❧ When eating out, what words suggest lower-fat or higher-fat food preparation?

Lower-fat dishes are often described as baked, broiled, roasted, sautéed, stir-fried, and grilled. Many restaurants will also accommodate your specific cooking suggestions. For example, you may be able to request that olive oil be used in preparing your food, or that your food be cooked with little or no oil. Avoid fried foods and dishes described as creamy, rich, or containing butter- or cream-based sauces, signaling high-saturated-fat preparation. Again, remember the Mediterranean Diet Pyramid. Butter, margarine, and high-fat dairy foods sit on the top, which means they are best consumed only on rare occasions.

❧ Olive oil has a strong taste. Is it versatile? How can I replace the fats in my diet with olive oil if I don't care for the taste, or if the dish I am preparing would not taste good with olive oil?

Olive oil can be an acquired taste, although some people love it on first try. If you are not immediately charmed, rest assured that in cooking, the strong taste is neutralized. Also, some brands of olive oil taste lighter than others. You can even start with a "light" olive oil, although these are more processed. In general, the lighter in color the olive oil, the lighter in taste. As you get used to the taste of olive oil, you can move on to the darker, richer, more flavorful (and more nutrient-rich) oils.

If you are not yet used to the taste of olive oil, use it when it will be heated to minimize the taste. In salads and other dishes where oil is not cooked, use canola oil, which is relatively tasteless. You will not receive the same phytochemical benefits, but you will receive the benefits of a monounsaturated fat source. Then gradually introduce olive oil into your diet more often.

Experiment with olive oil in dishes you might not have considered, and you may find you are pleasantly surprised at the result. Olive oil in baking imparts a luscious flavor (the baking minimizes the strong olive taste, but leaves just a hint of fruitiness). Quick bread and pastries become more distinctive with olive oil. Stir a tablespoon into a ho-hum soup to boost its taste and texture. Leave the butter in the refrigerator (or best, at the store) and drizzle a little olive oil on your bread instead. The possibilities are endless.

❧ *Is it true that oils contain more than one kind of fatty acid?*

Yes. When we say that olive oil is a monounsaturated fat, we mean that it consists primarily of monounsaturated fatty acids. However, olive oil also contains some polyunsaturated fatty acids, and even some saturated fat. All oils contain at least some saturated fat, although in differing amounts. However, the following chart compares a variety of common oils, and as you can see, olive oil and canola oil are the best sources of monounsaturated fat, that type of fat that has been found to promote "good" HDLs in the blood.

	Saturated	*Mono- unsaturated*	*Poly- unsaturated*
Butter	62%	29%	4%
Canola oil	6%	62%	32%
Coconut oil	87%	6%	2%
Corn oil	13%	24%	59%
Margarine (tub)	14%	32%	31%
Olive oil	14%	77%	8%
Peanut oil	17%	46%	32%
Soybean oil	15%	43%	38%
Sunflower oil	10%	20%	66%

This chart is adapted from the ADA's complete *Food and Nutrition Guide by Roberta Larsun Duyft, Minneapolis: Chronimed, 1996, p. 57.*

❧ **Is olive oil expensive? How long does it stay fresh? Should it be refrigerated?**

The extra virgin olive oil on your grocery store shelf is probably the highest quality and least processed of all the oils commonly available, but you will find that a modest bottle often costs quite a bit more than a large bottle of highly refined corn, safflower, sunflower, or canola oil (however, a little olive oil goes a long way). Most oil will last longer if kept in a cool, dark place, preferably in an opaque bottle. The refrigerator is a fine option, and even if it causes your olive oil to congeal or cloud, the oil will return to its clear state when allowed to sit at room temperature. If stored properly, olive oil should last for at least a year. Exposed to light and heat, however, it can quickly turn rancid, like most oils.

✤ How much olive oil can I eat?

Olive oil is "drizzled" over the top of our Mediterranean Diet Pyramid to indicate that olive oil should be enjoyed as a highlight to a Mediterranean way of eating, but not to drown out the other healthy benefits. We did not specify actual amounts of oil to be consumed because the amount should really be based on individual calorie needs. Calorie needs are determined from your height, weight, activity level, and state of health. As you can imagine, this can vary greatly from person to person. We strongly suggest consulting with a registered dietitian or other health care provider for guidelines on your individual needs. In general, however, fat should be used in moderation (no need to limit fat intake for children under the age of four, as infants and toddlers need fat for their growth requirements, yet we would suggest avoiding trans fats for children).

And remember how many other spectacular and delicious foods are integral to a traditional Mediterranean diet. Just take a look at the Mediterranean Diet Pyramid if you need a reminder. If too many of the calories in your diet come from olive oil, you won't have room in your calorie allowance for the other good stuff—the whole grains, vegetables, fruits, nuts, beans, and so on—that make up such an important part of a healthy diet.

Olive oil is certainly one of the highlights of the traditional Mediterranean diet and the Mediterranean Diet Pyramid, but it is not the only element. To get maximum health benefits that the traditional Mediterranean diet has to offer, enjoy olive oil in moderation.

4: *Vegetables: The Heart and Soul of the Traditional Mediterranean Diet*

How about a heady minestrone brimming with bright zucchini and carrots, green beans and butternut squash, fragrant garlic and onion, and slivers of plump cabbage leaves for dinner? Or perhaps you would prefer a simple pizza slathered with ruby-red tomato sauce and flecked with fresh basil? Maybe artichoke hearts and tomatoes stuffed with minced onions, cilantro, and a rainbow of chopped bell peppers, Moroccan-style, are more your speed. Chilled tomato-and-pepper gazpacho, anyone? A Greek eggplant salad with red bell peppers, tomatoes, and wild marjoram? Or maybe just a simple antipasto featuring grilled vegetables, marinated olives, and ratatouille?

Fresh and plentiful in the Mediterranean region, vegetables and herbs give traditional Mediterranean cuisine much of its character and flavor, not to mention its beauty and vibrant color. The traditional Mediterranean diet is naturally heavy on vegetables—not surprising, considering the garden-friendly Mediterranean climate. Traditionally, many people in the Mediterranean made their living farming the land. Others simply grew food to feed their own families.

What would classic Mediterranean cuisine be without vegetables? From eggplant Parmesan and tomatoes Provençal to stuffed vine leaves and spinach-cheese pie, vegetables provide the people of the Mediterranean with variety, color, and flavor without the high cost of meat-based meals. But vegetables, it seems, do much more than provide low-cost meals for people eating them in great quantities in the Mediterranean. Many of the health benefits of the traditional Mediterranean diet are undoubtedly due to the high proportion of fresh vegetables.

Many studies have examined the protective effect of vegetable consumption against certain chronic diseases. Some have uncovered an inverse association between vegetable and fruit consumption and the risk of many types of cancers, especially cancers of the upper respiratory and digestive tracts, lungs, stomach, pancreas, and cervix, as well as colorectal and ovarian cancers.

Could vegetable consumption in the Mediterranean be linked to low chronic disease rates? Evidence mounts to support this theory, even when the evidence doesn't directly involve the Mediterranean. Not too long ago, researchers Kristi Steinmetz, Ph.D., R.D., and John Potter, M.D., Ph.D., compiled more than two hundred population and animal studies that looked at plant food consumption and cancer rates. Indeed, there appears to be a strong relationship between plant food consumption and cancer rates. The researchers could only speculate that cancer can be a disease resulting from a diet devoid of sufficient amounts of plant foods. Human bodies, it seems, are better able to maintain and even regain their health when plant foods make up the majority of calories in the diet. But that is no surprise to people studying the cuisine and health status of people living in the Mediterranean.

High vegetable consumption seems to have a profound effect on the occurrence of other chronic diseases, not just cancer. The risk of heart disease, arthritis, macular degeneration (age-associated loss of sight due to gradual degeneration of the macula, a part of the retina), age-related cognitive decline (such as Alzheimer's disease and other forms of dementia), and other age-related health problems may all be reduced as vegetable consumption increases.

In addition to decreasing the risk of chronic diseases, research suggests that once chronic disease is present, certain components in vegetables may slow or even reverse the progress of the disease. This process occurs perhaps by offering a boost to the immune system, as well as assisting in the fight against cell-damaging free radicals (more on free radicals later in this chapter). In short, research on many fronts strongly suggests that a plant-centered diet rich in vegetables, as well as fruits and whole grains, may add both quality and quantity to your years.

⊘ WHAT MAKES VEGETABLES SO GREAT?

More than beautiful and delicious, adding variety and interest to meals, vegetables brim with nutrients such as cancer-fighting folate and selenium, as well as other essential vitamins and minerals. Potent phytochemical storehouses, vegetables contain beta-carotene, lycopene, flavonoids, and thousands of other compounds nutritionists are only beginning to discover. Phytochemicals are nonnutritive substances in plants that may serve a variety of protective functions in the human body, from blocking carcinogens and flushing them out of the body to strengthening the immune system (more on phytochemicals later in this chapter).

Vegetables contain few calories in exchange for such high nutrient levels, making this the food group for serious indulgence. On top of all these benefits, vegetables contain fiber, which is linked to decreased cancer risk and also helps to fill you up and keep your digestive tract working smoothly.

Every vegetable contains its own unique package of nutrients and phytochemicals, so to reap the most benefit, eat a wide variety of vegetables. Remember the Mediterranean Diet Pyramid, and the USDA's emphasis on variety? Studies show too much variety in other food categories, such as meat or sweets, can actually lead to overconsumption and overweight, but eating a variety of vegetables is inversely proportional to body fat. In other words, the more vegetables you eat, the less body fat you are likely to have. The great variety and range of flavors, textures, and colors make vegetables the perfect food group around which to base a meal.

Remember to sample vegetables from all the following categories. A handful of veggies from each category thrown into a soup pot with some chicken stock or vegetable stock and some dried oregano, fresh basil or thyme leaves, and a clove or two of minced garlic makes a fantastic, Mediterranean-inspired vegetable soup!

- **Cruciferous Vegetables.** These vegetables, which include broccoli, Brussels sprouts, cabbage, bok choy, cauliflower, kale, kohlrabi, and greens like watercress, mustard, rutabaga, and turnip, are so named because their flower petals are arranged in a cross shape (crucifer means "cross-bearing"). Even though not all these mentioned vegetables are native to the Mediterranean regions (such as bok choy), they fit nicely into a Mediterranean-inspired diet when fresh and preferably organic. Cruciferous vegetables have many nutritional benefits, and none more so than broccoli, a nutritional "star" rich with fiber, vitamins A and C, folate, calcium, iron, potassium, magnesium, and a host of phytochemicals including beta-carotene found to be active in the human body. Many cruciferous vegetables feature prominently in traditional Mediterranean dishes: cabbage in minestrone soup or boiled and then baked with olive oil and garlic; steamed broccoli with garlic, olive oil, and hot peppers or cooked until tender and tossed with a variety of pasta shapes; Brussels sprouts in a white sauce with a little grated cheese, nutmeg, and pine nuts; kale tossed with chestnuts, onion, and just an ounce or so of bacon.

- **Solanacae Vegetables.** This family of vegetables includes the tomato, pepper, potato, and eggplant. These vegetables are good sources of vitamins A and C and potassium. Tomatoes have recently been in the spotlight because of a phytochemical called lycopene that gives them (as well as watermelons and red grapefruit) their red color. Consumption of lycopene, which is particularly concentrated in tomato sauce and tomato paste, has been linked with reduced risk of prostate cancer and some other cancers. The solanacae family of vegetables may be the most heavily featured in traditional Mediterranean dishes. What would Italian cuisine be without the tomato? What more does a good pasta require than a simple sauce of ripe, fresh crushed tomatoes and a little olive oil? (Because lycopene is fat-soluble, it becomes even more available to the body when tomatoes are cooked in a small amount of oil). When tomatoes combine with eggplant in fragrant dishes such as ratatouille or eggplant Parmesan, these vegetables make a mouthwatering treat. Other favorite dishes include peppers roasted with eggplant; potatoes boiled with garlic cloves and mashed together; baba ghanouj, an eggplant dip popular in the Middle East; and any or all of these vegetables roasted, sautéed, or lightly boiled and tossed with pasta, rice, or polenta, or eaten on their own. (Fresh tomatoes with mozarella cheese, anyone?)

- **Umbelliferous Vegetables.** These vegetables have umbrella-like leaves. They include carrots, celery, parsnips, fennel, and the herbs parsley and cilantro. Rich in beta-carotene, vitamin A, and vitamin C, these vegetables further expand the vegetable lover's culinary repertoire. Parsley and cilantro, umbelliferous herbs, appear again and again in Mediterranean recipes. Raw fennel makes a sublime palate cleanser between courses; carrots add color, crunch, and flavor to salads and a sweetness to soups; and braised celery is a Mediterranean staple.

- **Cucurbitaceous Vegetables.** Offerings from this family of vegetables include the gourds and melons, those fleshy fruits and vegetables that grow on vines. These include pumpkins, summer squash, winter squash, zucchini, cucumbers, honeydew melons, and watermelons. Cucurbitaceous vegetables contain high levels of vitamins A and C, beta-carotene, phosphorous, iron, and fiber. While squash isn't typically considered a part of traditional Mediterranean cuisine, zucchini is the one exception. Ubiquitous in many Italian soups and stews as well as stuffed, grilled, baked, stewed, mixed with pasta, tossed into an Italian frittata, or cooked with tomatoes for ratatouille, zucchini is loved in Italy, and because this vegetable grows so well in the United States, we can easily enjoy authentic Mediterranean flavor in our own zucchini recipes.

- **Allium Vegetables.** These vegetables (some considered herbs) include those Mediterranean staples, garlic and onions. They also include shallots, chives, and leeks. Allium vegetables contain a host of cancer-fighting phytochemicals, and may also have antibiotic properties. Flip through any Mediterranean-inspired cookbook and you'll see garlic and onions featured in many recipes. Garlic makes a fantastic and surprisingly mellow featured ingredient in Spanish garlic soup. Who can forget the rich aroma and savory taste of French onion soup brimming with tender sweet onions, flavored with a splash of brandy, and topped with a slice of French bread and a little grated cheese? The Italian version of liver and onions contains far more onions than liver, and stifado, a Greek beef stew, contains more onions than beef.

⏣ VEGETABLE TALK

Nowhere are vitamins, minerals, and phytochemicals more densely concentrated than in vegetables. If you do not typically include a lot of vegetables in your diet, knowing a little more about the health-boosting elements in vegetables may inspire you to increase your vegetable consumption. Let's start with vitamins.

⏣ VITAMINS

Vitamins are chemical substances in vegetables (and other foods) that have a variety of jobs in the body, from assisting the chemical reactions that make your body function to promoting growth to preventing infection. There are two kinds of vitamins: water soluble and fat soluble.

Water-soluble vitamins dissolve in water and move through your bloodstream quickly. These vitamins, which include thiamin, riboflavin, niacin, vitamin B_6, folacin, vitamin B_{12}, biotin, pantothenic acid, and vitamin C, must be ingested regularly because the body doesn't store them. Among the many life-supporting functions of water-soluble vitamins, folacin and vitamin C have been shown to have anticancer functions, especially when paired with the fat-soluble vitamin E and beta-carotene (a form of vitamin A).

The fat-soluble vitamins—A, D, E, and K—dissolve in

fat and are stored in your body for longer periods of time. (For example, the body is capable of storing up to a year's supply of vitamin A.) Beta-carotene (a form of vitamin A found in vegetables) and vitamin E have been given a lot of attention lately as powerful antioxidants (more on antioxidants later). Many studies have linked these nutrients with the prevention of certain chronic diseases such as cancer and heart disease. Although the major food sources of vitamin E are nuts (especially the almond), seeds (especially sunflower seeds), wheat germ, and certain oils, there are a few vegetables that also contain appreciable amounts of vitamin E, most notably the sweet potato and avocado. Because many vegetables contain vitamin A, we will highlight this powerful nutrient (along with the other cancer-fighting vitamins, C and folacin) below.

In keeping with the spirit of the traditional Mediterranean diet, we recommend getting your vitamins from vegetables (and the other foods listed in the daily and weekly sections of the Mediterranean Diet Pyramid) rather than from supplements. Unheard-of in traditional Mediterranean culture, supplements would have been unnecessary anyway, given the nutrient density of the diet. We suggest getting your vitamins and other nutrients the way nature intended!

Vitamin A

Famous for promoting good vision, this fat-soluble vitamin facilitates a number of other important bodily processes. Vitamin A plays a vital role in maintaining healthy skin and healthy tissues found in your mouth, genitals, and digestive and urinary tracts. It also assists with the proper development of fetuses, sperm production, growth of children, and more. In terms of cancer prevention, vitamin A's importance in supporting the immune system makes this nutrient a powerful ally in the fight against cancer.

Getting adequate amounts of vitamin A is easy in a vegetable-rich Mediterranean diet. Identify vegetable sources containing vitamin A by their orange color, and you've got beta-carotene—a substance that converts to vitamin A in the body. Beta-carotene, a phytochemical that we'll discuss below, is also a potent antioxidant. Sweet potatoes, carrots, and melons—staples in the traditional Mediterranean diet—contain lots of beta-carotene. Pumpkin, native to North America, also contains high levels of beta-carotene and can easily be included in a Mediterranean diet, especially when you grow it yourself or buy organic pumpkins from local growers.

Vitamin C

Vitamin C, also called ascorbic acid, first gained fame when nutritionists discovered it warded off scurvy in sailors. Scurvy, a condition characterized by swollen, bleeding gums and tooth loss, rarely occurs today, and typically signifies malnutrition. Vitamin C's next claim to fame has been its apparent ability to fight off the common cold. Because of this potential cold-busting capacity, many Americans customarily load up on vitamin C supplements, but nutrition scientists still aren't sure how much vitamin C may actually help ward off the common cold. What scientists do know is that taking large doses of this vitamin can lead to more serious problems, such as the formation of kidney stones and diarrhea. Vitamin C also helps the body absorb the iron found in plant foods. So, the vitamin C–rich Mediterranean diet helps to ensure adequate iron absorption for the average adult.

Recently, this vitamin has become associated with chronic disease prevention, namely heart disease and cancer. Vitamin C's antioxidant abilities and its important role in maintaining a strong immune system is one reason, but its other role of collagen production makes vitamin C all the more beneficial in cancer prevention. Collagen is a protein-based substance that acts as structural material in skin, muscle, lung, and bone. The stronger this structural material, from a diet rich in vitamin C, the less likely cancer will invade these tissues. The presence of vitamin C in the digestive tract has been shown to prevent the formation of nitrosamines, those believed cancer-causing substances found in cured meats. Vitamin C also works hand in hand with vitamin E to deactivate cancer-promoting free radicals.

In addition to cancer prevention, vitamin C helps to promote a healthy heart. There is even some evidence that increased intake of vitamin C may help to improve one's blood cholesterol profile by lowering the level of "bad" LDLs and raising the level of "good" HDLs.

The recommended daily allowance (RDA) of vitamin C for the average adult is 60 milligrams. Pregnant women need 70 milligrams, and breastfeeding moms need about 90 to 95 milligrams per day. Many researchers feel that more than this is needed to prevent disease, although just how much is still unknown. Smokers do need to get more than the standard RDA, about 100 milligrams daily, because smoking can deplete the body of this nutrient. Getting adequate amounts of vitamin C can easily be accomplished in a varied Mediterranean-type diet rich in fruits and vegetables. Eat just one orange, and you've already consumed 60 milligrams of vitamin C. Many vegetables are also rich sources of vitamin C. Those most relevant to the traditional cuisine of the Mediterranean include tomatoes, green and red peppers, broccoli, spinach, potatoes, and asparagus.

Folacin

The word *folacin* is from the Latin word *folium*, or "foliage," because folic acid was first discovered in leafy green vegetables. Also known as folate or folic acid, this water-soluble B vitamin is essential for several important functions in the body. For one, it is crucial in the synthesis of DNA, and because of this, any body tissue that is dividing and growing needs ample amounts of folacin. Cells lining our digestive tract are continually regenerating themselves and therefore rely on folacin to do so. Pregnant women need substantial amounts of folate (more than twice the RDA for the average adult) to support the growing fetus. The U.S. Public Health Service recommends that all women of child-bearing age eat 400 micrograms of folacin daily to ensure adequate stores of folacin to support the large demands of this nutrient in pregnancy. Women who enter into pregnancy without adequate folacin stores and/or those who do not eat enough folacin during pregnancy (particularly in the first trimester) run the risk of bearing a baby with inadequate brain and spinal cord development.

Folacin's supporting role in DNA synthesis appears to make this nutrient important in the battle against cancer, particularly cancer of the colon. Reports in the *Journal of the National Cancer Institute* showed that a high folate intake lowered colon cancer risk. Some researchers feel that intakes of 400 to 800 micrograms of folacin are needed for cancer prevention, but this is still being determined. The Mediterranean diet provides ample amounts of folacin, especially with its emphasis on bean and vegetable consumption (see the following Questions and Answers section). The vegetables richest in folacin include avocados, artichokes, asparagus, spinach, mustard spinach (tendergreen), and turnip greens.

⊘ THE POWER OF ANTIOXIDANTS

Antioxidants are substances that combat the negative effects of oxygen in cells. When the body uses oxygen for energy, it produces by-products called free radicals that have a potentially damaging effect on cells. Antioxidants neutralize this effect, essentially shuttling free radicals and even carcinogenic substances out of the body before they can do damage.

Three of the most potent antioxidants are the vitamins C, E, and the substance beta-carotene, which the body converts to vitamin A. These vitamins have been a long-time research focus in disease prevention, and have been repeatedly linked to decreased risk of many chronic conditions, including heart disease, cancer, cataracts, and more. Research with the AIDS virus suggests that vitamin E and beta-carotene may slow the progression of HIV to AIDS. Vitamin E may protect from heart disease in a number of ways, by slowing or preventing oxidation of "bad" (LDL) cholesterol, and possibly by reducing the tendency of blood to clot.

The protective antioxidant power of vitamin E has also been shown to increase dramatically when vitamin C and beta-carotene are consumed. Shown to work in concert to modify the risk of many chronic diseases and age-related degenerative conditions, a balance of these three antioxidants seems to be most effective in the body, and the absence of one seems to negatively impact the effectiveness of the others. For example, vitamin C flushes out free radicals in the body's fluids, while beta-carotene and vitamin E neutralize free radicals in fat tissue.

Beta-carotene was once a star in the world of cancer prevention, and supplementation with this nutrient became popular. It seemed to make sense, given its antioxidant capabilities. However, research using beta-carotene supplements brought about some surprising results. In one famous study, beta-carotene supplementation was linked with an increase (not a decrease) in lung cancer among smokers. (This is an example of the possible dangers of supplementation.) Study subjects who did not smoke, however, were not negatively affected by the supplementation. Smokers typically have depleted stores of vitamins C as well as E.

Significantly, no such toxicity has been shown to exist when beta-carotene is consumed via vegetables. On the contrary, studies suggest that vitamins from food sources have a positive effect on a number of chronic conditions. One study linked increased vitamin C and beta-carotene consumption primarily from food (as opposed to supplements) to better old-age memory in a long-term Swiss study begun in 1971 and published in 1997. However, the results of studies seeking to determine the value of vitamin supplements are, in general, hazy. Some research seems to suggest supplements can have a positive effect on health (especially with vitamin E). Other studies suggest supplements have no effect. Still others indicate that vitamin supplements, especially in megadoses, can actually be injurious to health. However, vitamins in their natural form—potently supplied in vegetables—appear to be beneficial to health in countless, complex ways, as yet only minimally understood.

Just about every vegetable is packed with vitamins, and the traditional Mediterranean diet supplies vitamin-rich vegetables in abundance, and in far higher proportion than is typical in the American diet. Eating more vegetables, and a wider variety of vegetables, is an excellent first step toward eating in a Mediterranean-inspired fashion. It is also the safest and probably most effective way to reap the benefits of the many vitamins—antioxidants and others—your body requires.

⊛ MUST-HAVE MINERALS

Minerals work with vitamins in many bodily processes, and regulate a few essential functions, such as muscle contractions and nerve impulses. They are also part of our bodies: bones, teeth, and nails all contain minerals. The major minerals, including calcium, magnesium, and potassium, can all be found in certain vegetables. Many vegetables contain trace minerals as well, such as iron, selenium, and zinc.

Selenium has been the subject of much research. Another antioxidant, selenium appears to boost the action of certain anticancer enzymes in the body, and may even prevent premature aging. Plants incorporate selenium from the soil in which they are grown. Garlic is a good source of selenium.

Calcium is essential for bone strength and to slow the rate of bone loss associated with aging. Calcium also assists muscle contractions, including the heart muscle; facilitates proper nerve functioning; and helps the blood to clot. Calcium deficiencies can result in osteoporosis and may contribute to high blood pressure and possibly colon cancer. While most people think of dairy products as the best sources of calcium (they are indeed good sources), many vegetables supply calcium as well. In fact, the calcium in some vegetables (such as kale) is even more available to the body than the calcium in dairy products. Other calcium-rich vegetables include dark leafy greens such as mustard greens, turnip greens, and broccoli.

Magnesium is another mineral essential to bone strength and growth, as well as to nerve and muscle cells. It warrants a mention here because magnesium and calcium work together in the body to perform many important functions, and a magnesium deficiency also hinders the body's ability to use calcium (as well as potassium and sodium). Rich sources include dark green vegetables like spinach, as well as other foods common to the Mediterranean diet such as whole grains, nuts, and legumes.

⊗ PHYTOCHEMICALS: NATURE'S FIRST LINE OF DEFENSE

The buzz about vitamins and minerals has lately been replaced by the buzz about phytochemicals. Phytochemicals are nonnutritive substances in plants. Thousands exist, and every plant food contains them. What can they do for us? Knowing what they do for plants may shed some light on the question.

Some phytochemicals protect plants from invaders of all kinds. Predators like leaf-munching insects and animals, bacteria, viruses, and fungi can all be put off by the action of phytochemicals, whether that action comes in the form of an unpleasant taste, a repugnant smell, a startling color, or a poisonous effect. Also, the antioxidant action of certain phytochemicals protects plants against an oxygen-rich environment (remember, plants "breathe" carbon dioxide, not oxygen).

What happens when we consume phytochemical-laden vegetables? Only some of the thousands of phytochemicals have been found (to date) to have an effect on the human body, but these few apparently have enough of an effect to make a difference. (The thousands of phytochemicals as yet uninvestigated represent great research potential. The field of phytochemical research is still in its infancy and may well reveal many other benefits to human health.)

When humans consume certain phytochemicals, we appear to enjoy protective effects similar to those plants receive. Phytochemicals, in many ways, seem to defend the human body against free radical damage (see below) and age-related degeneration, not to mention viruses, bacteria, and fungi.

The phytochemical-cancer connection has been widely researched, and results suggest that phytochemicals may disrupt cancer in more ways than one. Phytochemicals may protect DNA or repair damaged DNA, helping to prevent cancer from developing. They may prevent cancerous cells from multiplying and/or spreading through the body. Phytochemicals may help the body to help itself, giving carcinogen-blocking enzymes a boost.

Much cancer research has focused more generally on vegetable and fruit consumption, which implicates phytochemicals by association. Raw and green vegetable consumption appears to reduce the risk of stomach, lung, mouth, esophageal, colon, rectal, breast, and bladder cancers. Research in other areas has supported general vegetable and fruit consumption as well, suggesting that a diet rich in vegetables and fruits may lower the risk of heart disease and stroke, and boost the effectiveness of the immune system. Some of the phyto-chemicals more relevant to humans include the allium com-pounds (in onions and garlic); carotenoids (in dark green and deep orange vegetables), including lycopene (particularly rich in tomatoes and red grapefruit); glucosinolates (in cruciferous vegetables such as broccoli); and flavonoids (in many foods including tomatoes).

Aromatic Allium

Allium compounds, also called organosulfides, exist in onions, garlic, leeks, shallots, and chives. These compounds give these vegetables their unique smell and pungent taste. They also appear to increase the effectiveness of the body's own cancer-fighting enzymes, halt the production of nitrates into carcinogens, lower cholesterol and blood pressure, and reduce the tendency of the blood to clot. Allium compounds appear to be most potent in raw vegetables, and may be de-stroyed by the cooking process.

Colorful Carotenoids

Carotenoids are potent antioxidant phytochemicals that fight free-radical cellular damage in the body, possibly guarding against a wide range of chronic diseases. They are the substances in plants that provide their bright red, orange, or deep yellow colors. More than six hundred carotenoids are known, but fewer than fifty have been found to be active in the human body. Examples of beneficial carotenoids found in vegetables are as follows:

- Alpha-carotene is a substance that the body converts to vitamin A. Research has linked alpha-carotene to a reduced risk of lung cancer. Carrots are full of it.
- Beta-carotene (as discussed previously) is another substance the body converts to vitamin A. Well pub-licized for its anticancer benefits, beta-carotene may

also prevent cataracts, slow the progression of heart disease, and boost the immune system. Good sources include most red, orange, and yellow fruits and vegetables, as well as dark, leafy greens.

- Gamma-carotene is just starting to get attention as an anticancer agent, and research with gamma-carotene is just beginning. The best sources of gamma-carotene are tomatoes and apricots. The above three carotenoids—alpha-carotene, beta-carotene, and gamma-carotene, are thought to be powerful allies against cancer.
- Lycopene, the carotenoid that gives tomatoes, watermelon, and red grapefruit their rosy hues, has been linked to decreased risk of prostate and breast cancer, and may also protect skin from the damaging effects of ultraviolet radiation.
- Lutein and zeaxanthin have been found in the eye and may help prevent age-related macular degeneration by protecting the retina from potentially harmful light exposure, and also by neutralizing the effects of free radicals formed by the negative effects of sunlight on the retina. One study demonstrated a lower incidence of macular degeneration in people who ate increased amounts of spinach and collard greens, both of which contain lutein and zeaxanthin.

Protective Flavonoids

Flavonoids include a huge class of compounds (more than four thousand) called phenolic compounds and are found in plants of all types. Flavonoids give plants color, have antifungal properties, slow or prevent damaging oxidation, lower cholesterol, prevent the clotting of blood, and protect cells from carcinogens. The most studied flavonoid is quercetin, abundant in onions, wine, and tea (more on wine in the next chapter). Unlike the allium compounds, quercetin remains intact and available after cooking, and may have an anticancer effect in the body.

Other flavonoids available to the human body from food include isoflavones, found primarily in soybeans (although soybeans aren't part of a traditional Mediterranean diet, they should be consumed in the Mediterranean spirit of eating). Isoflavones are thought to have an estrogenlike effect on the body, possibly guarding against hormone-related cancers like breast cancer. Catechins are another type of flavonoid, which may be responsible for the anticancer properties apparently inherent in green tea. Flavonoids may also be a factor in the heart-protective benefits of red wine.

⊘ PHYTOCHEMICAL SYNERGY

One of the most intriguing qualities of phytochemicals, and the most convincing argument for receiving your phytochemicals from food rather than from supplements, is their synergistic nature. Science has only begun to understand the effects of individual phytochemicals on the body. The combined nature of phytochemical interactions in the body—of eating a whole plant, rather than a supplement of artificially produced or isolated single compound—is still largely a matter of speculation, but many experts assert that eating plant foods in a form close to their original state (minimally processed) is the best way to ensure receiving the health benefits, both those understood and those not yet understood.

Even if the term *phytochemical* was unknown in the Mediterranean during the time when the traditional Mediterranean diet was the pervasive way of eating, phytochemical benefits were at a premium in this diet of locally grown, seasonally consumed, minimally processed plant foods. Understanding the nature of phytochemicals provides one more good reason to return to more traditional dietary practices.

⊘ FREE RADICALS, OXIDATION, AND ANTIOXIDANTS: SUMMON YOUR DEFENSES

Vitamins C, E, and beta-carotene aren't the only antioxidants. Many phytochemicals also have antioxidant properties, from which we derive great benefit. *Antioxidant*, once again, is a term referring to any substance that helps to nullify the deleterious, albeit natural, side effects of oxygen consumption within cells. Oxygen may seem like a harmless substance. We breathe it in all day long. All cells require oxygen to function. Oxygen is necessary for human life. However, oxygen consumption releases by-products that are potentially damaging to cells.

In our bodies, when cells use oxygen for energy, they produce by-products or waste products called free radicals. Free radicals are oxygen by-products missing an electron, which they have given up during the oxidation process. Free radicals "roam" through the body searching for electrons to correct the imbalance. The nearest molecule with an available electron is "robbed" by the free radical, and every cell robbed of an electron is slightly damaged. This is a natural process. Our cell membranes contain vitamin E to help neutralize free radical activity before cell damage can occur. However, our bodies weren't designed to handle the onslaught of free radicals produced by environmental pollutants common to everyday life today: car exhaust, cigarette smoke, certain chemical additives in foods, and so on. Without sufficient antioxidant protection, over time, free radical damage can become an insurmountable obstacle to good health. Many scientists believe that cumulative free radical damage contributes to chronic diseases like cancer, heart disease, arthritis, and macular degeneration.

The name *antioxidant* suggests that these compounds nullify the negative effects of oxidation on cells, and that is exactly what they do. If you dipped a cut piece of apple in lemon juice, it wouldn't turn brown as quickly because lemon juice contains ascorbic acid (a common form of vitamin C), an antioxidant. Another form of oxidation occurs when fat turns rancid. Tocopherols, a common form of vitamin E, are often used to preserve foods with fat because the vitamin E retards the oxidation, or spoilage, process. Exactly how antioxidants work is still largely unknown, but they appear to work in several ways in the body. Antioxidants seem to prevent free radical damage in the first place. They also may shuttle carcinogenic compounds generated by free radical damage out of the body before they can do any damage. And, as we've mentioned before, while the verdict is not yet in on whether antioxidant vitamin supplements do any good at all in the prevention of chronic disease, antioxidant consumption from fresh vegetables does seem to offer a significant measure of protection against free radical damage.

MEDITERRANEAN WAYS TO ADD VEGETABLES

How did the people eating the traditional Mediterranean diet pack so many vegetables into their daily meals? Easily and deliciously. In the Mediterranean, vegetable consumption is not just a matter of eating any vegetable at any time, in whatever state is most convenient. Vegetable selection is a matter of pride, vegetable preparation an art, and vegetable consumption a pure pleasure. Most essentially, in the Mediterranean, vegetables are chosen according to what is in season.

Outdoor produce markets throughout the Mediterranean offer the season's best, freshest, most vibrant vegetables. Your local grocer, farmer's market, or produce stand is also likely to feature the freshest locally grown produce. Even if the vegetables in season in your area aren't those in season in the Mediterranean, eating the freshest seasonal produce is still eating in the Mediterranean way. Seek out the best sources for vegetables in your area, and you may discover that vegetables taste much better than you think. Here are a few more Mediterranean-inspired tips for adding vegetables to your day. You'll wonder how you ever ate without them!

- Looking for a fast-food lunch? A wedge of hearty wheat bread, a small chunk of feta or other cheese, a few slices of ripe tomato, a handful of leafy greens drizzled with olive oil and a squeeze of fresh lemon juice, and a ripe peach or other seasonal fruit for dessert take less time to prepare than going through the drive-through. Bring your Mediterranean lunch to work with you and everyone will wonder what upscale deli supplied your meal.

- The next time you make spaghetti, stir a shredded carrot and a finely chopped green or red pepper, a few mushrooms, or a handful of chopped spinach into the sauce. Vegetable additions add color, flavor, and nutritional power to your pasta dinner.

- Instead of grilling burgers, grill vegetables, Mediterranean style. Slice onions, peppers, zucchini, portabella mushroom caps, eggplant, and tomatoes into thick slices, drizzle with olive oil, and grill. If you want to add a Middle Eastern flair, skewer the vegetables into shish kebabs. A chunk or two of chicken or lamb among the vegetables would be authentic and would add an extra dash of protein. Serve with lemon wedges.

- Drizzle those plain vegetables with a little olive oil and a sprinkling of fresh grated cheese, or garnish with a splash of tomato sauce or a few sun-dried tomatoes. Tomato sauce also adds culinary interest to broiled fish.

- If you can relate to former U.S. President George H. W. Bush when it comes to broccoli (his aversion to this beautiful vegetable was well known), maybe you just haven't had it cooked really well. Try steaming broccoli just until it is very bright green and tender. Toss with a little olive oil, sea salt, minced garlic, and a few flakes of red pepper. Serve and eat immediately. Perfectly cooked broccoli is a joy. Overcooked or old broccoli is enough to make anyone dislike the stuff.

- Leafy green salads are an important part of many Mediterranean meals. Get in the habit of including a bowl of leafy greens with olive oil and a little lemon juice or vinegar with at least one meal every day. A few extra chopped vegetables and a little grated cheese will make your greens even more interesting and nutrient-rich. (Just remember to forgo the creamy dressing in favor of a dressing with an olive oil base.) Do you think you don't have enough time to chop up a salad? Take advantage of food industry technology and splurge on ready-to-eat bagged veggies and greens. Selections are plentiful, many types are organic, and they come prewashed. What could be quicker?

- Eat pizza in the Mediterranean style. Unlike American pizzas, Mediterranean pizzas are typically thin, light concoctions with just a few toppings. Fresh tomato sauce and one or two featured vegetables (mushrooms, garlic slices, onion, zucchini, broccoli, peppers) and a very light sprinkling of mozzarella or Parmesan cheese on a fresh-baked (or store-bought, if you are pressed for time) whole-grain crust makes a perfect light dinner. Many Mediterranean pizzas don't even include cheese. In the mood for something more substantial? The more veggies, the better! Add roasted eggplant, mushrooms, red peppers (better than green if you want that lycopene punch)—you name it! See how much your pizza can hold. Load up and enjoy!

- Are you or your kids getting bored with peanut butter sandwiches? Add chopped or shredded carrots for a surprising, refreshing, flavorful crunch.
- Pumpkin is an American vegetable, but its nutritional value is Mediterranean in spirit! Stir canned pumpkin into hot oatmeal for breakfast with a little cinnamon and brown sugar. Add a generous spoonful to applesauce for a light dessert, or stir some into vanilla yogurt for an added zing.
- Microwave a sweet potato or yam until soft for a quick, carotenoid- and fiber-rich snack, or try baked sweet potato fries or yam chips, brushed lightly with olive oil and baked at 400 degrees until lightly browned and fork-tender, about twenty minutes, or longer if you've got a large pan full.

The one thing you can do to make your diet more "Mediterranean" is to begin eating more fresh vegetables today. Whether or not they were traditionally grown and consumed in the Mediterranean, the very concept of eating the vegetables grown on the land around you captures the essence of the traditional Mediterranean diet. Vegetables add beauty to your plate, excitement to your palate, and a host of vital substances to your body.

☙ QUESTIONS AND ANSWERS

❧ *If allium compounds are destroyed in the cooking process, what is the best way to include them in the diet? Raw onions and garlic?*

To many people, raw onions and garlic are too strongly flavored to be palatable when eaten alone. However, minced or even thinly sliced raw onions make an aromatic addition to a salad, and minced fresh garlic tastes great in an olive oil vinaigrette salad dressing. Raw chives are another delicious addition to salads and make a crunchy garnish to other foods, from the traditional cottage cheese to grain-based dishes and pasta dishes. When you do cook onions and garlic, try to cook them for as short a time as possible. When making soups and stews, sprinkle a few chopped onions on top, and/or add the garlic (or half the garlic) toward the end of the cooking time.

❧ *Are the familiar herbs and spices used in Mediterranean cuisine of any nutritional value, or are they purely for flavoring?*

Herbs and spices are plant foods and are rich with nutrients and phytochemicals, just like vegetables, although research hasn't focused its attention on herbs and spices the way it has on vegetables (at least partially due to the fact that these plant foods are consumed in much smaller amounts and so may have a less potent, although quite possibly cumulative, effect). Some plant foods such as garlic are often thought to be either an herb or a vegetable, and the distinction is indeed blurry at times. The dictionary even defines vegetables as "a usually herbaceous plant cultivated for its edible parts." Herbs are, technically, plants with fleshy rather than woody stems, and are also defined as "aromatic plants used in medicine or as seasoning." Similarly, spices are "aromatic or pungent plant substances used as flavoring."

While different Mediterranean countries tend to emphasize different herbs and spices, the region as a whole seems particularly partial to the following, listed below along with their nutritive and/or phytochemical highlights:

- **Garlic and chives.** Members of the allium family, these herbs contain organosulfides, the compounds that give allium vegetables their unique odors. Organosulfides are thought to have anticancer properties and to benefit heart health. Garlic also contains phenolic acids, antioxidant compounds that may disrupt cancer development in several ways, and monoterpenes, substances that appear to slow or reverse cancer development and contribute to favorable blood cholesterol profiles. Chives contain the carotenoids lutein and zeaxanthin, antioxidants that concentrate in the eye. Dried or dehydrated chives provide an even more concentrated source of these phytochemicals. Garlic is highly versatile and can flavor almost any savory dish. Sprinkle chopped chives, fresh or dried, on eggs, fish, or a salad.
- **The rosemary family of herbs.** Oregano, basil, thyme, marjoram, sage, mint, and rosemary are all members of the Labitaceae family and all contain the powerful antioxidant quinone. Oregano, basil, and thyme are pervasive in Mediterranean, especially Italian, cuisine, and give dishes like pizza, spaghetti, and lasagna their familiar flavors.
- **Parsley, cilantro, and Italian (flat-leaf) parsley.** These members of the umbelliferous family of vegetables (related to the carrot) are nutritional power herbs. The most widely used herb in the United States today, parsley dates back to the third century B.C.E. and was popular among the Romans. Parsley

can be more than a garnish. Its flavones and carotenoids, particularly lutein, zcaxanthin, and beta-carotene, make it worth using more often to flavor soups and stews, salads, meat dishes, pasta, rice, and anything else that needs a splash of green. Although more commonly featured in Mexican cuisine, cilantro is a relative of parsley. Both contain immune system–boosting polyacetylenes.

- **Chili peppers.** The ingredient in cayenne or hot pepper, chili peppers contain a phytochemical called capsaicin, thought to fight cancer and possibly decrease pain. Chili peppers also contain carotenoids, including lutein, zeaxanthin, and beta-carotene, and a dose of vitamin C. Use chili peppers to spice up any dish. Although chili peppers are more familiar in the cuisines of non-Mediterranean cultures such as Mexico and India, cayenne pepper (dried ground chili pepper) is widely used in North African cuisine. Authentic or not, add zip to paella, gazpacho, fish or shrimp, and eggs with chili peppers.
- **Turmeric.** Brilliant yellow turmeric is used extensively in Indian and southeast Asian cuisine, but is also a component of many African dishes. Turmeric contains the phytochemical curcumin, a phenolic compound with powerful antioxidant effects.

The above is just a sampling of the many herbs and spices used in Mediterranean cuisine. Experiment with herbs and spices to broaden your culinary spectrum and add both intense flavor and a phytochemical boost to your favorite foods.

℘ Are sun-dried tomatoes as nutritious as fresh tomatoes?

Yes. Just as a raisin is as nutritious as a grape, the sun-dried tomato is full of lycopene and contains all the nutrients of a vine-ripe tomato. The only element missing is the water. The sun-dried tomato also contains the same number of calories as a fresh tomato. However, because it is smaller, it is easier to eat more sun-dried tomatoes than fresh tomatoes. Of course, the calories in vegetables are minimal and these are calories with nutritional power, so there's no need to limit yourself. Sun-dried tomatoes make a flavorful addition to many dishes and are even a tasty addition to homemade bread.

✸ Are frozen vegetables as nutritious as fresh vegetables?

Not always, but sometimes the frozen version of your favorite veggie is actually more nutritious than the fresh version. Many vegetables are flash-frozen and bagged right in the field after picking, preserving many nutrients that might otherwise be destroyed by rough handling and extreme temperatures, not to mention too-long exposure to the air during the long transport to your local supermarket and finally to your refrigerator. Some nutrients are easily oxidized and depleted during this trek.

That's not to say you shouldn't seek out fresh produce! Seek out local produce stands or, better yet, grow your own vegetables. The trip from garden to dinner plate is much shorter, and you'll be getting the best flavor and most nutritional value possible. When good fresh produce isn't available, however, you can rest assured that frozen and canned vegetables are a pretty close second when it comes to nutritional value. Be aware, however, that sodium may be added to frozen and canned vegetables. Briefly rinse these vegetables with water before preparing to wash away the excess, should you be salt-sensitive or if your recipe doesn't call for extra salt.

✸ How much folacin is in different kinds of foods?

Many kinds of beans, vegetables, fruit, whole grains, nuts, and seeds contain folacin. All of these foods are recommended to be consumed on a daily basis in the Mediterranean Diet Pyramid, making it easy to get adequate amounts of folacin. The recommended daily allowance for the average adult is 180 to 200 micrograms. Women in childbearing years, and those who are pregnant, are recommended to get 400 micrograms of folacin per day. Some researchers feel that folacin intakes should be from 400 to 800 micrograms per day to help prevent cancer. Below is a chart of some foods and their folacin content:

Food	Folacin (micrograms)
Artichoke, boiled (1 medium)	155
Asparagus, boiled (1/2 cup, or 6 spears)	130
Avocado, raw (1 medium)	160
Blackberries (frozen, unsweetened, 1 cup)	50
Boysenberries (frozen, unsweetened, 1 cup)	85
Broccoli, raw (1/2 cup chopped)	30
Chickpeas (garbanzo beans), boiled (1 cup)	280
Orange juice (8 ounces)	110
Red kidney beans, boiled (1 cup)	230

Food	*Folacin (micrograms)*
Rye flour, dark *(1 cup)*	80
Sunflower seeds, *toasted (1 ounce)*	65
Turnip greens, *boiled (1/2 cup, chopped)*	85
Whole wheat, wheat flour *(1 cup)*	55

Note: These figures are rounded numbers. Source: Jean Pennington, Bowes & Churches, Food Values of Portions Commonly Used (17 ed), Philadelphia: Lippincott, 1998.

5: *The Fruits of Good Health*

Who can resist a perfectly ripe piece of fruit? Tender, blushing peaches; rosy slices of watermelon; mahogany plums dripping with garnet-colored juice; crisp, crunchy apples; luscious, sunny oranges; sweet, mellow bananas; succulent berries in a rainbow of hues. Few things are more pleasurable than eating really good fruit. So why don't we eat more, and why do we so often fall short of the recommended absolute minimum of two servings of fruit per day? Why do Americans seem to prefer a box of store-bought cookies or cake from a mix for dessert?

In the traditional Mediterranean diet, fruit is a meal's crowning glory, the ultimate finish to a delicious dinner. The Mediterranean climate is perfect for growing a wide variety of fruits, and whatever is freshest, juiciest, loveliest, and in season provides the final flourish to meals already rich in color, texture, flavor, vitamins, minerals, fiber, phytonutrients, and good old-fashioned pleasure.

Fruits are full of great nutrition. Most fruits are high in that ever-helpful and healthful antioxidant vitamin C (for more on the antioxidant powers of vitamin C, see the previous chapter). All fruits are full of essential vitamins and minerals, as well as fiber (more on fiber in Chapter Six). Many contain high doses of carotenoids and other phytochemicals such as caffeic acid and coumarins, which help the body to rid itself of carcinogens; ferulic acid, which may help to shuttle potentially carcinogenic nitrates out of the body; cryptoxanthin, a carotenoid associated with decreased cervical cancer risk; and flavonoids.

Additionally, many studies have linked high fruit consumption (in conjunction with high vegetable consumption or on its own) with lower rates of certain cancers. A study published in the *American Journal of Clinical Nutrition* examined the specific effect of fruit consumption on cancer, and found "strong protective effects . . . for cancers of the upper digestive and respiratory tracts," as well as a lesser effect "on cancers of the oral cavity, pharynx, esophagus, and larynx." The study also found that the farther a tumor was from the digestive tract, the weaker the protective effect of fruit. Nonetheless, the study also found "significant protective effects of fruit . . . for cancers of the liver, pancreas, prostate, and urinary tract."

Yet, despite fruit's demonstrated healthfulness and great taste, in America, eating desserts higher in both refined sugar and fat than a simple piece of fruit seems to be the norm. A fancy pastry, a chocolate sundae, or a candy bar are weekly, even daily treats for many. Such high-sugar, high-fat fare is only an occasional treat in the traditional Mediterranean diet, never a daily or even a weekly indulgence.

While people in some parts of the Mediterranean enjoy a small bite of something sweet during the late afternoon, rich desserts never follow a meal, and portions are relatively tiny. Fruit appropriately follows a heavily plant-based meal, offering both the fulfillment of that desire for something sweet, fiber to provide a feeling of satiety, and one last dose of nutrients and phytochemicals to send the diner on his or her way.

While a ripe, juicy piece of raw fruit is the ultimate treat, fruit can also be delicious cooked, stewed, or added to recipes. Check out Part II of this book, "Recipes for Enjoying the Mediterranean Diet," for some Mediterranean-inspired fruit ideas.

Many of the fruits listed below have been enjoyed for centuries in the Mediterranean. A few are native to North America, or are more often consumed here than elsewhere. While we will mention the availability of each of the following fruits in the Mediterranean, the important point we would like to make is that any high-quality, ripe, juicy, fresh fruit available to you is appropriate for your diet, and finishing your meals with any fruit is eating in the true Mediterranean spirit.

⊛ APPLES

Apples are a part of the cuisines of many countries, and have existed in the Mediterranean as early as the third century B.C.E., when Cato, a Roman writer, mentioned seven different varieties of apples. The Roman Pliny, writing in the first century C.E., names thirty-six varieties of apples in his writings. Caesar's invading Roman legions are credited with introducing apples to Britain, and the first American settlers brought apple seeds to the New World.

One medium apple has about 80 calories and supplies 5 grams of fiber, more than a serving of oatmeal and about one-fourth the daily fiber recommended by the American Dietetic Association. Most of the fiber in apples is soluble fiber, a substance demonstrated to lower cholesterol levels. But the benefits don't stop there. A daily apple may indeed keep the doctor away, especially if that daily apple remains unpeeled. Recent research out of Cornell University has uncovered a host of phytochemicals in apple skins, including the flavonoids known as quercetin glycoside, phloretin glycoside, chlorogenic acid, and epicatechin, most heavily concentrated in the skin. Apples have been shown to exhibit higher antioxidant activity than oranges, grapefruits, carrots, spinach, onions, and green peppers, according to the Cornell study. (Wash and rinse apples well with vinegar and water if they aren't organically grown.)

Yet Americans only eat, on average, an apple every three days. Apples are one of the hardier fruits that keep well and ship well, and compared to many fruits, they are amazingly long-lived. This durability adds to apples' convenience. You can buy them in bulk and eat them, as long as they are stored in a cool, dry place, for months. Some apples can keep for six months or more (such as the popular Red Delicious) under the right conditions. What food could be more convenient than an apple?

Look for apples with firm flesh and without bruises, soft spots, depressions, cuts and nicks, or little holes. If the inside flesh is showing and has been exposed to the air, vitamins and minerals may have been destroyed. Apples grown locally or regionally are great if you can get them. Big or small, apples can be surprisingly sweet and juicy. Color varies among apple varieties. Red Delicious, for example, are a bright or deep red, while Gala apples are yellow overlaid with a rosier red.

Avoid apples with a brilliant shine. Lots of shine probably means lots of wax, which traps pesticides. If you can find only waxed apples, peel them before eating. Whether you peel or not, wash all apples with vinegar and water, and scrub with a brush. Cut out any bruises or nicks. Apples last longer in the refrigerator and ripen faster at room temperature (as is the case with many fruits).

Some of the more widely available apple types, all great for eating out of hand, are Braeburn, Empire, Fuji, Gala, Golden Delicious, Granny Smith (also perfect for pies), Jonagold, Jonathan, McIntosh, Red Delicious, Rome Beauty (also ideal for baking), and Winesap. Many other types exist, too. Check your local market, produce stand, or grocery store. Apples are widely available all year round in the United States, and the many types, flavors, colors, and uses make them irresistible. Shouldn't you be eating more?

☉ APRICOTS

Apricots are familiar to denizens of the Mediterranean, particularly in Turkey. Americans like their apricots fresh, canned, and dried, and each form has its gastronomical and nutritional benefits. The bright orange-yellow color is a dead giveaway that these velvety little fruits are potent sources of beta-carotene in any form. Dried apricots are a concentrated source of energy and fiber, as well as many other essential vitamins and minerals. Fresh apricots are richer in vitamin C, and when eaten at the peak of ripeness and slightly warmed by the sun, are an utter delight.

The problem with fresh apricots is that they are incredibly delicate and don't last long. The apricot season in the United States is approximately May through July, but if apricots aren't grown near you, you may have trouble finding good fresh ones. Ripe apricots are soft and have a lovely apricot aroma. If apricots are greenish when picked, they will probably spoil before they ripen, but you can attempt to ripen them by storing them at room temperature in a brown paper bag. Dried apricots and cooked or canned apricots are other delicious and nutritious alternatives.

☉ BANANAS

Although you may not think of bananas as being a typical Mediterranean fruit, bananas are a part of the cuisines of Africa and Spain. Descriptions of bananas can be found in Greek texts from the time of Alexander the Great. Spanish missionaries introduced bananas to many parts of the world, and these cousins of the lily (which, incidentally, grow on very tall plants, not trees) exist in many forms and types throughout the world. Conveniently wrapped in their own package, bananas are a good source of potassium, that mineral needed for our heart to beat normally. When potassium levels fall dangerously low, which can happen during fasting or with severe diarrhea or vomiting, sudden death can occur. Potassium is also involved in maintaining our body's fluid balance and keeping our cells healthy. (Oranges, dates, and figs are actually richer sources of potassium than bananas.)

Bananas are delicious when the tips are still green, when the flavor is tangier, and at every stage until the skins are quite dark. The riper the banana, the sweeter it tastes. Cooked bananas are even sweeter, and grilled bananas are a delicious dessert, or even a side dish with a main course. Firmer, less ripe bananas are best for grilling or frying, while very ripe bananas mashed to a pulp are a superb addition to baked goods, and can even take the place of some of the fat.

⊛ BERRIES

What a glorious category of fruit! Berries are colorful, fun to eat, juicy, delicious, even fun to pick. They are perfect for cooking or eating raw. Freeze them for an icy treat, bake them into bread, or pop them one after another for a snack. Berries are delicate and they don't last long, so buy them, rinse them, and eat them immediately—and often.

Berries are beloved in the Mediterranean. Fragrant wild strawberries are a much-anticipated component of produce markets in Italy, and although the strawberries cultivated in the United States are somewhat different, the spirit remains the same. Blueberries, cultivated in North America, make a lovely Mediterranean-type dessert and are reminiscent of their cousins the lingonberries, the blueberry's European (and Mediterranean) equivalent. Plump, juicy blackberries, tangy raspberries, tart, globe-shaped gooseberries, and the all-American cranberry are other delicious choices. (Cranberries are too tart to eat raw for most people, but they are wonderful cooked into recipes.)

The vibrant colors of berries are a giveaway that these juicy fruits, perfect for snacking, are loaded with cancer-fighting phytochemicals. Flavonoids make blackberries purple-black, blueberries deep blue, and strawberries and raspberries rosy red. Berries are also full of vitamin C, fiber, and folate, all cancer fighters, too. In fact, in the fight against cancer, few foods are more powerful than berries.

Unlike some fruits, berries will last only a day or two in your refrigerator, and a little mold on one berry can transform the whole bowlful into a moldy mess overnight. Even berries untouched by the mold can take on an unpleasant taste. The best choice is to pick your own berries or buy them from a local produce stand or farmer's market.

Alternatively, berries from the supermarket can be stored layered between paper towels, and lightly rinsed just before serving. Blueberries last slightly longer than other types, such as strawberries, blackberries, and raspberries. Firmer and best used in cooking, cranberries are the exception. They keep well in the refrigerator and will keep for months in the freezer. When you can't find them fresh, frozen berries are similarly high in nutrients.

⏱ CHERRIES

Although the cherry tree's unfortunate fate at the hands of little Georgie Washington is the stuff of American legend, cherries have been around for centuries and were probably first domesticated over two thousand years ago in southern Turkey or Greece. The Romans loved them, and they have been planted and consumed all over Europe for centuries.

The cherry varieties most available in the United States

are sweet cherries—the popular, mahogany-skinned Bing cherry, the yellow-pink Rainier cherry, the dark red Lambert cherry, and the sweet Vans cherry—and sour cherries, most often used in pie fillings and other cooked desserts. Gaining in popularity are tart-sweet dried cherries.

Cherries are in season in midsummer and arrive at the market fully ripe. They are best handled gently, washed right before eating (when feasible—if not, wash and pat dry, then store in the refrigerator), and eaten as soon as possible. Choose plump, glossy berries with deep color and strong, intact stems. If you don't plan to eat your cherries right away, store them in the refrigerator, as you would berries, unrinsed between layers of paper towels, then wrap in plastic or store in an airtight container. Rinse just before serving. Cherries are rich in quercetin and kaempferol (flavinols), plus other powerful antioxidants. Tart cherries may also have anti-inflammatory properties, making them possible allies in the fight against arthritis pain (the Cherry Marketing Institute suggests eating twenty tart cherries per day to reduce inflammatory pain).

⊘ CITRUS FRUIT

Citrus fruit is plentiful in America, grown in abundance in Florida, Arizona, and California. It travels well, keeps well, and is plentiful all year in every state, making it a convenient (and self-packaged) food. Citrus trees are also familiar fixtures in the Mediterranean, as the climate is just right. Therefore, including lots of fresh oranges, grapefruits, tangerines, lemons, and limes in your diet is quintessentially Mediterranean. And don't forget the more unusual citrus choices, for variety: kumquats, tangelos, and tangors, if you can get them.

The orange juice industry has made it known that orange juice contains the folic acid so important for women of childbearing age. Deficiencies of folic acid have been linked to fetal abnormalities, and the United States Food and Drug Administration has stated that women of childbearing age can dramatically reduce the risk of having a child with neural tube defects such as spina bifida and anencephaly by consuming enough fruits and vegetables to assure adequate folic acid intake. Although some legumes and vegetables are even richer sources of folic acid, the orange still ranks as a good source.

Citrus fruits' real claim to fame is its high concentration of the antioxidant vitamin C. Although vitamin C is present in most fruits, one medium orange supplies the entire recommended daily allowance (currently 60 milligrams, although recent studies have suggested that 100 to 200 milligrams daily best saturates cells with vitamin C). Many studies have linked vitamin C consumption with reduced cancer risk. In addition to vitamin C's antioxidant properties (discussed in detail in the previous chapter), vitamin C gives the immune system a boost and aids the body in the absorption of iron, particularly that from plant-based sources, which aren't as readily absorbed by the body as the iron in animal meats. If you down a glass of orange juice with your iron-fortified cereal (for an extra C boost, throw in a few strawberries, too), your body will absorb more iron than it would without the extra vitamin C (for more on iron, see Chapter Seven).

Vitamin C is also important for maintaining the body's collagen supply. Collagen is necessary for healing wounds, strengthening blood vessels, and maintaining bones and teeth. Collagen has also been linked to a decreased risk of cancer metastasizing (spreading through the body).

Too much vitamin C (in daily megadoses of over 1,000 milligrams) could lead to kidney stone formation in certain people, and even higher doses have been shown to cause abdominal cramping, diarrhea, and nausea. Such megadoses would be virtually impossible to achieve from food, and are only a problem when people take vitamin C supplements, so we recommend getting your vitamin C from food sources— and what better food source than citrus fruits?

In addition to vitamin C, citrus fruit has other star qualities. Red grapefruit has been the subject of recent cancer research because of its high level of lycopene, the phytochemical that has been linked to lower rates of prostate and possibly breast and colon cancer. Red grapefruit is sweeter than yellow grapefruit—just one more reason to enjoy it. Even those who don't normally appreciate grapefruit's puckering tang might enjoy the sweeter red variety.

Don't worry about the color of the rind when choosing your citrus. Most commercially produced citrus is waxed and much of it is dyed. The citrus rind and citrus oil are also potent sources of the phytochemical limonene, a monoterpene often used in household products like detergent and furniture polish (which you should not, of course, eat!). Limonene has exhibited extremely strong anticancer effects, even causing complete regression of mammary tumors in laboratory rats. Try slicing organic citrus rind and candying it for a unique treat, made even more special when dipped in chocolate (for special occasions only—despite the orange rind, this is basically candy). Many cookbooks contain recipes for candied lemon, orange, and grapefruit peels.

Store citrus fruits in the refrigerator to keep them fresh the longest. Citrus can also be stored in a cool, dry place but will need to be eaten more quickly. Make sure the citrus can breathe. Airtight bags or containers tend to encourage molding. If allowed to come to room temperature, citrus fruits will be juicier and more fragrant.

⊘ GRAPES

Whether or not you are a fan of wine, you very well may be a fan of the noble grape. Whether green, red, or blue-black, grapes are fun to eat, deliciously juicy, and as sweet a fruit as anyone could wish for. Grapes are one of the oldest cultivated fruits known to man, and hieroglyphic evidence exists that the people of ancient Egypt were growing grapes and making wine.

Some grapes are native to North America, but the Mediterranean region was the first to cultivate grapes, transforming them from small, sour fruits to the juicy globes of sweetness we know and love today. European grapes brought to North America from Europe sparked the consumption of fresh grapes, the making of raisins, and the California wine culture.

Even today, Italy leads the world in the production of table grapes. (Chile is second and California is third.) However, in the United States, 97 percent of the table grapes available come from California. Other states producing grapes include Arizona, Michigan, and New York. The most popular eating grape in this country is Thompson seedless, a delicious variety of green grape. Because it is seedless, Thompson grapes (and other seedless varieties) make convenient snack foods.

Grapes are available all year, adding to their convenience. They are harvested ripe, so choose any grapes that look plump and fresh, are firmly attached to their stems, and have a healthy bloom (the white powdery cast to fresh grapes). Green grapes should have a golden cast, and red and blue-black grapes should have a deep, even color. Grapes brought to room temperature before serving are the most flavorful. Rinse just before serving.

Grapes (especially the red varieties) are rich sources of flavonoids, the substances in wine suspected to offer so many health benefits (see page 137 for more on wine). Grapes also contain caffeic, ferulic, and ellagic acids, phenolic acids with strong antioxidant properties that give both grapes and wine their color and flavor as well as the characteristic tartness. Grapes additionally contain the phytoestrogen resveratrol, a phenolic fungicide that may support a healthy heart. (Peanuts also contain resveratrol.) A small bunch of fresh grapes makes a satisfying conclusion to any meal. Raisins are also great for snacking, in breads, and in recipes where fruit is cooked.

⊘ MELONS

A highly perfumed melon evokes ancient times in exotic lands. Watermelon is native to Africa and was first cultivated there; the first recorded watermelon harvesting was nearly five thousand years ago in Egypt, according to the National Watermelon Promotion Board. Pharaohs stocked watermelons in their tombs, and legend has it that the Roman governor Demosthenes, after ducking half a watermelon that was thrown at him during a political debate, set the watermelon on his head and thanked the thrower for the helmet to wear while fighting Philip of Macedonia.

Watermelons are thought to have grown along the banks of the Nile even before 2000 B.C.E., and cantaloupe seeds brought from Armenia as a gift to the pope were first planted in Cantalupo, Italy—hence their contemporary name. Melons of all types spread all over the Mediterranean region centuries ago and have been a part of the Mediterranean diet ever since. Whether scooped out of their rinds with a spoon for dessert or cut into small slices and wrapped in strips of prosciutto as an antipasto, melons are a Mediterranean favorite. While the melons grown in the Mediterranean aren't widely available in this country (such as the dark green Spanish melon), other melons, such as juicy cantaloupe and honeydew melons, are available during much of the year, although they are in season in late summer through fall. Once only available during the summer when they are in season, watermelons are now also available all year, depending on where you live.

To pick a perfect honeydew or cantaloupe, look for a fruit with a pleasing melony scent at the smooth end. It should yield slightly to pressure at the stem end and be heavy for its size without cracks or spots. Cantaloupe should have a golden netting over light yellow. Honeydew melons should be creamy white or light yellow in color with a slightly oily film on the outer rind. Melons that stand for a day or two at room temperature will be juicier and more aromatic.

Watermelons should also seem heavy for their size and their bottom side should be pale yellow, signifying that the watermelon ripened on the ground. Folklore suggests balancing a broom straw on top of a watermelon to determine ripeness. If the straw rotates slowly, the melon is ripe.

Melons are heavy on nutrition. They contain many vitamins and minerals, as well as fiber. The watermelon's red color is the result of the powerful antioxidant carotenoid lycopene, that cancer fighter also present in tomatoes and red grapefruit thought to reduce prostate cancer risk and possibly breast cancer risk. Cantaloupe is high in vitamin C and beta-carotene (obvious from its orange color). Honeydew melons are also good sources of vitamin C.

Although melons do not cook well, raw melons make a lovely dessert or even part of the main meal, served in slices, cubes, or balls alongside meat or grain-based dishes. For a truly Mediterranean appetizer, serve slender cantaloupe and honeydew slices wrapped in strips of prosciutto (an admittedly pricey dry-cured Italian ham), or Canadian bacon or thinly sliced ham. All versions are tasty.

⊛ PEACHES AND NECTARINES

Peaches and nectarines (a smooth-skinned type of peach) are spectacular summer fruits when you are lucky enough to get good ones. In the Mediterranean, where peaches are abundant in the summer, the quality is high. In the United

States, peaches and nectarines bought out of season are frequently disappointing, even inedible. Nothing compares to the perfect, juicy, fragrant peach or nectarine, however. These fruits don't need any adornment.

However, peaches stuffed with chopped nuts and the crumbs of almond cookies are a popular Italian dish (see the dessert recipes in Part II of this book), and fresh peaches or nectarines poached in a little wine are a not-so-sinful pleasure, considering the high nutritional content of these fruits: rich in vitamin C, beta-carotene, and other carotenoids (again, the color is the clue), peaches and nectarines are a nutritious way to wind up a great meal. Cooking brings out more of the flavor in even the ripest peach, so consider cooking peaches whenever the mood strikes you. In addition to poaching, peaches are delicious grilled, baked, or even lightly sautéed in a fruity olive or nut oil. Peaches are closely related to almonds, so any combination of these two "fruits" is pleasing.

Peaches and nectarines don't keep well, but once ripe, will keep longer, in the refrigerator. Both are best purchased tree-ripened. Skin color is irrelevant to ripeness, but the peach should yield slightly to light pressure and have a fruity aroma. To ripen an unripe peach or nectarine, place one to three fruits in a paper bag for two or three days. Peaches and nectarines are in season (increasing your chances of getting good ones) in July and August. When you can't find good fresh peaches or nectarines, canned and frozen peaches are an acceptable alternative, retaining most of their nutritional value (they lose some vitamin C but the carotenoid content remains the same).

⊘ PEARS

Known throughout the Mediterranean for centuries, pears are second only to apples as the favored baked fruit. Baked pears are far less common in this country, although we aren't sure why. A fresh baked pear is a mouth-watering, sweet, buttery treat, and easy to prepare (see the recipe on page 306). Ripe pears are tasty, too—juicy, sweet, fragrant, and tender.

Most pears purchased from the supermarket aren't yet ready for eating, however. Pears are far more edible when they ripen off the tree, so green pears are picked and shipped (convenient, since the unripe pears are harder and sturdier, so they travel better). Unripe pears are long-lived, and rival apples when it comes to long-term storage potential. Chill them and they'll last and last (the harder varieties like Bosc and Comice can keep for up to seven months). A week or so before you are ready to eat them, bring them to room temperature and ripen in a brown paper bag.

When purchasing pears, look for firm fruit without cuts, bruises, or blemishes. Superficial nicks are fine if you plan to eat the pears that week. Bruises and soft spots should be avoided. Pears need to sit for a few days to soften sufficiently for eating once you bring them home. A ripe pear yields slightly to pressure on the stem end, and spoils quickly. Keep it in the refrigerator for a couple of days at most.

Pears are generally available all year in the United States, but their peak season is August through October. Sample the different pear varieties in most supermarkets: Anjou, Bartlett, and Bosc are among the most widely available, but you'll often see other types. Asian pears are crisper and are best in the fall.

Pears may not sport the orange color that distinguishes carotenoid-heavy fruit, but they have plenty of other nutritional properties to recommend them. Pears are full of vitamin C, and fresh raw pears are particularly high in fiber. They also contain many other vitamins and minerals. Dried pears are great for snacking and are a more concentrated source of nutrients.

⊛ PLUMS

Plums are no strangers to the traditional Mediterranean diet. Spiced plums cooked with sugar, cinnamon, and cloves is a French specialty, served chilled. Many types of plums are available in the United States, including the juicy Japanese plums perfect for snacking and the drier European plums best suited for cooking. Plums are available from May through October.

Plums range in color from yellow to blue-black, with every shade of red, purple, and blue in between. Plums are best when tree-ripened, but because plums soften (without developing additional sweetness) after picking, ripe and unripe plums can both feel soft and ripe in the store. If your market allows it, you will be better off taste-testing the store's plums before buying. Plums are a nutritious and complexly flavored dessert.

Let us not forget plums in their dried form! Supernutritious prunes have a reputation for promoting regularity, but they do far more than provide fiber for our bodies. Prunes are a concentrated source of many vitamins and minerals, and have high levels of caffeic and ferulic acid, phenolic acids demonstrated to have potent anticancer effects in animal studies.

⊛ THE GREAT WINE CONTROVERSY

On November 17, 1991, a segment aired on the popular television show *60 Minutes* that changed the world—or at least the world as wine fanciers and wine producers know it. The show examined the diets, lifestyles, and health of people living in southwestern France, where saturated fat intake (primarily from butter, cream, and cheese) was high. The surprising finding was the low heart attack rate among the

French—one of the lowest in the world! This discovery flew in the face of everything the American public had been told about how to lower the risk of coronary heart disease. What were the French doing to keep their heart attack rates so low? The study concluded that they were drinking wine.

Hallelujah! the world responded. We can eat whatever we want, follow it with a glass of wine, and everyone will be fine! Within a few weeks of the airing of the notorious *60 Minutes* episode, red wine sales rose 40 percent in the United States.

Of course, as with any purported panacea, the picture is far more complicated than it seems at first glance. While wine does appear to have many benefits, from a high flavonoid content to antibacterial effects, the French study subjects didn't overindulge. Red wine consumption in France is, on average, daily but moderate—about 8 ounces per day for men, half that amount at most for women.

A recent study published in the January 2003 issue of the *New England Journal of Medicine* showed that men who drank alcohol reduced their risk of heart attack by one-third, but consumption was moderate. The men in the study drank no more than two (roughly 4-ounce) glasses of alcohol. In this study, the alcohol consumption was in the form of wine, beer, or hard liquor, no more than seven times a week, which averages to no more than two glasses of alcohol a day. This is right in line with the amount of wine (alcohol) consumption seen in the traditional Mediterranean diet, but note that the study did not include women.

One study out of Denmark suggests that wine drinkers tend to have better eating habits. Wine drinkers, according to the study, tended to eat more fruits and vegetables, fish, salads, and olive oil, making the health benefits of wine a little less clear. Research in the United States additionally suggests that wine drinkers are, in general, more moderate drinkers who smoke less and are better educated than non-drinkers of wine.

Alcohol consumption of any kind has been linked to increased risk of breast cancer in women, so women may think twice about a daily glass of wine. One study suggests that two to five drinks a day can increase a woman's risk of developing breast cancer by 40 percent. While the recommended single 4-ounce daily serving of wine (red or white) may be small enough to make little difference in cancer risk, those otherwise at risk for breast cancer (and anyone else, for that matter) needn't feel compelled to drink any.

Anyone at risk for alcohol-related problems should also forgo wine in favor of more fruits and vegetables. Alcohol intake has been associated with an increased risk of accidents, cirrhosis (liver failure), stroke, and all causes of death, and alcohol is certainly not a necessary component in any healthy diet. While many researchers suspect flavonoids are the key to the protection wine may offer against heart disease, plenty of other fruits and vegetables have more flavonoids than a glass of wine (see chart on page 140).

For those who already enjoy wine in moderation, however, the research investigating the link between wine consumption and health is intriguing. Research has shown a U-shaped curve linking alcohol consumption with longevity. People who drink alcohol in moderation seem to enjoy a longer life than people who don't drink at all or people who drink heavily. "Moderation" generally refers to two or fewer 8-ounce glasses of wine per day for men, and less than one 8-ounce glass of wine for women.

Although some research suggests a longer life for moderate alcohol drinkers, alcohol consumption certainly has its risks, and other studies dispute the claim that moderate drinkers live any longer than nondrinkers.

The link between wine consumption and a reduced risk of heart disease is even more compelling. Many studies have associated moderate alcohol intake with improved cardiovascular health, especially a reduced risk of suffering a heart attack, and much research has been conducted in an attempt to determine what particular aspects of alcohol and/or wine consumption are responsible for this protective effect. One theory is that alcohol has a protective tendency to raise HDL ("good") cholesterol and lower LDL ("bad") cholesterol; another centers on alcohol's tendency to inhibit blood clotting. Other researchers are investigating wine's particular antioxidant phytochemicals, specifically phenolic compounds like flavonoids and the phenolic fungicide resveratrol. Again, however, most of these studies included male subjects only. Keep in mind, also, that most plant foods contain phenolic compounds, many in concentrations higher than in wine. Grapes and peanuts are also good sources of resveratrol, and flavonoids are present in many plant foods, especially red grapes, green leafy vegetables, and fruity vegetables like tomatoes. If these antioxidant compounds are the "magic ingredient" in wine, then consumption of grapes and other foods with high levels of phenolic compounds should offer similar protection. The following chart demonstrates the relative flavonoid content of various fruits and vegetables.

Flavonoid Content	Beverage	Fruit	Vegetable
Low flavonoid content (<10mg/kg or mg/L)	Coffee Orange juice White wine	Peaches	Cabbage Carrots Mushrooms Peas Spinach
Moderate flavonoid content (10–50 mg/kg or mg/L)	Red wine Tea Tomato juice	Apples Grapes Strawberries	Broad beans Lettuce Red peppers Tomatoes

Flavonoid Content	Beverage	Fruit	Vegetable
High flavonoid content (>50mg/kg or mg/L)	None	Cranberries	Broccoli Celery Endive French beans Kale Onions

Table adapted from "Alternative Approaches to Lowering Choles-terol," Patient Care *29, no. 18 (November 15, 1995): 110 (21).*

The problem with wine consumption involves the American tendency to do everything in a big way, and also to choose only those aspects of a healthy program for eating or living that are most desirable. The traditional Mediterranean diet is most effective and beneficial for health if followed completely—not just red wine, olive oil, and extra bread, but all these as part of a low-saturated-fat, plant-based diet combined with a high level of physical activity. If you enjoy wine, maximize its health benefits by consuming it in the Mediterranean way:

- Only with meals, never recreationally.
- Only in small amounts—8 ounces daily for men, 4 ounces daily for women, at most.
- As one part of an overall low-saturated-fat, plant-based diet and active lifestyle.

Don't forget that while small amounts of daily alcohol have indeed been associated with lower risk of heart disease and other chronic health problems in men, as well as lower rate of death from all causes and greater longevity, consumption of larger amounts of alcohol have been linked to a higher risk of accidents, including car accidents; heart disease; certain cancers; stroke; birth defects; and an increase in death rate from all causes, not to mention alcohol dependence and a tendency toward obesity. So, to sum up, drink if you like to, but if you can't do so in moderation, abstain. The health risks from overconsumption of alcohol far outweigh any possible lack of benefits from abstinence.

☞ QUESTIONS AND ANSWERS

ℬ Is fruit juice just as good as fruit?

Generally, no. While fruit juice is a preferable substitute to beverages with higher refined-sugar content such as cola, fruit juice—especially the kind you buy in the store—is fruit without the fiber and serving for serving contains a lot more calories than a piece of fruit. Whenever possible, choose the fruit over the juice. If you can't live without your juice, select the kinds that contain pulp. The fruit juice with pulp also may have retained more vitamins and phytochemicals than a highly processed juice. If you own a juicer, juicing your own fruits can be fun, and you can be assured the juice is fresh and wholesome—certainly a fresh and healthful alternative to a cocktail or after-dinner drink. However, when you clean the juicer of all that pulp, you'll see how much of the fruit you are throwing away.

ℬ Is it true that apples can keep other foods fresher and help other fruits ripen faster?

Apples do help. Put an apple in your bag of brown sugar to keep the sugar from drying out, and toss another in with your potatoes to keep them from sprouting. Baked goods stay moister in the company of an apple. Apples also make other fruit ripen faster. If you want to speed up the ripening of other fruit, put a few apples in the fruit bowl. If you want your other fruit to last longer, however, don't put apples in your fruit bowl, or have a separate bowl just for apples in a different area.

✅ What are other interesting ways to include fruit in the diet?

- Freeze green grapes and watermelon cubes to use as ice cubes in beverages or to eat on a hot summer day instead of sugary Popsicles or high-fat ice cream.
- Toss dried fruit into a stir-fry.
- To jazz up plain brown rice, add a few raisins, chopped dried apricots, currants, and walnuts.
- Whenever possible, add fresh fruit to your bowl of cereal.
- Use dried fruit to add texture and flavor to hot cooked cereal. Also try stirring fresh blueberries into oatmeal.
- Whenever possible, add fresh fruit to your yogurt.
- Stir dried fruit, chopped apples, or chopped cherries into your next batch of homemade bread.
- Tired of peanut butter and jelly? Peanut butter and pear or even date sandwiches are more nutritious and far more delicious.
- As long as we are on the subject of peanut butter, don't miss the ultimate kid-friendly treat: peanut butter and ripe banana sandwiches!
- Add crisp apple slices to your turkey sandwich instead of cheese.
- Add dried cherries to provide tang and interest to salads.
- Cranberry sauce isn't just for Thanksgiving. Make it with apple juice concentrate instead of sugar and serve alongside any meat or as a spread for bread or toast.

❧ *Which fruits can be cooked and which can't?*

Don't cook melons. They lose their sweetness. The exception is cantaloupe, which is tasty sliced and very briefly grilled. Most other fruits can be cooked one way or another. Apples and pears are superb when baked in the oven, and also work well in breads, pies, and cakes, providing sweetness and tartness. Grilled bananas are a special treat. Berries of all types work well cooked for jam or jelly, in breads, pies, cakes, muffins, and cooked into sauces. Citrus fruits and juices are often used in baking and in cooking, as they are a good complement to many main dishes, meat or otherwise. One delicious way to prepare your Thanksgiving turkey or roasted chicken is to baste it with orange juice during cooking, and brush orange marmalade over the skin during the last fifteen minutes of cooking.

Fruits with pits, like peaches, apricots, nectarines, and plums, make superb jam, cobblers, breads, cakes, puddings, and pies, and are also a delicious complement for meat or other main dishes. Try grilling peach and nectarine halves basted with citrus juice for a summer treat. Dried fruits are perfect for cooking. In addition to their use in breads and other baked goods, dried fruits are delicious cooked on their own terms. For a warm, satisfying breakfast on a cold morning, combine raisins with chopped dried apples, dried apricots, dried dates, walnuts, and a little fruit juice, and warm on the stove until the fruit is plumped. Good morning!

❧ *This chapter makes fruit sound so great, but the fruit in the supermarket isn't anything like you describe. Why not?*

Perhaps one reason that Americans don't consume as much fruit as people in the traditional Mediterranean region is that the fruit available in American supermarkets is often of inferior quality. Picked before ripeness, shipped hundreds or even thousands of miles, heavily waxed and sprayed, much of the fruit in the American food supply isn't particularly tender, juicy, or flavorful.

How many times have you opened the produce drawer of your refrigerator only to find that your fruit has turned rotten, or that the peach that looks good on the outside is brown and hard or mushy and rotten on the inside? Fruit is delicate and doesn't respond well to rough handling, long-term storage, or transportation across an entire continent. However, knowing a little about fruit, how it ripens, how to choose the best pieces, how to store it, and what its nutritional star qualities are can make the difference between a fruit-poor diet and a diet loaded with nature's very own sweet treats. A few rules apply in general to most fruits:

- Wash fruit thoroughly and scrub with a good fruit or vegetable brush to remove pesticide residue, dirt, microorganisms, and so on. Too vigorous scrubbing can bruise delicate fruit, however, so be gentle. Buy organic fruit if it is available and affordable. If fruit is waxed, consider peeling. Wax is virtually impossible to scrub off and can trap undesirable substances. Even though the skins of many fruits (like apples) are heavy with nutrients and phytochemicals, their pesticide residues may prove to be worth forgoing the extra nutrients when children will consume the fruits.
- Don't scrub fruit with soap, which isn't meant to be eaten, either. Try a fruit and vegetable wash instead, or a mixture of vinegar and water.
- The greater the variety of fruits you consume, the fewer of one type of pesticide residue you'll be subjected to, and you'll receive a wider range of nutrient and phytochemical benefits.
- Most fruit will last longer when refrigerated and will ripen faster at room temperature. To speed up

ripening, store a couple of pieces of fruit in a brown paper bag and roll the bag shut. Keep at room temperature and turn the bag daily to promote even ripening. Check frequently (once or twice a day), because some fruits ripen very quickly this way. This method works great for fruits with pits, like peaches, nectarines, plums, and apricots. It also works beautifully for unripe pears, and bananas ripen extra quickly this way.

- Fruits are delicate. Handle gently, store carefully, and check often for bruises, cuts, mold, soft spots, or rot. Don't eat the bad spots.
- Fruits soak up water, diluting their flavor and encouraging spoilage. Whenever possible, wash fruit just before eating it. However, if it means the difference between not eating fruit and washing it before you store it, wash, dry, then store, and enjoy at will straight from the fridge. We understand that convenience is often the determining factor!
- The potent antioxidants in citrus juices (lemon juice, orange juice, etc.) work their magic on cut fruit that tends to brown. When cutting fruit for a fruit salad or for cooking, sprinkle or brush with citrus juice to keep the fruit from turning dark.
- Dried fruits like raisins and currants are more tender and pleasant to eat if you let them plump up in a little water, wine, or fruit juice for at least ten minutes before serving or using in a recipe.

6: *The Grains, Legumes, Nuts, and Seeds of the Mediterranean*

If vegetables make up the soul of traditional Mediterranean cuisine, then grains, legumes, nuts, and seeds comprise the body. This food group constitutes the bulk of the traditional Mediterranean diet, and the many manifestations of grains, legumes, nuts, and seeds make delicious, comforting, fragrant, filling, and deeply satisfying food.

Nothing distinguishes a Mediterranean kitchen more than the aroma of fresh-baked bread. Whether a dense, round loaf of country bread from France or crispy Moroccan flatbread, whole-grain bread accompanies most Mediterranean meals in one form or another. Imagine steaming pots of pasta in shapes ranging from prodigious lasagna noodles and giant shells to rice-shaped orzo and the "little ears" called orecchiette to couscous, the grainlike pasta so common in African and Middle Eastern cuisine. The types of pasta are endless: spaghetti, linguine, fettuccine, penne, rigatoni, ziti, conchiglie, and fusilli, to name just a few.

Creamy risotto, a heavenly Italian rice concoction, may be flavored with any number of vegetables from artichokes to zucchini. Other rice dishes are prevalent as well: saffron-colored Spanish rice that is the one consistent ingredient in a Spanish paella, the classic Greek rice pilaf, and various combinations of rice with vegetables or seafood, baked in the oven or added to soup.

Porridgelike when fresh, crispy when chilled, sliced, and grilled, cornmeal-based polenta is an Italian specialty, as are gnocchi, little Italian dumplings made with flour and often potatoes. From the Middle Eastern shores of the Mediterranean comes bulgur wheat, cooked into pilafs or tabouli salad. And then there are pizzas, calzones, vegetable and meat pies, moussaka. Anybody hungry?

Grains sit at the base of the Mediterranean Diet Pyramid, which suggests eight or more servings of whole-grain breads, pasta, cereal, rice, bulgur, couscous, polenta, and others each day. One of the best ways to eat Mediterranean is to add more whole grains to your diet.

Grains of all types become even heartier and more delectable with the addition of protein-rich legumes, nuts, and seeds: penne with white beans, rice with peas, chickpeas with bulgur wheat, spaghetti with walnut sauce. Legumes exist in every Mediterranean country, often taking the place of meat as a main course and, even more often, serving to stretch very small amounts of meat to serve many. Legumes contain many vitamins (such as folacin) and minerals (such as selenium), are protein- and fiber-rich, and are satisfying dressed with nothing more than a little olive oil and a splash of lemon juice. Their sizes, colors, and types are far too numerous to list here, but some of the more common Mediterranean legumes are white canellini beans, chickpeas (garbanzo beans), fava beans (broad beans), black beans, green and red lentils, tiny white haricot beans, red kidney beans, lima beans, and Egyptian ful beans.

Many cultures have used legumes for centuries as a primary protein source, and the Mediterranean region is no exception. The Mediterranean Diet Pyramid suggests at least two half-cup servings of legumes each day.

Nuts and seeds (technically, nuts are large seeds of fruits with hard husks, except for peanuts, which are actually legumes) are often used to add flavor and crunch to raw and cooked foods, whether part of an appetizer, such as almond paste mixed with chickpeas for hummus; a feature of the main meal, such as pasta with pesto rich with pine nuts; or sprinkled over stewed fruit for dessert. Nuts and seeds can add significant nutrients, phytochemicals, protein, and mono-unsaturated fats to a traditional Mediterranean-inspired diet. Although most nuts and seeds can be high in total fat, generally only 10 percent of this fat is saturated. Frequent nut and seed consumption has been linked to low rates of many chronic diseases such as certain cancers and heart disease. Despite many fears that eating these beneficial foods (especially nuts) will cause weight gain, recent studies have shown otherwise. Walnuts, almonds, hazelnuts (filberts), pine nuts (pignolia), pistachios (in the Middle East), and peanuts (technically a legume) are the nuts most common in the Mediterranean.

Mediterranean or not, all nuts and seeds, except for the coconut (which is high in saturated fat) can be added to a Mediterranean-inspired way of eating. Just be sure that the nuts and seeds you consume (whether in spreads, such as peanut butter, or in the "whole" form) are not packaged with added hydrogenated oils, which spells trans-fatty acids. Other types of nuts and seeds include chestnuts, cashews, pecans, pumpkin seeds, sesame seeds, and sunflower seeds. The Mediterranean Diet Pyramid suggests that nuts and seeds be consumed daily in quantities of at least 1 ounce, depending on your individual caloric needs or allowances. Nuts and seeds, either plain or roasted without added oils and salt, make a wonderful and convenient snack food. A handful of nuts and another handful of dried fruit—raisins, currants, dates, dried cherries and blueberries, and so on—make a nutritious quick fix between meals.

Grains, legumes, nuts, and seeds are delicious and filling

sources of good nutrition in the true Mediterranean style. Let's talk about some of their more stellar nutritional—and in the case of fiber, nonnutritional—health benefits.

⊛ FABULOUS FIBER

Fiber, that nonnutritive stuff that gives plants their shape and sturdiness, is a word for carbohydrates that the body doesn't digest. If it isn't nourishment, how is it helpful? Even without nourishing the body, fiber does plenty to facilitate good health. Fiber alone is sufficient justification to choose whole grains over refined because of its many benefits. Fiber adds roughage to the diet—that noncaloric bulk that keeps the digestive and elimination systems running smoothly. New research suggests that fiber may also keep the body from digesting some of the calories it consumes. The study, conducted by the United States Department of Agriculture Human Nutrition Research Center in Maryland, put people on diets with the same number of calories but with differing, and changing, fiber content. When fiber intake was higher, absorbed calories were lower, making fiber a great ally for attaining and keeping body weight within a desirable range.

Fiber seems to do more than its famed role of preventing constipation. Studies have linked high fiber intakes to the decrease of certain cancers, such as cancer of the colon and rectum. It also appears to help stabilize blood sugar in people with diabetes and improve high blood cholesterol levels by lowering the "bad" LDL cholesterol. Fiber is bulky, therefore filling. A meal rich in fiber doesn't leave much room for high-fat foods.

Fiber isn't all the same, however. It comes in two types, and each type performs a specific function in the body. Soluble fiber, present in many fruits and vegetables, dissolves in water and forms a gellike substance in the body. It works in the body to lower cholesterol levels, particularly levels of LDL ("bad") cholesterol, by bonding with bile acids, which are made of cholesterol, and moving them quickly through the intestines and out of the body so that less cholesterol is absorbed into the blood. Types of soluble fiber include pectin, guar gum, oat gum, and psyllium, and these are the substances linked to decreased risk of heart disease and diabetes. Soluble fiber is the much-publicized type of fiber in oat bran, which is why oatmeal and other oat-based cereals are now heavily advertised as heart-disease preventives. However, oats are not the only source of soluble fiber. Other good sources include whole-grain bread, barley, kidney beans, pinto beans, navy beans, lentils, split peas, black-eyed peas, green peas, corn, prunes, pears, apples, and citrus fruits.

Insoluble fiber is sometimes easier to spot. It is, and looks like, roughage, and includes substances like cellulose and lignin. This is the fiber that gives plants their structure. One of the best sources is wheat bran. Insoluble fiber doesn't dissolve in water. In the body, insoluble fiber expands because it soaks up water. It helps move waste through the body quickly and is the fiber that may decrease the risk of certain chronic diseases by minimizing the time potentially harmful substances spend in the colon.

While whole wheat-based products are among the richest sources of insoluble fiber, some fruits and vegetables contain insoluble fiber, too: most notably, dates, blueberries and blackberries, green peas, and lima beans.

Many foods contain both types of fiber, and many fiber-rich foods are low in fat and high in vitamins and minerals, making the benefits of fiber hard to isolate. One thing is clear, however: Fiber-rich foods are good for your health!

Yet most Americans don't consume as much fiber as many health officials would like—in one survey, the national average totaled about 11 grams of fiber per day, not impressive next to the levels recommended by many health organizations. The American Heart Association, the American Cancer Society, and the American Dietetic Association recommend 25 to 35 grams of fiber per day for the maximum health benefit. Those who consume too little fiber may be putting themselves at risk for colon cancer, as well as constipation, hemorrhoids, high blood pressure, diabetes, obesity, and coronary heart disease, to name just a few of the conditions linked to low-fiber diets.

To get more fiber of both the insoluble and soluble types into your diet, follow the Mediterranean way of eating, choosing fiber-rich foods daily: whole grains in breads, pastas, and cereals; a variety of legumes, nuts, and seeds; and a variety of fresh raw fruits and vegetables.

⊛ B VITAMINS, HOMOCYSTEINE, AND YOUR HEART

While fruits and vegetables contain many vitamins and minerals, when it comes to many of the B vitamins, whole grains and legumes can't be beat. B vitamins are water-soluble vitamins that include thiamin (B_1), riboflavin (B_2), niacin, folacin, pantothenic acid, biotin, pyridoxine (B_6), and cobalamin (B_{12}). They perform many functions in the body, from helping the body turn carbohydrates, fats, and sugars into energy, to making cells.

B vitamins may also help to protect against heart disease. Heart disease researchers have linked high levels of a substance called homocysteine in blood to higher risk of heart disease. Homocysteine is a chemical formed naturally in the body from a breakdown of amino acids from protein foods. Generally, homocysteine levels don't pose a problem in the body. They are kept within a safe range by the action of three of the B vitamins: folacin, B_6, and B_{12}. However, when homocysteine levels rise, the walls of the arteries become sticky, catching blood cholesterol and encouraging its accumulation along arterial walls. This accumulation can eventually result in artery blockage, restricting blood flow to the body, including to the heart and brain. One study suggested that 15 to 30 percent of all patients with artery blockages had too-high levels of homocysteine in their blood.

While the homocysteine–heart disease connection is still being explored, it makes sense for people already at risk for heart disease to have their homocysteine levels tested and to take steps to lower homocysteine levels over 12 micromoles per liter. (Talk to your doctor if you are concerned.)

It certainly makes sense to eat foods rich in B vitamins, like whole grains and legumes. These foods are good for your health in many ways, and are a great way to keep homocysteine levels in check for anyone, whether or not you are currently at risk for heart disease. For those eating a Mediterranean-inspired diet, getting enough folacin, B_6, and B_{12} (the last available mostly in animal foods—more on B_{12} in the next chapter) is easy. For those whose diets consist primarily of "junk food"—candy bars, sodas, chips, and the like—deficiencies of these essential nutrients become far more likely.

☙ THE PHYTOCHEMICALS OF GRAINS, LEGUMES, NUTS, AND SEEDS

Vegetables and fruits aren't the only phytochemical-rich elements of a healthy diet. Grains, legumes, nuts, and seeds are plant foods, too! Some of the phytochemical stars in this group include:

- **Phytosterols.** These cholesterol-lowering, anti-cancer phytochemicals are contained in many nuts and seeds, such as almonds, cashews, peanuts, sesame seeds, and sunflower seeds. Phytosterols are also abundant in whole wheat and soybeans (again, the last not a "Mediterranean" legume, but one that can easily be included in a Mediterranean-inspired diet), as well as in some vegetables (such as corn) and vegetable oils.

- **Lignans (or Phenolic Lignans).** Abundant in whole grains and flaxseed (not a Mediterranean original, but well worth a mention in any discussion regarding chronic disease prevention), this powerful "phyto" or plant estrogen helps protect the prostate and breast from cancer. Lignans contain antioxidant properties, and can also be found in some berries and vegetables.

- **Flavonoids.** These plant phenolic compounds are featured in wine, tea, and many fruits and vegetables, but they are also present in many types of legumes and cereal grains.

- **Phytic Acid.** This compound is found in cereal grains, including wild rice, nuts, and seeds, especially sesame seeds and soybeans. Some researchers believe that it is phytic acid, not fiber, that provides the anticancer effect of diets rich in whole grains, nuts, and seeds. Phytic acid seems to slow cancer formation and stabilize blood sugar, cholesterol, and triglyceride levels.

- **Saponins.** These phytochemicals may keep cancer cells from multiplying as well as keep blood sugar, cholesterol, and triglyceride levels in check. While most vegetables and herbs contain some saponins, beans and legumes are the richest sources.

- **Resveratrol.** This phenolic fungicide that gives wine its color and may contribute to wine's heart-protective function is present in even greater concentrations in peanuts than in wine.

⊛ GETTING THE WHOLE GRAIN

While grain-based foods aren't always made from the whole grain (whole grains are grains that have not been stripped of their bran and germ), traditional Mediterranean foods, especially breads, are far more likely to be made from whole grains than many of the grain products popular with American consumers: white or "wheat" (but not "whole-wheat") breads, refined pastas, and white rice, not to mention a host of specialty products made with refined white flour: dinner rolls, packaged snack cakes, bagels, English muffins, breakfast muffins, and other sweetened baked goods from doughnuts to cookies to store-bought birthday cakes. Even so-called health foods can be deceiving: rice cakes, cereal bars, and "health" breads aren't always made from whole grains and are sometimes highly refined.

Grains are the fruits of grass plants, and grains contain three parts: the germ or seed, which contains protein and oil; the endosperm, containing carbohydrates and some protein; and the bran, or fibrous outer layer. Once upon a simpler time, people picked grains, ground them between stones to make flour, and that was that. When technology made the removal of the coarser bran and germ possible, a finer, whiter flour was the result. This white flour was nothing but the ground endosperm, and although the endosperm contains protein and carbohydrates, most of the vitamins, minerals, and fiber are contained in the bran and germ—those valuable parts of the grain people began to throw away.

In the 1940s, manufacturers began to restore some of the missing vitamins and minerals to refined grain products. This may seem like a roundabout way to get the goodness of grain products into your body, and indeed, it is. In the past few decades, people have begun to prefer the coarser, heavier, whole-grain products once again, as public understanding about nutrition grows. We now know that white bread, white flour, white rice, and other refined grain products lack the nutritional value of their whole-grain counterparts.

Scientists have also uncovered a whole host of health benefits from whole-grain consumption. Whole grains, which provide vitamins such as folacin and vitamin E; minerals such as selenium and magnesium; phytochemicals such as phytosterols and lignans; and fiber, have been implicated as strong allies in the fight against a number of chronic diseases. Some of these diseases include certain cancers, such as cancer of the colon and rectum, as well as heart disease.

Not too long ago, oats made headlines as protectors against heart disease. As a result, foods containing oats, whole oats, and whole oat flour began to flood the market with brightly colored labels claiming that eating these foods "may reduce heart disease risk." The Food and Drug Administration (FDA), a government "watch dog" that regulates health claims on food labels, researched these purported promises. The FDA, after examining studies involving soluble fiber and heart disease, approved that foods rich in whole oats can be deemed as heart-healthy, so long as they contain at least 0.75 grams of soluble fiber per serving (a daily intake of at least 3 grams of soluble fiber has been shown to lower high blood cholesterol levels). The labels must also be worded in a way that indicates the importance of a low-saturated-fat intake in addition to whole oats in the diet.

Whole oats are not the only grains associated with a reduced risk of heart disease. In a recent study from the University of Minnesota, women between the ages of fifty-five and sixty-nine who ate at least three servings of whole grains in general per day over a nine-year period were 30 percent less likely to die of a heart attack than women who ate less than one serving of whole grains per day.

What makes whole grains a heart-disease preventive? The answer isn't yet clear but probably involves a number of factors: more vitamins and minerals, more fiber, and more phytochemicals, including phenolic compounds like flavonoids and coumarins; glucarates, carotenoids, terpenes, phytic acid, and phytoestrogens.

The fiber in whole grains has disease-fighting properties, too. Diets rich in fiber have been linked to lower incidences of colon and rectal cancer, in particular. Scientists suspect that fiber fights cancer because it "dilutes" potentially carcinogenic substances in the colon with bulk, and it also moves these substances through the body more quickly, allowing the body less time to absorb them.

The good health of people living in the Mediterranean and eating a traditional Mediterranean diet is certainly due, in part, to the heavy consumption of whole grains. Mediterranean breads are typically (though not always) dense, hearty, and heavy, with the nutty, chewy texture of whole-grain wheat and other grains. Many other traditional Mediterranean ingredients, from the stone-ground cornmeal used to make Italian polenta to the fluffy millet so popular in North African meals, consist of grains never subjected to the refining process. Refining grain products does make them last longer, and makes them somewhat lower in total fat. The germ, which contains oil, is removed so the grain will become rancid far less quickly (oil becomes rancid, or decomposes, relatively quickly, and will last longer when refrigerated and not exposed to light). However, the germ in whole grains is an important source of vitamin E and other important nutrients, and shouldn't be left out of the diet.

☉ GO WITH THE GRAIN

While most whole grains have been used to some extent in the Mediterranean, some are more well known than others. Some of the most beloved and most nutritious grains in the traditional Mediterranean diet were wheat in its many forms, from the pale yellow, hard-wheat semolina used to make pasta to the hearty bulgur wheat used to make tabouli; stone-ground corn for polenta; and rice in its many forms, from arborio rice for risotto to yellow (from added saffron) Spanish rice.

These grains aren't the only choices today, however, as food production makes grains from all over the world available in the United States. Eating a variety of grains is the best way to assure plenty of soluble and insoluble fiber, vitamins, minerals, and phytochemicals. The high-nutrient, high-fiber grains commonly available today in health food and natural food stores include:

- **Amaranth.** This grain, revered by the ancient Aztecs, is high in protein, vitamins, and minerals, and contains lysine, an amino acid many grains lack. You can buy whole amaranth grains or find amaranth in grain products, such as breads and pastas. Amaranth makes a flavorful hot cereal or an interesting side dish when mixed with other grains, such as cornmeal.

- **Barley.** Many people have only encountered barley in its traditional American manifestation, as a traditional part of vegetable beef soup. Barley is delicious in many other forms as well: for breakfast, as a dinner accompaniment, in soups, salads, or combined with other grains. Pearl barley is the refined barley. It keeps longer but has less nutritional value. Scotch or pot barley is more nutritious and contains fiber.

- **Buckwheat.** This grain is featured in the cuisines of many countries. Kasha, a traditional Russian form of buckwheat commonly available, may not be Mediterranean, but it is delicious, nutty, filling, and satisfying.

- **Cornmeal.** Stone-ground cornmeal is the whole-grain variety and it makes a fine, hearty polenta, that dish beloved in Italy and just as delicious in the United States today. The version popular in the southern United States is better known as grits. Either way, the whole-grain cornmeal contains fiber and has lots of minerals and vitamins.

- **Millet.** This African grain is more often seen in this country in birdseed mixes, but why should we let the birds get all the great nutrition? Millet is delicious as a hot cereal or mixed with olive oil, garlic, and grated cheese as a hearty side dish to a main meal.
- **Oats.** Who doesn't love a warm bowl of oatmeal on a cold morning? Whole-grain oats are full of soluble fiber, and they taste delicious on their own or combined with other grains in baked goods. Process oatmeal in your blender to make oat flour and substitute it for half the wheat flour in baking. For best nutrition, avoid processed instant or "quick-cooking" oats, especially those that are preflavored and sugared.
- **Quinoa.** This traditional South American grain is high in protein and minerals, cooks quickly, and is a delicious substitute for rice or bulgur. Combined with nuts, it makes a hearty snack or alluring side dish.
- **Rice.** Brown rice is higher in fiber, vitamins, minerals, and phytochemicals than white rice. It has a nuttier, richer taste. White rice cooks more quickly and lasts longer in the pantry, but as with all refined grains, contains fewer nutrients and fiber. Rice combines well with many foods: tomatoes, beans, vegetables, nuts, herbs and spices, seeds, even dried fruit. Spanish rice is highly spiced with tomatoes, green peppers, garlic, and hot pepper; paella, another Spanish dish, consists of rice flavored with chicken or other meat, tomatoes, legumes, vegetables, and sometimes shellfish. Risotto is an Italian dish in which rice—Italian rice like arborio or medium-grained rice work best—is cooked with oil, stock, white wine, and Parmesan cheese (there exist numerous variations) to create a rich, tender, creamy dinner course.

- **Wheat.** This most ubiquitous of grains is highly versatile and present in virtually every cuisine worldwide. Notably, wheat was originally a Mediterranean grain. Perfectly suited for making bread, wheat is also available in numerous other forms: Wheat berries, cracked wheat, couscous and other semolina-based pastas, wheat germ, and bulgur wheat are a few. As mentioned previously, whole wheat contains the bran, germ, and endosperm and is full of vitamins, protein, minerals, phytochemicals, and fiber. Whenever possible, choose whole-wheat and sprouted-wheat products to get the maximum benefit. Wheat is one of the most fiber-rich of the grains, so enjoy it often—something easy to do in the United States, where wheat dominates the grain market.

✇ FULL OF BEANS

Whether you love beans or fear their aftereffects, they are undeniably a rich source of protein, fiber, minerals, vitamins like folate, and phytochemicals like flavonoids. Beans are just one type of legume, a category that also includes peas and lentils. For thousands of years all over the world, people have relied on legumes for survival. They are low in calories, high in nutrition, and much less expensive than meat. They are also delicious and extremely versatile, adding flavor and interest to an astounding variety of foods. Whether you prefer dry or canned, plain or fancy, try to include legumes in your daily diet or at the minimum, three times per week. Legumes come in many shapes and sizes. Follow package directions for cooking instructions. If you are a beginner and a bit bean-wary, order some bean-based dishes in restaurants first. You'll know a professional is preparing them. Try beans in your own homemade soups, on salads, in casseroles, rolled in tortillas, tossed with stubby pasta, or mixed with rice.

Mediterranean or not, include a variety of legumes for a diet in the Mediterranean spirit, such as black beans, black-eyed peas, cannellini beans, chickpeas, cranberry beans, fava beans, flageolets, great northern beans, lentils, lima beans, navy beans, peas, pink beans, pinto beans, red kidney beans, red beans, and split peas.

⊛ NUTS (AND SEEDS) TO YOU

Nuts and seeds are loaded with nutrition, and no healthy diet should be without them. High in fiber, phytochemicals, protein, vitamins, and minerals, these antioxidant-rich food sources are as healthy as any other Mediterranean-featured plant food. How can that be when they are so high in fat? Remember, nuts are low in saturated fat, and include fats more conducive to heart health, such as monounsaturated fat and omega-3 fatty acids (a type of polyunsaturated fat). Mono-unsaturated fat, the fat featured in olive oil, tends to lower your LDL ("bad") cholesterol without affecting your HDL ("good") cholesterol levels, thereby keeping your total blood cholesterol levels in check and reducing your risk of heart disease. The omega-3s have also been linked to healthy hearts, as well as to a decreased risk of certain cancers and other diseases.

Recent studies have shown the beneficial effects of nut consumption in particular in the fight against heart disease. A highly regarded study from Boston's Brigham and Women's Hospital (BWH), called the Nurses' Health Study, showed that "women who ate at least 5 ounces of nuts per week reduced their risk for coronary heart disease by 35 percent compared to women who ate less than 1 ounce per month." Similar results may soon appear for men from an equally famous study, the Physicians' Health Study (also based out of BWH in Boston). In the DELTA (Dietary Effects on Lipoproteins and Thrombogenic Activity) study, which was funded by the Heart, Lung, and Blood Institute, participants who ate a diet with nuts being a primary source of the total fat calories substantially lowered their "bad" LDL cholesterol levels when switching from a high-fat typical American diet to a lower-fat diet that was rich in nuts.

In addition to diseases of the heart (which include coronary heart disease and congestive heart failure), the healthy fat content of nuts and seeds, as well as the fiber, phytochemical, and antioxidants they contain, have many researchers looking at the role of these foods in decreasing the incidence of other chronic diseases, such as certain cancers (like breast cancer), diabetes, stroke, and renal failure.

Unfortunately, many Americans avoid nuts and seeds, fearing that the fats in these nutritious foods will cause weight gain. Indeed, most nuts and seeds are sources of fat (as mentioned above), and therefore calories. But there have been many intriguing studies showing how frequent nut consumption will not necessarily lead to weight gain. In a large study involving more than 34,000 Seventh Day Adventists in California, those who ate nuts at least five times a week had lower body weights than the rest of the group. Another study looking at 508 people living in Reno, Nevada, also showed that frequent nut eaters kept their weights within a desirable range. While this does not suggest that eating nuts will keep us thin, it helps to support the argument that nut (as well as seed) consumption is not a one-way ticket to obesity. (Some study subjects actually lost weight after adding nuts to their diet.) Researchers speculated that those who eat nuts tend to be more conscious about their health. Those benefits, of course, were rendered from the "fresh" nut, or nuts that have not been processed in hydrogenated oils.

Indeed, eating any food to any large degree (especially if you don't substitute a certain food calorie for another) will cause weight gain. But although most nuts and seeds contain their fair share of fat and calories, they should not be condemned. If you follow the recommendations of this book, nut and seed consumption is listed in the daily food section in moderate amounts (to be adjusted for individual caloric needs). Meats, higher-fat dairy, and other high-saturated-fat foods have been pushed farther up on the pyramid, to be consumed on a weekly or monthly (if at all) basis, depending on their level of saturated fat. For many, these higher-saturated-fat foods will therefore be consumed less frequently, leaving calories to be replaced with nuts and seeds.

Let's look at the numbers. In an ounce of almonds, which is about twenty-four nuts, you've got roughly 165 calories. Alternatively, eat an ounce of potato chips, and you've comparably consumed about 155 calories. And which of these two foods is far more beneficial for your health? No question, the almonds! You may find that eating the almonds is a lot more satisfying than eating the chips, since the nuts contain a lot more fiber and feel more "wholesome" than the processed snack item. Hence, you may feel less compelled to keep on snacking, saving you even more calories in the long run. And some research has even indicated that the high fiber content found in nuts, as well as seeds, may prevent all the calories and fat in nuts and seeds from being absorbed anyway.

For another example, let's look at a breakfast. Instead of eating two strips of bacon (which contain about 100 calories and 8 grams of total fat), mix about ½ ounce of almonds (about twelve nuts) into your whole-grain cereal for 83 calories, 7.5 grams of fat. The numbers compare, and tossing ready-made almonds into your cereal is a lot more convenient than having to cook that greasy bacon. The almonds are much higher in monounsaturated fat, while the bacon is heavy on saturated fat. You may also find you are more satisfied with the almonds throughout the morning. See the following Questions and Answers section for a list of common nuts and seeds, and their fat and calorie breakdown. Substituting nuts and seeds for other less healthy foods has been done in some controlled studies, with the results proving positive, especially, again, in the realm of heart disease prevention. A study published in the *New England Journal of Medicine* found that when walnuts replaced 20 percent of the calories in the diet of one group (the walnut diet was adjusted to include lesser amounts of other fatty foods), total cholesterol levels went down and LDL-HDL cholesterol ratios improved. The study concluded that "incorporating moderate quantities of walnuts into the recommended cholesterol-lowering diet while maintaining the intake of total dietary fat and calories decreases serum levels of total cholesterol and favorably modifies the lipoprotein profile in normal men." The walnut, not incidentally, has been a part of the Mediterranean diet for thousands of years.

Whether the grains, legumes, nuts, and seeds you choose to form the bulk of your diet are those of the traditional Mediterranean diet or not, enjoy these most gratifying foods and reap their nutritional benefits daily. These foods are an endless source of interesting recipes and make filling, deeply satisfying comfort food. Some of the recipes in this book containing walnuts and beans are adapted from recipes provided by the Walnut Marketing Board in Sacramento, California, and the Bean Education and Awareness Network in Chicago.

⊘ QUESTIONS AND ANSWERS

ℬ *Fresh whole-grain bread sounds great, but I don't have time to make it at home. Any suggestions?*

Many bakeries and even grocery stores bake delicious whole-grain breads that can be purchased fresh each day. Also, consider buying a bread machine. These machines make homemade bread a breeze, and they have the added benefit of filling your home with the aroma of baking bread.

Just pour in the ingredients, press a button, and the machine does the rest. Fresh bread in a few hours!

When time does permit—a free weekend afternoon, for example—try baking your own bread by hand. Few things are more relaxing and rejuvenating than mixing, stirring, kneading, pounding down, kneading again, forming, and baking your own bread. It can be a fun-filled family activity, and good exercise, too!

❧ What if I don't like whole-grain products?

Like olive oil, whole-grain products can be an acquired taste, especially if you are accustomed to refined-grain products. Whole-wheat bread is usually an easy switch. It is more flavorful with a more interesting texture than white bread. Kids raised on whole-grain bread don't think much of the mushy white stuff, either. Whole-grain pastas, tortillas, and cereals are a harder sell for some, although others like them immediately.

Don't worry about transforming every single grain product in your diet to whole grain, especially right away. Make the steps gradually. The more you become acquainted with the interesting flavors and textures of different whole grains, the more willing to experiment you may become. But don't force yourself to eat something you don't like. Maybe for now, only white spaghetti will do, but perhaps you don't mind the nutty flavor of brown rice. Just keep an open mind. Eventually you may find yourself purchasing buckwheat groats for breakfast, sprouted-wheat pita bread stuffed with falafel for lunch, and amaranth vermicelli for dinner!

❧ What are additional ways to get more fiber into my diet?

One convenient way for Americans to add fiber to their diets is to eat a serving of whole-grain cereal every morning. If you like hot cereal, choose old-fashioned or steel-cut oats rather than instant. When purchasing cold cereals, check the labels and choose varieties with higher fiber content. Some brands now include omega-3–rich flaxseed! If you are a toast lover, choose from the wide variety of delicious whole-grain breads (preferably those that do not contain hydrogenated oils) and bagels. Make pancakes or waffles with whole wheat or oat flour for a change, or buy whole-grain, frozen waffles, served with a handful of walnuts and a dollop of applesauce, yogurt, fruit, real maple syrup, or honey.

For lunch, choose whole-grain bread for your sandwich, or toss some beans or chickpeas and a handful of sunflower seeds onto your salad. Choose a bean-based soup with rice or pasta.

For dinner, choose brown rice and experiment with different types of whole-grain pastas. Whenever possible, eat your fruits and veggies raw and chew them well (chopping and cooking can modify the fiber content of some foods). Wash produce well so you needn't discard the edible peels, often rich sources of fiber. Substitute beans in your meal for meat at least twice a week, and begin replacing half the white flour in cooking and baking with whole-wheat or other whole-grain flour. And don't forget to snack on high fiber items, such as plain or lightly salted popcorn, nuts, seeds, or whole-wheat bread sticks.

✿ How much fiber is required for a food to be labeled "high fiber"?

The nutritional information on packaged food will list that food's fiber content. However, any food labeled "high fiber" must contain at least 5 grams of fiber per serving. If the label says a food is a "good source" of fiber, that food must contain between 2.5 and 4.9 grams of fiber per serving. "More fiber" or "added fiber" means the food contains at least 2.5 grams per serving more than a serving of the traditional version of that food. Remember, the goal is to consume about 25 to 35 grams of total fiber per day.

✀ Will too much fiber cause digestive problems?

A sudden increase in fiber intake can cause temporary digestive problems such as flatulence and stomach cramps. Instead, increase your fiber intake gradually, giving your body a chance to adjust. First switch to whole-wheat bread. A week later, choose a whole-grain cereal. A week after that, add more raw vegetables. And so on.

Legumes are notorious for their gas-producing quality. However, discarding the water in which you've soaked dried beans and cooking the beans in fresh water can significantly lower the gas-producing effect of beans. If you prefer the convenience of canned beans, rinse them well before cooking and eating (this step will also minimize the high sodium content of some canned beans). For some, smaller portions take care of the problem.

If you do notice unpleasant digestive effects from an increased fiber intake, cut back just a little until your body doesn't seem to notice, then increase again, gradually. If you are willing simply to ride out the effects, they won't last long. Once your body adjusts to your healthier, fiber-rich diet, you shouldn't notice any ill effects. Special enzyme additives can decrease the flatulent effect of beans, too. For painful gas problems, several over-the-counter remedies are available (but if pain persists, please see your doctor).

Exceptionally high intake of fiber (over 50 to 60 grams daily) has been shown to cause serious intestinal problems when the fiber is taken as a supplement rather than received through the consumption of natural, whole-grain foods like bread, pasta, and cereal. We recommend you receive your fiber through your diet, not through supplements, fiber powders, or fiber pills. Also, people with certain digestive diseases may need to limit fiber intake or consume fiber in specific ways. If fiber is a problem for you because of a health problem, contact a registered dietitian to help you work fiber into your diet.

❧ What is the best way to soak dried beans for cooking?

To minimize gas content, soak dried beans in room-temperature water in a large container (the beans will approximately triple in size) for at least four hours, or put them in soaking water before you go to bed at night, then cook them the next day. When you are ready to cook them, drain off the soaking water and boil them in fresh water until they are fork-tender. Don't add salt or any acidic foods like vinegar or tomato products until the very end of cooking time. These will hinder the beans from becoming tender. A dash of olive oil will keep the bean water from foaming.

If you don't have time to soak the beans for four hours and cook for another few, boil water, remove from the heat, and soak the beans in the hot water for one to four hours, then cook. Or use canned beans. They are as nutritious as dry beans, although they are typically softer and, some say, less flavorful. Rinse canned beans well before use.

❧ Are garbanzo beans and chickpeas the same thing?

Yes.

❧ What is the fat and caloric content of the more common nuts and seeds?

While most nuts and seeds contain their fair share of fat, and therefore calories, the fat that they contain is principally the beneficial monounsaturated kind. Nuts and seeds also contain omega-3 fatty acids. Both monounsaturated fat and omega-3 fatty acids have been shown to help guard against many chronic diseases, such as heart disease and cancer.

The chestnut is one nut that is actually a low-fat food. In an ounce of roasted European chestnuts (which is about three and a half nuts), there is only 0.6 grams of total fat, 0.1 grams of saturated fat, and 70 calories. The chestnut is definitely a food for indulgence (within reason, of course) during the holidays, or beyond, if you can find them in your local market.

Other popular types of nuts and seeds with their fat and calorie content are noted below.

Nut or Seed (1-ounce serving)	Total Fat (g)	Saturated Fat (g)	Calories
Almonds (24)	15	1	165
Cashews, dry roasted (about 18)	13	2.6	165
Chestnut, European, roasted (3½)	0.6	0.1	70
Peanuts, dry roasted (about 36)	14	2	160
Pecans, dried (31 large)	19	1.5	190
Pistachios, dried (47)	14	1.5	165
Sesame seeds, whole, toasted	13.5	2	160
Sunflower seeds / kernels, dried	14	1.5	160

Note in the preceding chart that an ounce of most nuts and seeds can actually be quite plentiful. For example, 1 ounce of peanuts is thirty-six nuts, 1 ounce of pecans is thirty-one large nuts, and 1 ounce of pistachios is forty-seven nuts. That's quite a snack! The Mediterranean Diet Pyramid recommends eating a variety of nuts and seeds to be consumed throughout the day to equal about 1 ounce or so daily. Another way of getting nuts is through nut spreads such as peanut butter or almond butter that do not contain added hydrogenated oils (or trans-fatty acids), sugars, or other fillers. Two tablespoons of a nut spread equals 1 ounce.

7: Meat, Poultry, Fish, Dairy, and Egg Consumption the Mediterranean Way

The chapter that might, in many books about dietary considerations, be a book's centerpiece is put nearly last in this book—not because we don't like meat and dairy products, but because they were, in comparison to plant foods, of so little importance in the traditional Mediterranean diet. That's not to say people in the Mediterranean don't eat meat. They always have, and many of the most well-known and beloved Mediterranean recipes contain meat. However, the traditional Mediterranean diet is a near-vegetarian diet.

Near vegetarian? Sure! In a culture accustomed to a large slab of beef on the center of a dinner plate surrounded by a few paltry servings of vegetables, the term makes sense. In the traditional Mediterranean diet, beef, as well as veal, pork, fish, poultry, and rich dairy products like cheese, was more often used for flavoring rather than as the main event of a meal.

Nestled in a large platter of rice and vegetables, one might find a few small pieces of chicken or shrimp. A prodigious pot of pasta sauce might contain a few clams, some prosciutto, or perhaps some ground meat. Occasionally a whole

fish poached with vegetables and herbs will form the core of
a meal, and various types of shellfish are present in small
quantities in the diets of most Mediterranean countries. A
Turkish or Greek shish kebab typically includes cubes of
skewered lamb, but plenty of vegetables, too.

Eating some meat and dairy products certainly makes
good sense. High in nutrients, including certain vitamins
and minerals, meat and dairy products also add depth, di-
mension, and flavor to plant foods. Even red meat can be a
sensible part of a healthy diet, if the cuts of meat are lean
and the portions small, especially for high-fat meat and full-
fat dairy products, which contain high amounts of saturated
fat. Eating these foods in moderation is ideal because it
guarantees you the nutritional benefits of these animal foods
without the excess saturated fat, not to mention excess calories. Pushing animal foods to the side of the plate leaves
room for the highly beneficial plant foods we've been discussing throughout this book.

The Mediterranean Diet Pyramid illustrates how animal
foods can fit into a healthful Mediterranean-inspired diet. In
addition to fish (weekly consumption is recommended), you
can choose a serving of another source of lean meat about
once a week, if desired. Serving sizes are specified in a general range of 1 to 4 ounces on the Mediterranean Diet Pyramid, to be individualized according to dietary needs.
Remember, you needn't consume your entire week's allowance of fish, lean beef, chicken, veal, or whatever you
choose at one sitting. An ounce chopped and added to soup
one day, another ounce or two added to rice or pasta a few
days later, and a few more ounces in a casserole at the end of
the week is probably a more authentically Mediterranean
way to eat animal foods anyway. The same goes for
cheese—a few shreds here, a sprinkling there. A little high-
fat cheese, which is highly flavored, goes a long way. Although the Mediterranean Diet Pyramid specifies lower-fat
cheeses (such as mozzarella made with part-skim milk) be

consumed optionally on a weekly basis or high-fat cheese be consumed monthly (also optional), that month's serving can easily be portioned out over a number of satisfying meals.

Try to choose the animal products listed closer to the base of the pyramid more often than those listed higher—fish more than chicken, lean white-meat chicken more than lean beef, and so on. These animal meats are arranged by their saturated-fat content; the farther up they are listed, the more saturated fat they contain. The same goes for dairy products: High-fat dairy products, such as high-fat cheeses, butter, and so on, sit at the top of the pyramid, while lower-fat cheeses are listed within the weekly section. (We placed the lower-fat cheeses as an optional weekly treat because cheese was very much a part of the traditional Mediterranean cuisine, usually in smaller amounts per serving than typically seen in the United States today). Low-fat or nonfat dairy products are listed in the daily echelon of the Mediterranean Diet Pyramid—a great way to keep your daily protein and calcium intake at a satisfactory level.

Fish is the one animal meat we recommend consuming more than Americans are generally getting—up to 8 ounces of cooked fish per week—especially the fattier fishes like salmon, mackerel, trout, herring, and tuna. Fish contains omega-3 fatty acids that offer many health benefits (more on omega-3 fatty acids later in this chapter). If you choose to avoid fish because of concerns for possible contaminants, that's fine. Our fish recommendation is optional. Just be sure to include other sources of omega-3 fatty acids such as flaxseed, walnuts, and even strawberries.

And what about eggs, those high-cholesterol villains we all thought we knew to avoid? Actually, as we've mentioned before, dietary cholesterol isn't a threat to the heart health of most people. There are indeed some who are particularly sensitive to dietary cholesterol, usually a genetic condition. Consult your physician if you think this might be you. It is saturated fat, as we've mentioned throughout this book, that has been clearly linked to a higher risk of heart disease. Egg yolks do contain some saturated fat, which is the main reason that we generally suggest a moderate intake of four or fewer eggs per week (including eggs used in cooking). By the way, the egg white is virtually cholesterol- and fat-free, so indulge at will in this high-protein portion of the egg.

⌘ THE VEGETARIAN MEDITERRANEAN

Typically, the traditional Mediterranean was not a land of vegetarians. But what if you aren't particularly fond of meat, or eggs, or even dairy products? Perhaps you are a vegetarian and don't think the Mediterranean Diet Pyramid could be relevant for you. Please don't read our recommendations for animal products as a requirement. You needn't eat meat or eggs at all, especially if you are diligent about following the recommendations in the daily section of the Mediterranean Diet Pyramid. This level contains no meat or eggs. While a little animal meat or egg can go a long way, nutritionally speaking, and while fish certainly has demonstrated health benefits, none is a necessity in a healthy diet.

Probably the question vegetarians hear the most is: "How do you get enough protein?" You may have even thought the same thing when surveying the Mediterranean Diet Pyramid. Meat just once a week? How could that be enough? What about protein?

Actually, most Americans consume much more protein than their bodies need—about 90 grams of protein each day, mostly from meat and processed meat. The average man typically needs only about 60 grams of protein per day, the average woman about 50 grams. Because saturated fat can be high in animal food sources, plant-based protein sources, although often less protein-dense, may be a healthier protein source. Getting enough protein takes little effort for the average adult (pregnant and breastfeeding women need slightly more). Breakfast alone can knock off a third or more of this requirement: ¾ cup of oatmeal (dry) mixed with 1½ cups of low-fat soy milk (to be cooked), then topped with ½ ounce of nuts and a cup of strawberries comes to about 25 grams of protein.

Come lunchtime, a green salad with 1 tablespoon sunflower seeds and ½ cup garbanzo beans, 2 cups of hearty lentil soup, a whole-wheat roll, and a cup of nonfat plain yogurt mixed with fresh fruit comes to about 25 grams. For dinner, try 2 cups whole-wheat pasta topped with mushrooms, artichoke hearts, broccoli, green and red peppers, tomato sauce with Italian seasonings, ½ cup white beans, and 1 tablespoon of toasted walnut pieces; with a baked apple for dessert, the protein adds up to about 30 grams (or more, depending on the amount of vegetables—cooked vegetables contain roughly 3 grams of protein per ½ cup). This meal rounds out the total to a more than satisfactory 80 grams of protein. And what do you know—no meat or dairy!

And that's just one day! So you see, even if you choose not to eat meat despite the minor presence of meat in the traditional Mediterranean diet, you will still be consuming a heart-healthy, nutrient-dense diet. Of course, this book is specifically about the eating patterns of the traditional Mediterranean region, and these include a wide and fascinating variety of plant foods, as well as animal foods in small quantities sufficient to provide enough protein for the entire family, so vegetarians, please feel free simply to adapt the principles and recipes to your own taste. We won't dispute that animal foods offer the most complete source of protein, meaning they include all the amino acids our bodies need. However, protein-rich plant foods in abundance and in a wide variety can do a great job of meeting our amino acid requirements as well.

If you prefer to go completely without meat, eggs, and fish (a vegan diet), you could be at risk for a vitamin B_{12} deficiency. Without enough vitamin B_{12}, you could develop a severe blood disorder called pernicious anemia. Vitamin B_{12} is found mostly in foods of animal origin, most notably in certain fish, such as clams, mackerel, tuna, and shrimp, as well as beef and lamb. Milk and dairy products also contain some vitamin B_{12}, as well as certain fortified cereals (check the labels). Soy milk is a good source of B_{12}. If you consume no foods of animal origin whatsoever, we recommend consultation with a dietitian or other qualified health care professional to ensure adequate vitamin B_{12} intake.

Strict vegetarians may also have difficulty getting enough vitamin B_6 into their diets. The highest sources of this vitamin are certain fish such as bass and salmon. Certain plant foods are also rich in vitamin B_6. If you don't eat meat or fish, be sure to include in your weekly consumption those plant foods containing vitamin B_6, such as chickpeas, whole grains, potatoes, bananas, avocados, and dried figs. Again, consultation with a registered dietitian or other qualified health professional would be beneficial.

Minerals that could be deficient without the consumption of animal protein include zinc and iron. Meat, poultry, and fish are good sources of zinc, but so are whole grains and certain vegetables.

Iron is an essential mineral. Without it, people can develop an iron-deficiency anemia. People experiencing rapid growth stages—children, teenagers, menstruating and pregnant women—are especially in need of iron in their diets.

Iron comes in two forms: heme iron and nonheme iron. Heme iron is found only in animal meats and egg yolks. Nonheme iron is found primarily in plant foods such as whole grains, seeds, nuts, greens, legumes, and dried fruits. Nonheme iron is much less efficiently absorbed. However, the absorption of nonheme iron can be improved when combined with vitamin C or animal food sources containing heme iron.

Although our body needs iron, consuming amounts far above the recommended daily allowance can be dangerous.

Some researchers believe that excessive iron intakes can lead to heart disease, or even cancer, especially in those who are not in need of a lot of iron, such as adult men. The heart disease/iron theory was fueled by results of a 1992 study involving more than two thousand adult males in Finland. The study showed that those men with the highest levels of iron in their blood were more than twice as likely to experience a heart attack as the men with lower levels. There has since been more recent research disputing this claim, but many experts still believe that iron fortification of foods such as bread products should be stopped because of the possible health risks for people who are not in need of large amounts of iron. For now, however, consuming animal meats in moderate amounts will help keep iron, especially the easily absorbable heme iron, at more reasonable levels. For more information on iron, contact your local registered dietitian or other health-care professional.

Vegetarian considerations aside, for those who choose to eat in a manner as close as possible to the traditional Mediterranean diet, foods of animal origin do help to ensure prevention of vitamin and mineral deficiencies. Of course, anyone with special nutrient needs, such as children, teenagers, pregnant women, and lactating women can benefit from the advice of a registered dietitian to assure they are meeting their unique nutritional requirements.

The key is to remember that the traditional Mediterranean diet remains staunchly plant-based, and the ratio of plant foods to animal foods appears to be conducive to good health and longevity. While many aspects of the traditional Mediterranean diet have been implicated in its apparent healthful quality, low animal product consumption may be a significant key to the health benefits of the traditional Mediterranean diet.

Let's look more closely at how these foods fit into a cuisine that cherishes yet hardly relies on them for nutritional support, and how you can mirror the Mediterranean pattern of animal food consumption in your own life by centering your diet around plant foods, then flavoring it with animal foods. Your heart will thank you, and your grocery bill will be lower too!

⊘ MEDITERRANEAN MEAT AND POULTRY

The people in the Mediterranean like to eat meat. Make no bones about it! However, as much as they have always relished meat, people living around the Mediterranean Sea and eating a traditional Mediterranean diet simply don't eat much of it. Meat was expensive and hard to come by. A Mediterranean farmer was likely to have a few chickens and rabbits running around the farmyard, but cattle for beef? Mediterranean diet researcher Ancel Keys may have put it best: "Cows do not thrive where the olive tree flourishes—and vice versa!"

The Mediterranean landscape is particularly unsuited to grazing cattle into adulthood. The required pastureland simply isn't there, so the Mediterranean doesn't produce much dairy or beef cattle. Instead, cattle are slaughtered when young (veal) and, not inconsequentially, far lower in fat. In the traditional Mediterranean diet, veal, as well as lamb, were more common offerings than beef.

But even veal and lamb aren't present at every meal. What an expense that would be! In contrast, in the United States, beef is the most beloved meat (although red meat consumption has declined in recent years). Pork and chicken are also popular.

Poultry and game were also a part of the traditional Mediterranean diet, but again, quantities were small and a meal centered around poultry was rare. Wild rabbits and wild game birds such as wild geese and ducks, pheasant, and quail often provided flavoring for the soup pot. Game tends to be lower in fat than domesticated animal meat (see the Questions and Answers section for more on game meat). Wild rabbit is low in fat, with only 3 grams of fat per 3-ounce cooked serving. Domesticated rabbits can be high in fat, however—up to 8 grams of fat per 3-ounce cooked serving.

When meat is prepared as the center of a meal in the Mediterranean, it is often because of a holiday or celebration. Veal shanks braised with vegetables and served with risotto comprises the much beloved dish the Italians call osso bucco. Roast lamb, whether sliced and highly spiced or skewered and marinated, is the ultimate treat in Greece, and in many Mediterranean areas in North Africa.

In many other well-known Mediterranean dishes, meat enhances but doesn't dominate the flavor. Ground lamb flavors many Greek dishes such as moussaka or the stuffed grape leaves called dolmathes. Meatballs and other appetizers made with chorizo sausage are popular in Spain. Sausages of all flavors and containing different types of meat are available in most Mediterranean countries but are eaten in small quantities—their high salt and spice content made them a good way to preserve meat in the warm Mediterranean climate. Simmered with fava beans, sliced and baked with eggs and tomatoes, chopped and tossed into paella, dense and highly seasoned handmade sausages give many Mediterranean dishes their distinctive character.

Even when meat dominates a Mediterranean recipe, it is well surrounded by plant foods of all types. All the Mediterranean countries include meat, poultry, and seafood in their own versions of stews, soups, and casseroles, but these same dishes are brimming with juicy, fresh vegetables and tender grains. Meat is cooked with vegetables, roasted with olives, served alongside pasta, pilafs, and couscous, or variously sliced, skewered, ground, chopped, or cubed into salads. Meat can be found in risotto, legume-based baked dishes, mounds of fresh steaming pasta, or fancifully crafted appetizers, from Italian antipasti to Moroccan meze, that are as beautiful to behold as they are delicious to eat.

One last note about meat and the food pyramids we have discussed throughout this book: You may have noticed that the USDA Food Guide Pyramid includes fish, legumes, eggs, and nuts in the "meat" group. The Mediterranean Diet Pyramid doesn't. Instead, we suggest that lean meat, poultry, eggs, and fish be consumed weekly, while nuts, seeds, and legumes be consumed daily. Meat's higher fat and cholesterol content make it a better occasional choice—a weekly treat, or a semiweekly flavoring element for plant foods. With daily plant protein sources—legumes, nuts, seeds—you get the added benefits of fiber and phytochemicals.

⑦ PHASING OUT MEAT MAIN-COURSE MENTALITY

Much as you would like to eat a more plant-based diet, you may find it difficult to do. The United States is firmly entrenched in meat main-course mentality. Many of us retain that deep-down feeling that meat simply must be an important part of a healthy diet. Restaurants cater to this impulse by serving primarily meat-based entrées (although this is slowly changing, especially in ethnic and gourmet restaurants or restaurants with a health-conscious philosophy). When some restaurants do serve a meatless entrée, drowning the entrée's grains or vegetables in high-fat cheese sauces or mounds of melted shredded cheese often "compensates" for the lack of meat (as if a creative use of plant foods required any compensation). Striving to eat in the Mediterranean style certainly doesn't mean shunning animal products for the rest of your life, but it doesn't mean drowning your vegetables in them, either. Eating Mediterranean means including a wide variety of animal products in your diet, but decreasing their importance and frequency of occurrence on your plate.

Shifting to a plant-based diet isn't difficult, it just takes a little creativity. You may also find it easier to limit your consumption of meat if you know meat isn't forbidden. You can still enjoy meat (meaning beef, pork, veal, lamb, and poultry—we'll talk about fish separately) while you focus on an enjoyment and exploration of plant foods as your primary dietary objective. Following are some tips to help you gradually shift that focus, while shifting that piece of meat to the perimeter of your plate.

1. Begin planning your meals for the week. If you don't plan, you may be more likely to fall back on habit and rely on convenience or fast foods, many of which can be high in fatty meats, cheese, and refined-grain products. Planning ahead allows you to shop sensibly and it also cuts down on the hassle of trying to figure out what to make each night when everyone is hungry and wants to eat five minutes ago.

2. When planning, begin by allowing for four or five meals per week that include some meat (this can be further decreased later), but only one where meat is the center focus—for instance, a pork roast or sirloin steaks. Other choices could include meat but not emphasize it. Instead of beef burritos, use half the meat and stuff those tortillas with nonfat refried beans. Instead of fried chicken, chop some chicken and stir it, along with plenty of chopped vegetables, into yellow rice.

3. Each week, choose one piece of meat from the meat department and consider it a challenge to your creativity to make it last all week. You'll be more inclined to use small amounts to make the meat last. A roast can be served with potatoes and

salad one night, and leftovers can be cooked into rice, tossed with pasta, shredded over salad, and stirred into soup for the rest of the week. A little goes a long way. A package of lean ground beef or some skinless chicken breast can easily last all week when they make up a small component of the main course.

4. After a few weeks, you can begin to reduce the amount of meat in recipes even more. Aim for red meat as a flavoring element in a recipe once a week, poultry on another night, and fish on another night or two. Many Mediterranean-inspired recipes are conducive to such an effort. A Spanish paella varies from cook to cook in the Mediterranean, so why not experiment with your own versions? A few ounces of cooked chicken or lean turkey sausage and a few pieces of fish or chopped shrimp flavor a huge pot of yellow rice and vegetables. Sauce for pasta, eggplant moussaka, or other casseroles need contain no more than a few ounces of ground meat. Just a handful of any type of chopped meat is enough to enrich a soup brimming with vegetables and potatoes or pasta.

5. Experiment with substituting seafood or tofu where you would normally use meat or poultry. Shrimp, chunks of fish, or scallops are delicious with rice, stir-fried with vegetables, or tossed into a pot of soup. A grilled or baked (not deep fat-fried!) fish sandwich is a tasty alternative to the pervasive cheeseburger, and cooked shrimp or crab adds flavor and interest to salads.

6. Keep experimenting with nonmeat dinners like pastas with sautéed vegetables, rice casseroles, vegetable pizzas and calzones, flavored polentas and risotto, and salads of all types—chopped vegetable salad, bread salad, rice salad, bean salad,

bulgur salad, lentil salad, pasta salad, lightly dressed greens and citrus fruits, tomato salad with olive oil and feta cheese—the possibilities are endless.

7. Buy most of your groceries from the produce sections of your supermarket aisles. Eventually you may not even notice those brightly lit bins of cellophane-wrapped meat.

8. Get in the habit of shopping at farmer's markets or local produce stands when possible, stopping at the supermarket for staples only.

9. Finally, reserve the large pieces of roasted meat for holidays and special occasions. Turkey is a great low-fat food when eaten in moderation without the skin. The white meat is the lowest in fat. If your holiday traditions include a beef roast, pork roast, roast lamb, or even a roast goose, you will still be eating in the Mediterranean spirit, where roasted meats were cherished as a feature of special celebrations. Have a small portion, enjoy it, but get most of your calories from the plant-based side dishes.

10. Once you start to eat in a more plant-centered mode, you may find you don't miss meat much at all. At least, we've found this to be true in our own experience. A meal full of interesting plant-based dishes can be much more fun and enjoyable to eat than a plate of meat.

⊛ THE BOUNTIFUL MEDITERRANEAN SEA

Seafood, in contrast to meat, has been and continues to be far more popular in the Mediterranean than in the United States. Certainly, part of this has to do with the omnipresence of the Mediterranean Sea. Fish, especially small fish, and shellfish were readily available, fresh, and inexpensive. Of course they would represent a major source of protein for Mediterranean countries.

Every Mediterranean country uses seafood pervasively in its cuisine. Fish soup alone is a feature of almost every Mediterranean country: Called zarzuela de pescado in Spain, soupe de poissons in France, cioppino in Italy, and psarosoupa in Greece, all typically contain, along with a variety of fish, plenty of vegetables and a dash of olive oil. Baked fish is a feature of the Mediterranean as well, and each country has its additional seafood specialties. Along the Mediterranean coast of Spain, paella, studded with shellfish such as shrimp, scallops, and mussels, is a tradition and one of the hallmarks of Spanish cuisine. In France, bouillabaisse is the definitive seafood stew. Shellfish such as scallops cooked in olive oil and lightly dressed in a butter-garlic sauce are a delicacy, and a perfectly poached fish is a matter of pride in a French kitchen.

In Italy, risotto is often flavored with clams, shrimp, or squid. Swordfish may be served with pine nuts and dried fruit or baked with capers and olives. In the Middle East, fish may be served with any number of highly flavored sauces. Greek meals may begin with an appetizer of marinated octopus, and the main meal is more likely to include fish, often baked with vegetables and flavored with olive oil and lemons, than meat. Fish stuffed with spiced rice and baked or flavored with a seasoned charmoula marinade, then skewered and grilled, is a coastal Moroccan specialty.

In the United States, however, especially in the landlocked center, really good, fresh fish is much harder to come by, and many of the types of fish common in the Mediterranean are virtually unheard of in this country. However, we have many fresh fish and shellfish species of our own. The fresher, the better, and more Mediterranean in character. One need not eat a native Mediterranean fish to eat in the

Mediterranean style. Many easily available fish and shellfish species work well in traditional Mediterranean recipes.

Try salmon, snapper, haddock, halibut, or cod as a substitute for meat in your favorite beef recipes. The lobsters, crab, mussels, and shrimp may be of a different variety in this country than they are in the markets of France, but so what? As we've said many times before, substituting what is locally available and fresh is perfectly compatible with Mediterranean style. Or forget the recipes and go for simplicity: Bake, poach, steam, or grill your fish or shellfish with a little olive oil, then serve with a wedge of lemon.

Americans, in general, can certainly benefit nutritionally by eating more fish. Fish is a low-saturated-fat food, and in general, a low-calorie source of high-quality protein. Many kinds of fatty fish, such as salmon, contain the highly beneficial omega-3 fatty acids we've so often mentioned in past chapters of this book. These fats are most prevalent in fish that frequent the chilly ocean depths. Consumption of salmon, albacore tuna, sardines, mackerel, herring, and bluefish has been linked to lowered heart attack risk.

⊗ HEART-HEALTHY OMEGA-3s

The link between fatty fish consumption and lowered risk of heart disease was first well publicized in the late 1970s, when researchers discovered that the Greenland Eskimos, whose diets were heavy in fish, had extremely low levels of coronary heart disease. Omega-3 fatty acids seem to keep blood from clotting easily and accumulating on artery walls, and may even keep artery walls from hardening. Omega-3 fatty acids also appear to keep the heart pumping on a regular rhythm. (If the rhythm is disrupted, medically termed arrhythmia, a fatal heart attack can occur.) These actions have been linked to lower incidence of heart disease and heart attacks.

The relationship between high consumption of omega-3 fatty acids and lowered heart attack risk didn't end with the Greenland Eskimos. Many studies since, particularly in recent years, have reinforced the theory that fish is good for your heart. One study demonstrated how omega-3s may be even more beneficial to people who have already suffered a heart attack. In a study reported in the *Tufts University Health & Nutrition Letter*, men who had previously suffered a heart attack and were told to eat more fatty fish were 30 percent less likely to die during a two-year period than heart attack victims not told to eat fish. After two years, the fish-eating group had about one-fifth the cardiac deaths as the other group, and only one-third as many nonfatal heart attacks. Another recent study found a 29 percent decrease in overall death during a two-year period in men who ate fatty fish twice each week. Additionally, studies show that fish oil may hinder cardiac arrhythmia, or irregular heartbeats, by stabilizing the heart's muscle cells. Laboratory studies showed that omega-3 fatty acids kept myocardial cells from losing calcium, a mineral they require for normal operation. And other studies have demonstrated time and again that people who eat as little as one meal of fatty fish a week (usually salmon) suffer about half the cardiac arrests as those who don't regularly eat fatty fish.

Indeed, the data surrounding omega-3 intake and heart disease prevention have been compelling, particularly the impressive studies reported since 1999 that show a protective effect in keeping coronary heart disease (CHD) patients from developing further CHD incidents. The data have been so convincing that in January 2003, the American Heart Association officially recommended that patients with documented coronary heart disease should consume about 1 gram of omega-3 fatty acids per day—ideally from food sources such as a 3-ounce serving of fatty fish, such as salmon, herring, trout, or sardines. Those CHD patients who cannot consume 1 gram of omega-3 fatty acids per day through food are advised to take fish oil supplements—the first time ever that the AHA recommended a supplement to be used as an alternative to a recommended nutrient.

The American Heart Association also recommends that those who do not have heart disease should consume at least two servings of omega-3 rich fish per week, as well as incorporating other sources of omega-3s, which include flaxseed, canola oil, and walnuts. And those who need to lower their triglyceride levels to achieve a normal level of 200 mg/dl should consume 2–4 grams of omega-3 fatty acids per day to help achieve this result. Although fish can be an excellent source of omega-3 fatty acids, there are other sources of the heart healthy omega-3s, so vegetarians who don't eat fish or others concerned about possible pollutants or contaminants in fish, can also benefit from increased consumption. A type of omega-3 called alpha-linolenic acid is found in some plant foods and has also been linked to lower heart attack risk. Sources of alpha-linolenic acid include, as mentioned above, certain vegetable oils (most notably flaxseed oil, canola oil, and in lesser amounts, olive oil), walnuts, soybeans, and other beans. Traces of this omega-3 fatty acid can also be found in kale, wheat germ, avocados, strawberries, and broccoli. In one study, women who ate the most alpha-linolenic acid were about half as likely to die of a heart attack as women who ate the least amounts. Those who had the lowest risk of dying from a heart attack consumed about 1.4 grams of alpha-linolenic acid daily, the equivalent of about a tablespoon of canola oil, 1⅓ tablespoons soy oil, or a cup of olive oil (too much olive oil to consume daily, of course—canola oil or flaxseed oil are probably the most practical and widely available source).

It is easy to see how omega-3s can promote heart health, considering their effect on blood coagulation. Omega-3 fatty acids make blood less sticky and less likely to clump and clog arteries, as well as less likely to form blood clots. Yet they have been shown to benefit more than the heart.

⊛ OMEGA-3s FOR TOTAL HEALTH

Omega-3 fatty acids have been extensively studied, and the results are in: Omega-3s do more than help your heart to stay healthy. Research supports the theories that omega-3 fatty acids may help to prevent certain cancers such as breast cancer, ease arthritis pain, assist in infant development, treat depression, promote improved blood glucose control in type 2 diabetics, and even maintain healthy bones.

Omega-3s for cancer defense? Epidemiological studies have shown that populations that tend to eat a lot more fish than typical Americans have fewer incidences of breast cancer. It may be that omega-3 fatty acids help prevent the production of tumors in breast tissue, as some animal studies have indicated.

Clinical studies involving humans have yet to confirm whether omega-3 fatty acids prevent or cure breast cancer, but some studies have determined that omega-3 fatty acids do tend to settle in the breast, and because of this, these fatty acids may play an important role in maintaining normal breast tissue. In a recent study at the University of California at Los Angeles, women with breast cancer were placed on a low-fat diet consisting of 3 grams of omega-3s each day, which equates to about 6 ounces of fatty fish. After three months, the amount of omega-3 fatty acids present in their breast tissue was significantly higher than before the study. Another study showed that malnourished cancer patients with advanced solid tumors consuming 18 grams of fish oil each day along with 200 IU of vitamin E lived longer and demonstrated improved immune function. Even though these preliminary human studies involved large intakes of omega-3 fatty acids, amounts that are not easy to maintain on a daily basis, the results are interesting. Definitive proof of the correlation between omega-3s and cancer is still unknown.

Omega-3 fatty acids also appear to help with inflammatory diseases. One such disease, and one that affects millions, is arthritis. In a recent ten-year study, arthritis patients consuming large doses of omega-3s experienced less joint swelling, tenderness, and morning stiffness. Many of these patients were able to reduce their intake of anti-inflammatory drugs (such as ibuprofen products), and some were able to get off anti-inflammatories altogether. The use of omega-3 fatty acids in the treatment of arthritis is still being determined, but there does seem to be some promise.

Another inflammatory disease that has received some attention from researchers involved with omega-3 fatty acid is cystic fibrosis. Feeding mice large doses of docosahexaenoic acid, or DHA (a type of omega-3 fatty acid found in fish), reversed the signs of cystic fibrosis. Human trials are under way.

DHA happens to be one of the chief fatty acids in the brain, and a substance developing fetuses get from their mothers in the last three months of pregnancy, when brain growth is most significant. For premature babies who miss that last trimester in the womb and are put on formula (rather than breast milk, which contains DHA), lack of maternal DHA may result in compromised brain, central nervous system, and visual development.

Even full-term infants fed breast milk appear to have enhanced brain development. Breastfed infants have scored higher on intelligence tests than those infants who were given formula without DHA. Whether these differences remained once the children reach school age has yet to be determined, but the apparent health benefits of DHA has led many countries, including the United States, to start adding it to baby formulas. Some baby food is now also supplemented with DHA.

In keeping with the traditional Mediterranean way, we strongly recommend breastfeeding. Although some infant formulas now include DHA, tolerance to these formulas is not always guaranteed and there are many other benefits of breast milk for your baby. After all, traditionally women in

Mediterranean countries primarily breastfed their babies, and some speculate that this may be another reason for the low incidences of cancer in Mediterranean countries.

Preliminary research with omega-3 fatty acids has also shown promise for the treatment of depression. The rate of depression in the United States is on the rise. Today, more than 15 million Americans suffer from depression, and some researchers believe this increase is inversely proportional to the decrease in omega-3 consumption in this country. Serotonin, a mood elevator in the brain, may not work as well in a less fluid environment, something the brain uses omega-3s to accomplish.

Increased omega-3 fatty acid consumption may also help type 2 diabetics with improved blood sugar control. Population studies have shown that people who eat about 5 ounces of fatty fish each week appear to enjoy more controlled levels of glucose, as long as calorie intake is held constant. Substituting fish for other higher-fat meat sources (instead of simply increasing fish consumption) is advised. Excessive calories from any food can cause weight gain, and this can interfere with adequate blood glucose control. You thought bones needed calcium alone? New animal studies suggest that omega-3 supports bone formation and could help to prevent or slow osteoporosis. There may come a day when dietary recommendations for osteoporosis prevention will include food sources of omega-3s, in addition to calcium.

⍟ FABULOUS FISH

While many of the studies on the health benefits of omega-3s used fish oil supplements, side effects from too many supplements can be unpleasant—upset stomach, nausea, diarrhea, flatulence, weight gain, and the possibility of vitamin A and D toxicity and liver damage. No such side effects have been found from eating more fish, however. We should note that it appears that large amounts of fatty fish need to be consumed to reap most of the benefits listed in the above studies, but the jury is still out on how much we actually need. For now, why not eat more of this nutritious food in moderate amounts as recommended by the Mediterranean Diet Pyramid? Fish, as well as many types of nuts, canola oil, flaxseed oil, flaxseed meal, and whole-grain bread/cereal products made with flaxseed are excellent sources of omega-3 fatty acids. Fish cooks quickly, making it a convenient choice for dinner, and it is versatile, fitting into many recipes as a meat replacement or featured on its own with nothing more than a little olive oil and fresh lemon juice. Fish with fins, such as flounder, cod, haddock, and catfish, are particularly low in saturated fat and cholesterol, and shellfish, although higher in cholesterol than fin fish, is also exceptionally low in saturated fat, the real concern when it comes to heart health.

Warnings that some fish may have high levels of mercury and should be avoided by pregnant women and by children, or that seafood of various types may contain toxins should be considered. In general, however, up to 6 to 8 cooked ounces of fish every week may be safe and, indeed, beneficial to health. For added insurance, however, pregnant and lactating women may want to consume plant sources of omega-3 fatty acids, or, at the very least, avoid larger fish, like swordfish, shark, or king mackerel, which are higher on the food chain and more likely to be concentrated sources of any toxin. Salmon, sardines, bluefish, anchovies, and herring, on the other hand, have been reported to have low levels of mercury and are good sources of omega-3 fatty acids. If you're concerned, consult your doctor or pediatrician about how much fish you and your children should be eating. When free of pollutants, fish remains an excellent source of nutrition for the general population and is certainly in the spirit of the traditional Mediterranean diet—low in saturated fat and great for heart health. But remember, moderate consumption is the most true to the dietary patterns of the traditional Mediterranean.

☞ THE IMPORTANCE OF DAIRY

While dairy foods didn't constitute a large part of the traditional Mediterranean diet, they were certainly important. Milk wasn't consumed in the quantities it is enjoyed in the United States. Reserved usually for coffee and custard, milk didn't keep well in the hot Mediterranean climate. Yogurt and cheese, however, lasted longer because of their fermented character, and while never dominating a meal, these dairy products certainly supported many a Mediterranean feast.

Dairy products from the traditional Mediterranean came from goats, sheep, buffaloes, and camels, as well as cows, giving Mediterranean cheeses much of their unique character. Yet, once again, dairy foods made up a relatively small portion of the traditional Mediterranean diet, and the health of the people eating this diet may reflect why low dairy consumption is best.

There has been much controversy lately surrounding the American dietary recommendations for dairy consumption. While it appears that Americans are not consuming enough calcium, many researchers believe that increasing the intake of dairy products would primarily benefit the dairy industry, not the average American. Those in opposition to the recent push for Americans to strive for three servings of dairy foods per day (up from the recommended guideline of two servings per day) feel a better public policy message should be for Americans to improve lifestyle habits that have been shown to contribute to calcium loss from bones, such as inactivity, smoking, and high animal protein consumption, along with promoting the consumption of calcium-containing, highly beneficial plants foods, such as broccoli, mustard greens, and calcium-fortified soy milk.

The recent "three-a-day" dairy campaign was given a boost when dairy calcium consumption made headlines after research reports that ample intakes of calcium, particularly through dairy foods, appear to help in the prevention and treatment of obesity. One study outlined how dietary calcium seems to play a crucial role in the regulation of calorie metabolism, and high intakes of calcium caused accelerated fat loss in mice. But, obviously, much more research is needed before dairy calcium consumption can be equated as a magic weight-loss bullet.

Nevertheless, dairy products are a good source of calcium, and the current dietary recommendations for the average adult are 1,000 to 1,500 milligrams of calcium per day, primarily to prevent osteoporosis, a bone-weakening disease affecting millions of Americans, most of whom are women. Vitamin D helps the body absorb calcium more effectively, and vitamin D is added to most commercial milk.

While adequate calcium consumption is undoubtedly important, especially in the diets of children, adolescents, and pregnant women (for the developing fetus), as well as those over the age of sixty when bone mass declines significantly, dairy foods should not be regarded as the only source of calcium. Rather, dairy foods, particularly the nonfat or low-fat varieties, should be regarded as just one of several good sources of calcium. Calcium-fortified soy milk and calcium-containing plant foods should also be recommended, along with as much physical activity as possible.

Although people living in the Mediterranean countries traditionally did not consume a lot of dairy, they consumed plenty of calcium from plant foods like dark green vegetables. Some green vegetables, such as kale, contain calcium that is highly absorbable, but some other green vegetables, such as spinach, contain calcium that is not readily absorbed by the body. Eat a variety of different dark green vegetables, and you will probably get good calcium absorption from this plant food category. Other good plant sources of calcium include figs, sesame seeds, almonds, tofu (when processed with calcium salts), calcium-fortified orange juice, white beans, and other beans. Unlike high-saturated-fat dairy products, these plant foods have not been linked with an increased risk of heart disease.

So what is a dairy lover to do? As mentioned, dairy products are a good source of calcium. In low- or nonfat form and in moderation, they are good dietary choices. If you live for cheese, couldn't give up your fruit-flavored cup of yogurt, or require warm milk before bedtime, stick with low- or nonfat dairy products in moderation, with two servings (or more depending on different individual needs) per day as specified in the Mediterranean Diet Pyramid (a serving equals a cup of low-fat or nonfat milk or yogurt or 1 ounce of low-fat cheese). Some cheeses that are not considered low fat but are generally lower in fat than other cheese varieties can also be enjoyed in moderation on a weekly basis. These types of cheeses include part-skim mozzarella, part-skim ricotta, and reduced-fat feta (see page 200 for more on the fat content of selected cheeses). We've included these lower-fat cheeses in the weekly section because of their importance in flavoring many Mediterranean-inspired dishes. What would a homemade pizza be (preferably one loaded with a variety of vegetables for the ultimate Mediterranean treat) without a bit of part-skim mozzarella on top? Some researchers even believe the saturated fat in yogurt and cheese may not have as detrimental an effect on blood cholesterol levels as the saturated fat in butter and milk, although more studies on this are warranted.

There have been controversial studies on the dangers of bovine growth hormone (rBGH), a genetically engineered hormone injected into dairy cows to increase milk production, suggesting that nonorganic milk may pose a risk to human health. The FDA and the manufacturers of the hormone deny any health risk to humans. If you are still concerned, consider buying organic milk and organic or European-produced cheese (rBGH is banned in Europe).

☙ CHEESE, YOGURT, AND MILK

Cheese (as mentioned above) has been an essential component of Mediterranean cuisine for millennia. No dietary element could be more Mediterranean. As early as 4000 B.C.E., descriptions of cheese were recorded on clay tablets by the ancient Sumerians. Egyptian hieroglyphics depict cheese, and cheese was well known in ancient Greece and Rome. Recent research has indicated that the cheese consumed in the traditional Mediterranean diet was higher in omega-3 fatty acids than we may find in today's manufactured cheese products. This was because the animals producing the cheese in the traditional Mediterranean region were eating all-natural diets—consuming the omega-3-rich field greens that covered the Mediterranean countryside. The omega-3 fatty acids were passed through the animal's milk and into the cheese.

Even today, cheese is a Mediterranean fixture. Italy alone has some sixty kinds of cheese and more than three hundred cheese names that identify the locality of production. Spain is the exception when it comes to the Mediterranean love affair with cheese. Spanish cuisine isn't much concerned with cheese. In the other countries around the Mediterranean Sea, however, cheese was and is indispensable.

European cheeses are gaining in popularity in this country. Sales of feta cheese rose by 12 percent between 1995 and 1996. Sales of edam cheese rose 32 percent, and asiago 21 percent. United States cheese consumption rose to 31.2 pounds per person in 2000, up from a mere 11.3 pounds in 1970, according to the United States Dairy Council. Even so, for years the American cheese "ideal" was a far cry from cheese in the traditional Mediterranean diet. As much as Americans love cheese, the cheese most familiar to us—big orange blocks of cheddar; preshredded mozzarella; packaged, sliced Swiss; individually wrapped cheese sticks; or that stuff known enigmatically as "cheese food"—would be strange and possibly frightening to a resident of the traditional Mediterranean. Americans tend to prefer their cheeses mild and melted in large quantities over burgers, nacho chips, and Americanized versions of Italian food. This wasn't the way cheese was consumed in the traditional Mediterranean diet. A small cube of finely crafted hard cheese was often a dinner finale. When used in cooking, hard cheeses like Parmesan and Romano were grated lightly over vegetables or slivered and mixed in with vegetables. Softer cheeses like mozzarella were served in small amounts with tomatoes or marinated vegetables. A small chunk of feta is traditionally crumbled into Greek salads. Creamy cheeses would sometimes flavor or be stuffed inside vegetables or pasta in amounts just enough to impart a cheesy flavor without overwhelming the goodness of the principal components, the plant foods.

When it comes to cheese, the nutritional trick is to eat it in small amounts. Many cheeses are high in saturated fat and sodium. Eating cheese in the Mediterranean style means eating cheese in small amounts and, if weight loss is a concern, usually choosing lower-fat varieties. Genuine mozzarella is made from Indian buffalo milk, but the version in the United States is made from cow's milk, and part-skim mozzarella is widely available. When high-fat cheeses are appropriate for certain dishes, a little goes a long way in the traditional Mediterranean diet. Strongly flavored cheeses accentuated the taste of food rather than drowning it.

Low-fat cheese can certainly be part of a healthy daily diet. The Mediterranean Diet Pyramid recommends that nonfat or low-fat dairy products like low-fat or nonfat yogurt and skim milk be consumed daily. Lower-fat cheeses (such as part-skim mozzarella) can be enjoyed on a moderate, weekly basis. Save high-fat cheeses for special occasions or consume them in very small amounts.

Yogurt has enjoyed similar popularity in the traditional Mediterranean diet, most notably in Greece and the Middle East, but also in other Mediterranean countries. When made with nonfat or low-fat milk, yogurt is an excellent part of a daily diet. It is low in fat, high in calcium and protein, and rich with the bacteria that can help maintain intestinal flora.

Milk was a far less popular part of the traditional Mediterranean diet than of the American diet. As we've mentioned, the warm climate and lack of refrigeration made cheese and yogurt the more practical and long-lasting dairy products. As Americans happily guzzle milk into adulthood, people in the traditional Mediterranean typically drank milk only with their morning coffee or espresso. The Mediterranean Diet Pyramid suggests nonfat or low-fat dairy products like skim milk be a part of the daily diet because of their high calcium and nutrient content, or even better try low-fat, calcium-fortified soy milk in keeping with a plant-based Mediterranean model of eating.

⊛ EGGS

What Spain lacks in cheese cuisine, it makes up for in its heavy use of eggs, making eggs a peripheral but important part of the traditional Mediterranean diet, at least as the Spanish have always known it. During his travels through Spain, Ancel Keys discovered that along the Mediterranean coast of Spain, eggs are eaten "at almost every main meal," while heart attacks remain a rarity compared to levels in the United States, and blood cholesterol levels of people living in this region were much lower than average levels in the United States. Keys attributes this seeming paradox to the fact that dietary cholesterol is less significant for heart health than saturated fat, and that despite high egg consumption, total saturated fat consumption remained low.

But aren't eggs little packages of dietary cholesterol just waiting to induce heart attacks? One large egg yolk (the whites don't contain cholesterol) has about 260 milligrams of dietary cholesterol, and the American Heart Association recommends a total daily intake of only 300 milligrams of cholesterol at most. One egg almost meets an entire day's quota! But, as we've said before, recent research suggests that cholesterol really isn't a factor in heart health when consumed in moderation. Saturated fat is the dietary component to watch, and while eggs have some (one large egg also has about 6 grams of fat, of which about 30 percent is saturated), four eggs or fewer per week are fine for most adults. (Check with your doctor if you are unsure about whether you should be eating eggs.)

Moderate egg intake—that is, four or fewer per week as specified in the Mediterranean Diet Pyramid—is compatible with most of the dietary patterns seen in the traditional Mediterranean countries. It also just happens to be within the range recommended by the American Heart Association for people trying to prevent high blood cholesterol or treat blood cholesterol that is already moderately high.

⊘ QUESTIONS AND ANSWERS

❧ What cuts of meat are the lowest in fat?

In general, look for cuts of meat with the words *round* or *loin,* such as ground round, pork loin, beef tenderloin, and so on. For beef, choose extra-lean ground beef (95 percent lean), or buy lean cuts of meat and grind them at home. Eye of round, top round steak and roast, sirloin, or beef tenderloin are other low-fat choices. Bacon is much higher in fat than lean ham or Canadian bacon. A broiled pork chop has far less fat than pork ribs. The lowest-fat cuts of pork are pork tenderloin, top loin roast, top loin chop, center loin chop, sirloin roast, loin rib chop, and shoulderblade steak. White-meat chicken and turkey are leaner than dark meat. Lamb and veal are naturally lower in fat than beef if you can find them, afford them, and want to eat them.

See the following chart for a comparison of fat content in different types of meat products. All figures are for cooked meat, generally broiled or roasted, in 3.5-ounce portions. Other portion sizes used are 3 ounces for fish, 8 ounces for milk, and 1 ounce for cheese.

	Saturated Fat Grams	*Total Fat Grams*
Eggs (1 large)	1.60	5.30
Ground beef	8.10	20.70
Ground beef, extra lean	6.40	16.30
Halibut	.40	2.50
Ham, extra lean	1.40	4.30
Lamb, leg of, lean	3.30	9.40
Lambchop, lean	3.70	9.80
Pork tenderloin, lean	1.70	4.80
Poultry, dark meat with skin	4.40	15.80
Poultry, dark meat without skin	2.70	9.70
Poultry, light meat with skin	3.00	10.80
Poultry, light meat without skin	1.30	4.50
Salmon	2.10	10.50
Shrimp	.20	.90

❧ What is the fat content of different cheeses?

We have categorized cheeses by the amount of fat that they contain. Nonfat cheeses (as well as other nonfat dairy products) contain no fat. Low-fat cheeses and dairy products contain 3 grams of fat or less per serving. Lower-fat cheeses are those cheeses that have about 5 grams of fat or less per serving. Higher-fat cheeses contain more than 5 grams of fat per serving. The following table should help to decipher the fat content of some commonly used cheeses.

Cheese per 1-Ounce Serving	Fat Grams	Saturated Fat Grams
Blue cheese	8.1	5.3
Brie	7.8	4.9
Camembert	6.9	4.3
Cheddar	9.4	6.0
Cheddar, low fat	2.0	1.2
Colby	8.7	5.5
Cottage cheese, 1% fat (1 cup)	2.3	1.5
Edam	7.9	5.0
Feta	6.0	5.4
Gruyère	9.2	5.4
Mozzarella, part skim	4.5	2.9
Mozzarella, whole milk	6.0	3.7
Parmesan, grated (1 tablespoon)	1.5	1.0
Provolone	7.5	4.8
Ricotta, part skim (1/2 cup)	9.8	6.1
Ricotta, whole milk (1/2 cup)	16.1	10.3

Cheese per 1-Ounce Serving	Fat Grams	Saturated Fat Grams
Romano, grated (1 tablespoon)	1.5	1.0
Swiss	7.8	4.5

What are the best ways to cook meat to reduce saturated fat content?

When preparing ground meat, cook, drain, and then rinse in a colander to remove excess fat. Broil or grill meat rather than frying. Use just a little olive oil or even nonfat cooking spray to keep leaner cuts from sticking to broilers and baking pans. When baking meat, use a rack so the fat drains into the bottom of the baking pan.

I feel deprived if my meal doesn't include meat. Am I doomed to high blood cholesterol levels?

Not at all. Refer back to our section on phasing out meat main-course mentality. Even if it takes a while, you can probably find recipes you enjoy that don't include meat. Even if you do choose to eat meat more often than is recommended in the Mediterranean Diet Pyramid, you don't have to eat it in large amounts. Stick to lean cuts of meat and reduce portion sizes. Learn to use meat in recipes instead of on its own (see the recipes in Part II for some great ideas), and you'll find that what you thought was a single serving can easily serve four people. Even if you like to eat meat (as did the people eating a traditional Mediterranean diet), why not expand your culinary horizons to include an equal appreciation of the vast variety of plant foods available to you?

If you feel deprived, you won't enjoy your food, and that is certainly not in the Mediterranean spirit. Eating should be a pleasurable and fulfilling as well as filling experience. If that means including meat four or five times a week for now, that will be the plan that works for you. As long as your saturated fat intake remains at a sensible level (no more than 10 percent of your average daily calories from saturated fat), you should be able to maintain a healthy heart.

If, however, you already suffer from high blood cholesterol and are at risk for heart disease, you may need to learn to overcome your feelings of deprivation (eating too much meat is probably more habit than anything else) and trim your meat intake down to the levels suggested in the Mediterranean Diet Pyramid, or even lower. Talk to your doctor about what you should be eating and how much meat makes sense for you.

✎ What about other, less common types of meat? How do they fit into the Mediterranean way of eating?

Although we didn't include game meat in our Mediterranean Diet Pyramid, since it isn't commonly consumed in this country on a regular basis, it was consumed in the traditional Mediterranean diet. If you can find it, or if you choose to go out and hunt it, fit game meats into the Mediterranean Diet Pyramid as if they were red meat, in terms of frequency of consumption and portion size. A few additional considerations regarding game and other less common types of meat and fish:

- Water buffalo is very low in fat, with only 1.8 total grams of fat in a 3.5-ounce roasted portion, only .6 grams being saturated fat. This is a lean meat.
- Deer is also relatively low in fat, with only 3.2 grams of total fat and 1.3 grams of saturated fat in 3.5 ounces roasted meat.

- Elk is a lean meat, with 1.9 total grams of fat and only .7 grams of saturated fat in a 3.5-ounce serving of roasted meat.
- Goat is also a lean meat, with 3.0 grams of total fat and .9 grams of saturated fat in a 3.5-ounce portion of roasted meat.

❧ Are free-range chickens more heart-healthy?

Not necessarily more heart-healthy, but they may be healthier in other ways, and in our opinion, they taste much better. Free-range chickens may not be much different in their fat, protein, vitamin, and mineral content. But organic free-range chickens raised on food without antibiotics, growth hormones, and other additives are certainly more akin to the way chickens were raised and eaten in the traditional Mediterranean. For this reason alone, organic free-range chicken may be worth the slightly higher price tag.

❧ Should I buy shrimp from the guy in the van selling it on the street corner?

We wouldn't. It could be that the shrimp—or lobster or crab legs or whatever is being offered—is just fine. On the other hand, seafood spoils quickly, meaning that if it isn't properly refrigerated, bacteria growth can reach dangerous levels. Buy fresh or frozen fish from a dependable source.

❧ Which fish should go in which recipes?

Lower-fat fish—the kind that is lighter in color, like orange roughy and sole—is best for baking and cooking in the microwave. Fattier fish, such as salmon, tuna, and mackerel (the types with higher fat content but also higher omega-3 fat content) are ideal for grilling and broiling.

✿ How do I know if fish is fresh?

Fresh fish smells pleasantly like the sea with flesh that is firm, translucent, moist, and without brown spots. If fish flesh separates, a sign of dryness, it is probably less fresh. Ideally, mollusks like clams and mussels should be alive when purchased with undamaged, slightly open shells that close when tapped. Scallops should be moist and plump, and shrimp will smell "shrimpy" but not unpleasantly so. If any fish smells unpleasant, don't buy it.

Frozen fish should be frozen completely solid and without crystals or dry, discolored spots. It should have only a slight odor and be well wrapped.

Even if the fish you buy is fresh when you buy it, it won't stay that way for long. Eat fish and seafood the day you buy it or the next day. If you won't eat it that soon, freeze it, but fish that has already been frozen will deteriorate in quality if refrozen. Best to buy seafood the day you plan to prepare it, the way they did, and still do, in the Mediterranean.

8: *Embracing the Mediterranean Lifestyle*

Compare the typical day of an American man, let's say about forty years old, with that of a typical farmer of the same age living in the rural Mediterranean in 1950. Of course, we never lived in the Mediterranean region at this time, but we can make an educated guess, based on written research and documentation, about what life may have been like.

Both the American man and the Mediterranean man rise at about six A.M., the American man with the aid of an alarm clock that drags him from a groggy haze after a scant five hours of sleep, the Mediterranean man waking naturally with the first rays of the sun over the horizon after a satisfying eight hours of sleep.

The American man grabs a doughnut and a cup of coffee with white sugar and hydrogenated-fat-based nondairy creamer at a convenience store on the way to the office. The Mediterranean man sits down to a light breakfast of whole-grain bread and coffee with hot milk.

The American man gets frustrated and angry sitting in traffic for an hour. He sees nothing but concrete, overpasses, underpasses, interchanges, and other cars. The Mediterranean man opens his front door and is already at work. He breathes deeply the fresh, cool morning air and pauses momentarily to watch the sun rise over the lovely green hills of his farm. The distant sea sparkles.

All day, the American man sits at a desk in front of a computer screen except for a walk into the neighboring conference room for a long meeting. He is often on the phone, on line, or immersed in writing a report. His eyes ache but none of his other muscles do much moving at all. He breaks for lunch at one o'clock with his colleagues. His order might consist of a bacon cheeseburger or a corned beef on rye, French fries, a slice of cheesecake, and a large cola, or perhaps even a martini or two. He leaves work wearily at seven P.M.

All day, the Mediterranean man works hard in the field. His entire body gets a great workout, although he doesn't think of his efforts as "exercise." They are, quite simply, what one does. He breaks midmorning for another hearty slab of whole-grain bread, and again for lunch, the biggest meal of his day: more bread wrapped around a handful of greens cooked in olive oil with a little lemon or vinegar, whatever vegetables are seasonally available and in the house, a small piece of cheese, a glass of red wine, and a slice of melon for dessert. Back to the fields, the man works vigorously in the fresh air. The work is hard and tiring, and his muscles ache, but he sees the results of his work there before him—a newly plowed field, an acre of harvested olives, or a neatly tended vineyard.

The American man stops at the gym on his way home for a game of racquetball with a friend—his daily exercise requirement, and "requirement" is just how he sees it. He loses and it irritates him. He drives home in a bad temper, picks up a pepperoni pizza for his family, and he, his wife, and his two children eat the pizza in silence in front of a blaring television. The television stays on long after the children have gone to bed, and he watches it late into the night.

The Mediterranean man also works until about seven P.M. Tired and hungry, he comes home to a light salad, a dish of pasta, a glass of red wine, and a bowl of citrus fruit. He eats with his family and they talk. Perhaps the family from the neighboring farm joins them for the light meal and everyone laughs and eats and exchanges information about what happened that day in the fields, in the village, along the road. They exchange stories, news, farming or cooking tips. When the sun is fully set, everyone goes off to bed.

Which lifestyle sounds healthier? Of course, we've certainly oversimplified and, admittedly, romanticized the Mediterranean lifestyle in our description. Life was certainly hard for the working classes in the Mediterranean region. Money was often tight for farmers and laborers. A natural disaster or a physical injury could destroy a crop and a family's income for the year. Work must surely have been stressful more often than not. Children got sick. People didn't always agree. Sometimes there wasn't enough food to satisfy everyone.

But we compare the two—the American man and the Mediterranean man—to make a point: In the traditional Mediterranean, life was, most certainly, three things: technologically simple, physically rigorous, and in touch with the natural world. Not incidentally, although we used a man for our example, women's lives in the traditional Mediterranean were similarly physically active—cooking by hand without appliances, washing clothes without machines, washing dishes without washers and dryers, sweeping and dusting and scrubbing the home without machines or chemical cleaners, sewing clothes, gardening, going into town to shop, taking care of the children. And American women today, of course, lead lives much like those American men.

Could the Mediterranean lifestyle be a factor in the superior coronary health and longevity of the traditional Mediterranean people? Research says probably, and why wouldn't it? Study after study has demonstrated that exercise, in whatever form, lowers the risk and also the severity of many chronic diseases, from heart disease to depression. Chronic stress—which may be the result of a complicated lifestyle as well as a lifestyle largely removed from the natural world—has been linked to any number of health problems. While people in the traditional Mediterranean undoubtedly experienced stress—in other words, that physical fight-or-flight response to certain stimuli our bodies undergo, preparing us to deal with crisis—chronic stress over a period of months, even years, was probably far less prevalent than it is today in our overextended and hectic world.

The irony of life in the traditional Mediterranean was that, on the surface, it looked a lot more stressful than contemporary American life. Not enough food, never enough meat, hard physical labor day in and day out, an existence at the mercy of the elements and luck, large families in small living spaces, none of the modern conveniences of living.

Yet, for all our conveniences—cars, central heating and cooling, cable television, computers, overhead lights, fax machines, programmable coffee makers, credit cards, electric razors, clock radios, cellular phones, burglar alarms, riding mowers—we've sacrificed a life close to the earth, full of movement and strength-building activity, in physical contact with our friends and community. We've lost much of the old sense of belonging, of knowing and depending on our neighbors, of doing a job and seeing the result right there in front of us, of earning the money and using it to buy what we need, of building our own homes, growing our own foods, even of moving our own bodies. Many of us feel isolated, even depressed.

What price have we paid for modern life? And can we ever reclaim some of the simpler aspects of life so taken for granted by people living the traditional Mediterranean culture? Can we regain a sense of community, relearn how to live simply, and recapture an active lifestyle without sacrificing the jobs we love, the cars we need, the beautiful houses with our names on the mortgages, the conveniences that have become so necessary to get along in contemporary society?

Of course we can. We can have it all! It just takes a little planning, and a few priority adjustments. But first, let's look at the evidence, so we can be sure that moving toward a more Mediterranean-inspired lifestyle is really worth the effort.

⊛ TO MOVE IS TO LIVE

Physical activity was a natural part of life in the rural Mediterranean. People had to be active and endure often grueling physical labor just to make a living and get food on the table. We, on the other hand, often have to make time for exercise. It has to be something we "pencil in" to our busy schedules, and it is, all too frequently, the first thing to be crossed off the list when those schedules get too tight. You have to finish that report, or get to the grocery store, or drive the kids to soccer practice, or serve on that committee. The half-hour run through the park you had planned can wait . . . can't it?

Maybe not, if you want to stay healthy enough to write that report or pick up that gallon of milk. Studies on both men and women make compelling arguments that exercise is literally a matter of life and death.

A study published in a 1999 issue of the *New England Journal of Medicine* revealed that women who walk briskly for at least three hours each week or who exercise more vigorously—jogging or aerobic dance—for ninety minutes per week reduce their heart attack risk by 30 to 40 percent, and women who walk for five or more hours per week cut their heart attack risk in half.

Even shorter periods of exercise can have a positive effect on heart health. Research out of Loughborough University in Leicestershire, England, demonstrated that shorter exercise sessions—ten minutes three times per day rather than thirty minutes all at once—can indeed lower heart attack risk in young, healthy men by lowering triglyceride levels after meals.

Exercise can do more than cut your heart attack risk. Research out of the University of Illinois suggests that older people who begin a program of aerobic exercise such as walking can maintain their mental "fitness" better than older people who remain sedentary. The study examined sedentary adults between sixty and seventy-five years old and asked them to begin either walking or a stretching and toning program. After six months, mental reactions in the walking group (who worked up to forty-five-minute walks at about 3.8 miles per hour three times per week) were up to 25 percent quicker than mental reactions in the stretching and toning group.

A two-year study conducted at the Cooper Institute for Aerobics Research in Dallas studied a similar subject: the effect of more total aerobic activity each day accomplished piecemeal throughout the day, rather than in one chunk of structured exercise time. They found that many of the participants who exercised throughout the day in shorter, more frequent sessions, not only lowered their blood cholesterol levels but also lost excess weight.

Why is exercise so good for our bodies? An easier question may be, why is a lack of physical activity so bad for our bodies? It is a scientifically noted reality that people who live sedentary lives are more prone to a variety of chronic diseases such as heart disease, stroke, colon cancer, diabetes, and osteoporosis. Inactive people tend to suffer more often from obesity. They don't seem to live as long. On a less dramatic scale, physically active people tend to have fewer colds, better sleep, and a more positive attitude than the sedentary. Isn't that reason enough to get up and get moving?

Exercise helps prevent high blood pressure and also lowers already high blood pressure levels. Physical activity strengthens the heart muscle, helping it to work more efficiently. It also appears to lower the levels of certain immune system chemicals in the blood that promote atherosclerosis, and increase levels of certain chemicals that prevent atherosclerosis.

Exercise improves your body's ability to metabolize carbohydrates, increasing sensitivity to insulin and lowering the risk of developing adult-onset diabetes, which some believe is actually a disease of inactivity. Exercise also helps to move waste through your digestive system more quickly, which may be the mechanism whereby it lowers colon cancer risk—if toxins and carcinogens are in your digestive tract for less time, they have less chance of being absorbed by the body. Weight-bearing exercise strengthens bones, reducing the risk of developing osteoporosis.

Perhaps most compelling is the effect of physical activity on longevity. One British study showed that moderate exercise appeared to reduce the risk of death in older men. The death risk of moderately active men was half that of sedentary men, and deaths from all causes were highest among sedentary men.

A study of physical activity and mortality in postmenopausal women concluded that any kind of exercise seems to lower the risk of death in postmenopausal women. The study included postmenopausal subjects and found that the more women exercised, the lower their risk of death during the study's follow-up period. Even women who exercised only once a week experienced what the study called a "significant drop in mortality," but the women who enjoyed the lowest risk of death were those who exercised at least four times per week or who regularly exercised vigorously.

Even if exercise didn't add years to your life (which it apparently does), it certainly adds life to your years, as they say. Exercise is increasingly prescribed by physicians as a treatment for chronic diseases, such as high blood pressure, diabetes, and arthritis. Exercise can make the elderly stronger and more independent.

⊛ HERCULES WAS GREEK

As important as aerobic exercise is for your health, strength training is equally important. You probably couldn't find someone in the traditional Mediterranean lifestyle lifting weights, but that doesn't mean he or she didn't challenge muscles and bones with weight-bearing physical activity every day! In the Mediterranean, weight-bearing activities were a part of life on a farm: lifting, hauling, pulling, loading, pushing, chopping, digging. Americans don't do much of these activities anymore unless by choice, or unless they choose farming or some form of manual labor as a profession. Yet strength training can easily become a part of modern American life, even without having to purchase an expensive set of weights or a fancy machine.

Strength training requires less endurance but more short-term intense effort. Weight-bearing exercises not only build muscle, they also build bone. Studies indicate that older people who begin a strength-training program show improved muscle tone and function, improved bone density, and greater strength.

Stronger muscles do more than look better. They work better. We don't mean huge, bulky, incapacitating muscles (which are difficult to achieve, anyway, especially for women, who don't typically have the necessary testosterone). We mean fit, fully nourished, active muscles. Larger muscle cells more accustomed to moving can process oxygen better, taking some of the load off the hardworking heart muscle, which doesn't have to "push" so hard to supply those muscles with nutrients. Strong muscles surrounding arthritic joints help to take the pressure off joints. Muscle strength can also make small differences all day long—that grocery bag isn't such a load, those sacks of lawn trash are trifles, those twin toddlers aren't so heavy after all, even when they jump on you at the same time.

Work weight-bearing activity into your daily life by doing more things for yourself: carrying grocery bags, packages, small children; shoveling snow, raking leaves, digging in the garden; even walking up and down stairs lifts the body weight. Many people enjoy yoga, which employs weight bearing by lifting and manipulating the weight of the body in a controlled manner.

Whatever method you choose, don't forget that aerobic activity and weight-bearing activity go hand in hand, working together to improve your health.

⊗ NO TIME TO LOSE

But you've heard this story. You know exercise is good for you. Yet you still have trouble fitting it into your schedule. We live in a nation of convenience. Where else would you find convenience stores on every other corner? These stores do well because Americans truly believe they don't have enough time to do it all.

Do you think you don't have time to exercise? Do you think you don't have the energy? The important thing to remember is that regular exercise will give you more energy, which will make you feel as if you have more time. Some other tips for fitting exercise into your day are as follows:

- Remember that exercise in bits and pieces throughout the day is just as effective as exercise all in one session, as long as the total time and exertion is the same.

- Climb up and down the stairs in your home or office as often as possible. Forget elevators.
- Park in the most distant parking space from your destination. Think of the time you'll save circling the parking lot looking for the choicest space! And your car will be easier to find.
- Save gas, save the environment, and save your muscle tone—walk everywhere possible! While some cities and environments are less conducive to pedestrians than others, you may find plenty of opportunities for walking you hadn't considered. Some people even drive to their mailboxes, or to the next-door neighbor's house. That need not be you.
- If you take the bus or subway to and from work, get off a stop or two earlier and walk the rest of the way. Wear your athletic shoes and carry your work shoes.
- If you work at a computer all day, make it a habit to get up every fifteen minutes and stretch. A brisk three-minute walk around the office or outside every hour or two is even better.
- Try cooking the old-fashioned way. Knead bread dough, whip up cake batter, or beat eggs by hand. Get the kids involved and make cooking an enjoyable exercise event for all!
- If your attempts to exercise always fail because you've planned to get up earlier and exercise in the morning, change your plan. Some people have a higher energy level later in the day. A brisk walk right after work each day might suit you better, or maybe an evening run is more your speed (if so, wear reflective gear—not a necessity in the rural Mediterranean but an important safety precaution in our busy cities!).
- Play with the kids (or the dog). Don't let the shorter members of your household play in the backyard or

the park alone. Engage them in a game of tag, keep-away, Frisbee, or whatever game is "cool" in school this week. Not only will you get some great exercise, but you'll be engaging in family time, an essential part of the traditional Mediterranean lifestyle.

• Exercise with your partner or friend. If you aren't in the mood to exercise, your buddy can talk you back into the mood, and vice versa. Jog together, play tennis, ride bicycles, skate, swim, even mall-walk. Exercise is more fun when you've got someone to talk to, and once again, such a social endeavor is certainly in the Mediterranean spirit.

• Don't hire the neighborhood kids to do your lawn chores. Do them yourself. Rake the leaves, weed the garden, mow, shovel snow. You'll get exercise and a sense of accomplishment when you see the results. You'll also save the money you would have paid to have the service performed for you.

• Instead of spending your weekend night out at a movie, go dancing, ice skating, or roller skating.

• Getting together with friends? Why not go canoeing or cross-country skiing? Hit the courts for a friendly game of basketball, or the green for a game of golf (without the golf carts, of course!).

• Turn off the TV! The more active alternative activities are staggering in number and variety. Go for a walk. Clean your closet. Visit the zoo or the museum. Organize your pantry alphabetically. Scrub the bathtub. Dance to your favorite music. Jump rope. Bring in a load of firewood. Chop more firewood! Or, if you absolutely must have the television on, pop in an exercise video and get off that couch!

• If you like your exercise in a more spiritual form, take a yoga, tai chi, or martial arts class. Not Mediterranean, but exercise is exercise!

❁ A MEDITERRANEAN-INSPIRED EXERCISE PLAN

The American College of Sports Medicine recently recommended that everyone, no matter age, shape, or fitness level, should exercise for at least thirty minutes per day on most days of the week. For weight loss, the ACSM recommends forty-five to sixty minutes of aerobic activity each day. Strength training is important, too.

That may sound like a lot, but if you follow our Mediterranean-Inspired Three-Day Exercise Plan, you'll find that the recommendation is actually fairly easy to accomplish. And fun, too! The beauty of this plan is its simplicity. You don't need equipment, special instruction, or even any special skills. You just need to know how to walk.

The following plan is just a guide. You can follow it exactly or you can tailor it to your own needs. You can increase or decrease the length or intensity of any of the activities. You can mix and match activities. You can do the plan for three days and take a day off, or do some version of the plan every day. (This plan isn't so strenuous as to require a day off. It can be performed every day.)

The intensity at which you exercise depends on your fitness level. You should feel like you are working hard, but not so hard that you can't carry on a conversation. Sweat, but don't knock yourself out. Don't think a leisurely stroll around the block will do the trick, either, however. Remember—move it or lose it!

Day One
- Do five minutes of gentle stretching and fifty jumping jacks before breakfast (or start with five jumping jacks and work your way up to fifty). Good morning!
- For your midmorning coffee break, take a brisk ten-minute walk (in the fresh air, if possible).
- Take a fifteen-minute walk during lunch.

- Before dinner, either at your job or elsewhere, find a flight of stairs and go up and down a few times.
- End your day with as many sit-ups and push-ups as you can do with some effort but without pain (increase by a few repetitions every week or two), and finally, some gentle stretching. If you have kids, they'll probably be happy to join you on the floor, and you can set a great example!

Day Two

- Begin your day with gentle stretching, then march in place briskly for five minutes.
- Take the bus to work and get off one stop early. Walk the rest of the way (ten minutes).
- Move more, eat less. Pack a light lunch and take a fifteen-minute walk.
- For your afternoon coffee break, do some stair climbing.
- Before dinner, go on a bike ride with a friend (or play a game of tennis or golf, or do some in-line skating).

Day Three

- Begin your day with gentle stretching, then put on some wake-up music and dance for five minutes. (Nobody has to see . . . or let the whole family join in!)
- Rally your coworkers and take a brisk, twenty-minute lunchtime walk.
- For your afternoon coffee break, jog in place for two minutes, do ten jumping jacks, then try twenty push-ups against a wall. You won't need the coffee!
- After a light supper, enlist your partner, children, or your dog for a brisk, fifteen-minute (or more) evening walk.
- Before bed, grab two cans of food (or one- to two-pound weights, if you have them), hold one in each

hand, and see how long you can keep your arms extended. Then try your sit-ups with the cans of food held against your chest, for extra weight. If you are already used to heavier weights, use 5-, 8-, or 10-pound dumbbells.

☙ STRESS AND THE BODY

We don't want to give the impression that people living in the Mediterranean and eating a traditional Mediterranean diet didn't experience stress. Contemporary America is plagued by a different kind of stress, however—an insidious, chronic stress that often goes unrecognized. People who have all their basic needs met—food, clothing, shelter, warmth—fall prey to stresses from other sources. Financial difficulties, difficulties with relationships, demanding careers or jobs, parenting, or any number of other problems can become sources of long-term, chronic stress.

Exercise can help your body deal with stress more efficiently. Even if you exercise daily, however, you probably are still under plenty of stress. What is stress, exactly? Stress is a reaction in the body, sometimes called the fight-or-flight reaction, that prepares the body to handle extreme circumstances. Stress can be a good thing, and a survival mechanism. If we are confronted with danger, our body prepares us to react quickly to preserve our lives and the lives of those we protect.

When we sense danger (whether an approaching tiger or an approaching exam or an approaching speech), our bodies do certain things, all triggered by the release of two stress hormones, adrenaline and corticotrophin-releasing hormone. These hormones induce certain physical changes in the body:

- Blood platelets clump together, in preparation for a potential wound (to stop any bleeding).
- The immune system activates in readiness for trauma.

- Blood and blood sugar rush to the extremities and the muscles to prepare them for action.
- Muscles contract in readiness.
- Heart rate and breathing rate speed up and blood pressure rises.

After the danger has passed, a steroid hormone called cortisol signals the body to return to its normal state. The problem is that in modern life, some people are under so much stress that the body fails to return to its normal state. In others, cortisol, for whatever reason, doesn't signal the body as it should. The stressed or fight-or-flight state is not intended to be a permanent or long-term state. The immune system reverses its elevated function and becomes depressed, leaving the stressed person vulnerable. The clumping action of blood platelets over the long term can increase the risk of heart attacks. Too much cortisol in the body can depress immune function, trigger bone loss, and increase insulin production. One study on aging animals and humans links chronically high levels of stress hormones to memory loss.

The entire chemical process that takes place in a body under stress can go awry in many ways, but the upshot is that gearing our lifestyles to reduce stress is healthier both for our bodies and for our overextended minds. It is also quintessentially Mediterranean.

⊘ PEOPLE WHO NEED . . .

In traditional Mediterranean culture, people had many mechanisms for dealing with stress. Family bonds were often strong and of utmost priority. Friends and neighbors supported each other, helped each other when someone was in need, and spent time together.

People were also closer to the natural world than many of us are today. They worked the land, they spent time outdoors, and they weren't isolated most of the time from the natural world by cars, insulated and sealed homes, shopping malls, and hermetically sealed office buildings.

Whether exposure to nature has an effect on stress levels may be a matter of debate. Research on the subject is slim, but anecdotal evidence supports the theory. A more studied area concerns strong social ties as a weapon against stress. Strong friendships and a social network of support may strengthen the immune system, slow the aging process, reduce disease risk, even increase longevity.

A 1989 Stanford University study demonstrated that women with metastatic breast cancer who were involved in support groups lived an average of eighteen months longer than those who were not in a support group, and other research has demonstrated highly active natural killer cells in cancer patients who say they feel emotionally supported. Social support, it is theorized, increases white blood cell activity by decreasing stress. Another investigation published in a 1997 issue of the *Journal of the American Medical Association* linked a lack of diverse social contacts to an increased risk of developing colds—even more of an increased risk than for smokers, people with low vitamin C intakes, or people with elevated stress hormones!

⊛ LOW-STRESS LIVING

But how do we engage in more low-stress living? Moving to southern Italy or to a Greek island and living off the land with our best friends may sound nice, but it isn't very practical for most. Yet we can capture the spirit of such a life even as we continue living in our fast-paced society. Here are some tips.

- **Cherish your friends.** Nurture and expand your social contacts. If you sometimes feel isolated and unable to meet people, ask family members or acquaintances for ideas. Support groups, community groups, religious organizations, and universities or community colleges often have groups open to interested members of the community.

- **Try meditation.** Meditative techniques can be effective for relieving stress. We like visualization. Spend five or ten minutes each morning and each evening in solitude, eyes closed. Envision wandering the Grecian coastline, relaxing in a café in southern France, strolling through a museum in Florence, basking in the sun on a beach in southern Spain. A mini-vacation every day can recharge you and help your body to remember how relaxation feels.
- **Spend a little time outside every day.** Let the sun warm your skin (but wear a sunscreen!). Feel the breeze. Breathe the fresh air. If you live in a place where fresh air is a mere memory, make it a point to drive out of the city at least every few weeks so you can recall what the natural world looks like! In the meantime, plant a patio or windowsill garden with a few flowers or fresh herbs. Even in the winter months, you can enjoy, even cherish, the outdoors. Many of us who live in wintry climates know well the sense of calm and exhilaration of walking through new-fallen snow (stay safe, of course, and don't walk in blizzards or on icy pavement).
- **Put things in perspective.** So your toddler spilled a gallon of milk on the floor, your report blew out the window of your car, your son wants to join a heavy-metal rock band, and your computer crashed. These things may be inconvenient, irritating, even life changing, but they needn't throw you off course to such an extent that you get sick. Remember the Serenity Prayer about accepting what you can't change, changing what you can, and being wise

enough to know the difference? The words are of
Irish, not Mediterranean, origin, but their wisdom is
universal.

- **Exercise every day.** The world will seem like a
much nicer place. Whenever possible, forgo the
convenient machine and do things by hand.

- **Speak your mind—within reason.** Telling people
how you feel and what you think may help to relieve
stress if you can air your anxieties and get problems
out into the open. On the other hand, speaking in
anger may result in saying things you don't mean,
which can cause more stress in the future. Your best
bet may be to talk out your anxieties and worries
with an unbiased or sympathetic third party—family
members, friends, your partner, or a counselor.

- **Write about it.** A 1999 study of people with asthma
or rheumatoid arthritis revealed better health among
those who kept a journal to express their feelings
about stressful events in their lives. Writing how you
feel can be a great outlet for stress, and it doesn't
hurt anyone's feelings!

- **Embrace life.** Live in the here and now and treasure
every moment rather than letting your days slip
away unlived. Savor your food, stop and enjoy a
beautiful view, take time out for a walk in the fresh
air, take a hot bath, really listen to your loved ones,
and try to experience everything you do rather than
living on "automatic pilot."

- **Offer support, and ask for it.** Take advantage of
your friends and family in the best way, by being
there for them and letting them be there for you. A
long-term HIV-infected "nonprogressor" (someone
who has HIV but has remained healthy without developing full-blown AIDS) named Stephen Foster
described what other long-term HIV survivors have

in common: "This is a generalization, but people who are long-term survivors seem to be more concerned about living than dying. Instead of depending solely on pharmaceuticals, they reach out to as many types of support as are available to them. They do not isolate themselves, and they are willing to ask for support and give it to others."

- **Don't smoke and don't drink excessively.** One or two glasses of red wine per day is more than enough alcohol for most people.
- **Make relaxation a priority.** Schedule five or ten minutes each day to relax profoundly, undisturbed. Consider it an investment toward productivity and efficient functioning.
- **Rechannel your anger.** Anger can elevate cholesterol levels and raise blood pressure, and has been linked to depression. One of the best ways to control anger is to raise your exercise level and to identify things that trigger your anger and avoid them. When something bothers you, let people know instead of repressing your feelings. If your anger is out of control, seek counseling. A professional counselor can help you learn to deal with your anger.
- **Don't forget to follow the Mediterranean Diet Pyramid.** Eat accordingly.

⊛ QUESTIONS AND ANSWERS

⊛ How much longer do people live who exercise regularly?

About two to three years, which may not sound like much, but it is slightly longer than the amount of time average longevity would increase if all cancer was completely eliminated tomorrow.

❦ *Are certain activities more effective for certain health problems like heart disease or arthritis?*

Most moderate exercise is beneficial for most health problems, but some conditions necessitate an adjustment in an exercise plan. For example, arthritis can make exercise painful, so good ways to strengthen the heart and the muscles with minimal stress to joints include low-impact exercise like swimming and walking; stretching and toning exercise like yoga; and strength training.

Strength training is important for people suffering from osteoporosis. Studies show weight-bearing exercise may actually stop or reverse bone density loss.

Aerobic exercise appears to be most beneficial for diabetes, and moderate aerobic exercise works best for high blood pressure. Depression seems to respond to both aerobic exercise, especially in a social or group setting, and weight training.

❦ *Do people need more or less exercise as they age?*

More. Unfortunately, people tend to get less and less exercise as they age and as muscle strength and flexibility decrease, endurance decreases, and hormonal changes speed up certain changes such as loss of bone density. Exercise can halt or counteract many of these changes, making old age largely a matter of numbers, not of limitations.

❦ *Exercise is so boring! I can't keep it up for more than a couple of weeks.*

Exercise needn't be boring, and is most often considered boring by those who have a relatively narrow view of what exercise is. Exercise isn't limited to this or that machine at the gym, or a same ol' aerobics routine. Simply doing more for yourself rather than relying on automation can raise your activity level. Walk more, and walk faster. Spend your spare time moving—playing games, bicycling, swimming, or again, walking. You don't need to join a fitness club or buy any equipment to enjoy a more active lifestyle.

I live in an area where air pollution is a problem. Should I still exercise outdoors?

Exercising in air pollution can actually be detrimental to your health, increasing your risk of heart disease, suppressing your immune system, and increasing your chances of developing respiratory problems. Runners take in ten times as much air per minute as people standing still, and if that air is polluted, those pollutants enter your body ten times faster. If you have allergies or asthma, you are at an even greater risk of developing health problems from exercising in a polluted environment.

As nice as outdoor exercise is, if you live in a polluted environment, your best bet probably is to exercise indoors, whether that means finding a walking track at a local gym, joining a fitness center, or walking the local mall with your buddies. Whenever possible, take a day trip or a vacation to a nonpolluted area and take advantage of the fresh air by staying as active as possible.

In general, air pollution is at its worst during the hottest part of the day, so exercising in the early morning or evening will expose you to slightly cleaner air. If you hear on the news that pollution levels are high on a given day, stay inside. Don't walk or run near high-traffic areas, if possible. May to September is smog season, so summer may be the best time to exercise inside if you live in a big city.

❧ Is exercise important for children?

Yes! Obesity and even high cholesterol are increasing problems for American kids today. Too much television and too many video games? Too much junk food? Whatever the reason, the results are real. Encourage kids to get outside and stay active. Stock the cupboards and refrigerator with healthy snacks like fresh fruits, vegetables, and whole-grain bread and crackers. Low-fat cheese, low-fat milk, and low-fat yogurt are good snacks, too. The Mediterranean Diet Pyramid is also meant for children over the age of two. Perhaps most important, set a good example for your kids. If they see you eating healthy foods and staying active, they will want to do the same (even if they won't admit it!).

❧ My job is very stressful. Should I quit?

All jobs are stressful some of the time. If your job is a source of extreme stress in your life, however, you may want to consider what it is about your job that is causing you so much displeasure. Is it the working environment? The people? Are your skills underused or have you neglected to follow your dream?

We strongly support finding a life's work that engages and excites you. This can be a source of great pleasure and satisfaction. However, you may be able to fulfill this need with a hobby, a small business on the side, or another sort of part-time venture while keeping the job that provides you with security. If you are in a position to quit and follow your dream without risking the health or livelihood of people who depend on you, then why not go for it? It never hurts to have a sensible backup plan just in case. You should also have a realistic, researched, and detailed plan of action. However, you may be one of those who can someday say, "I lived my dream!"

❀ **The Mediterranean lifestyle sounds perfect for me. Should I move there?**

Ah, the dream of many. Keep in mind that the Mediterranean has changed a lot since the days when Ancel Keys was researching the traditional Mediterranean diet. Many of our modern conveniences have entered the region and transformed it. There are still plenty of rustic and rural pockets left, however, and lots of really great food.

You may be able to satisfy much of your Mediterranean longing by reading. Travel accounts abound, and tourist guides for the area are also in plentiful supply in bookstores. Browse the Internet for Mediterranean information, recipes, and traveling tips.

If you have the means, you might also consider vacationing in the Mediterranean. Try the food, the climate, and the lifestyle for yourself. Consider a hiking tour or other active endeavor, and don't forget the local cuisine. Just remember to eat like the people in the Mediterranean eat, not like the tourists eat. You'll save yourself a 20-pound weight gain. The more you visit, the more friends you make, the more you may indeed decide to move there. You wouldn't be the first American to relinquish modern life for a simpler existence in the Mediterranean.

If you do visit, write us a letter and tell us how you liked it. We wish we were there right now!

❀ **Is the Mediterranean diet and lifestyle really something practical to live with every day in America?**

The Mediterranean Diet Pyramid, an active lifestyle, more contact with the natural world, strong social ties, a sense of community, and diligent practice of stress-management techniques? Why, this is modern living at its finest. Welcome to the twenty-first century!

9: *Losing Weight and Living Well on the Mediterranean Diet*

Americans are hungry. We eat a lot, and in general, we weigh a lot . . . a lot more than we should, for good health! According to the National Heart, Lung, and Blood Institute, more than half of American adults are overweight or obese, a number that has steadily increased over the years. It seems no matter how much we learn about nutrition, exercise, and how to stay healthy, as a nation, we just keep getting fatter!

If you have a body mass index, or BMI, of over 29, current research suggests that you are indeed dangerously overweight, or obese. A BMI of 25–29 usually signifies overweight, and a BMI between 19 and 25 is typically in the healthy range. A BMI of under 19 is considered underweight. What's your BMI? Here's how to figure it out (it just takes a little math, so get your calculator ready): weight in kilograms divided by height in meters squared equals BMI. For us Americans who don't use the metric system, figure your BMI via the following formula:

1. Multiply your weight in pounds by 704.5
2. Multiply your height in inches times itself (square it).

3. Divide the first number by the second number. The total equals your BMI.

So, for instance, if you weigh 150 pounds and you are five feet, seven inches tall, you would multiply 150 by 704.5, which equals 105,675. Then, you would take your height in inches, which is 67, and square it, to equal 4,489. Finally, 105,675 divided by 4,489 equals 23.5, which is a BMI in the healthy range.

Unfortunately, many of us have BMIs above and beyond the healthy range. To combat our expanding waistlines and growing susceptibility to chronic diseases like heart disease and cancer, Americans love to spend time and money exploring the diet du jour—whatever new fad diet promises easy weight loss without deprivation or effort. Of course, most of us know that sensible food choices and an active lifestyle are the best way to combat overweight, but then again, what we know and what we do are often worlds apart.

Some recent trends in the diet wars include low-carb, high-protein diets; high-carb, low-fat diets; diets based on blood type; diets based on raw foods; vegetarian or vegan diets; diets that exclude certain types of foods like dairy products or wheat; pro-soy or anti-soy diets; diets that advocate six small meals each day, and diets that advocate one huge meal per day in combination with a twenty-hour daily fast.

On top of that, the media bombard us with conflicting information about exercise for weight loss. Should we exercise just twenty minutes three times a week, or an hour every day? Should we lift weights, or focus on aerobic activity? Should we train hard, or take it easy? Is walking the best exercise, or is it running, or kickboxing, or yoga, or the latest gym machine? It's enough to make a person throw up his or her hands and order a pepperoni pizza with extra cheese! How the heck are we supposed to know what to eat and what not to eat?

Americans try to make sense of the conflicting information by trying the latest fads that might work. The recently popular trend toward controlled carbohydrate diet plans such as the Atkins Diet, Sugar Busters, and Protein Power may well be a backlash from the last decade's high-carb, low-fat diets, which resulted in a high refined-carb intake and a lot of health problems for a lot of people. Unfortunately, reports of scientific studies are often oversimplified, and a lot of Americans were led to believe that replacing high-fat foods with "low-fat" or fat-free commercial products containing high sugar and refined flour, rather than focusing on vegetables, fruits, and whole grains was healthy. Many "fat-reducing" dieters who did not increase their vegetables, fruit, and whole grain consumption, but simply replaced high-fat fare with commercial fat-free products, got hungrier and hungrier, and ultimately consumed more and more calories.

When people heard they could actually lose weight with a seemingly simple diet focused on protein, many felt great relief. The logic behind these diets appeared sound. As a nation, our sugar consumption had risen considerably, and replacing sugar with protein to battle the bulge seemed sensible.

And what was more convincing was that high protein diets appeared to work for many people. All around us, people were swearing by tightly controlled carbohydrate eating plans and they were losing weight—at least in the short term. But the longevity of the initial excitement and results of these diets has proven to be questionable. It appears restricting your carbohydrate intake is hard for many to maintain, making long-term weight maintenance difficult. Eating strictly high-protein foods can be difficult, and many find themselves craving carbohydrate foods after a while. And there appear to be side effects to these diets, such as bad breath and lethargy, which result from a low-carbohydrate, metabolic condition called ketosis. And the jury is still out as to whether eating a low-carbohydrate, high-protein diet will produce lifelong healthy weight maintenance, not to mention an ideal health profile.

Although the general high-protein, low-carbohydrate diet craze is not new—having been popular during the 1970s—a dietary concept that has recently come into center focus is something called the *Glycemic Index* (GI), a scale that rates foods according to how quickly they break down and release sugar into the bloodstream. The GI system was originally developed to help people with diabetes stabilize blood sugar levels, and some scientists believe the system can also work for insulin-sensitive people who may be "pre-diabetic," or prone to developing diabetes. Those advocating GI-based diets believe that foods with a high GI number cause insulin levels to rise and fall more quickly, and promote a faster carbs-to-fat transformation in the system. The result: weight gain. GI-based diets limit processed foods like white flour, white rice, and sugar, because of their high GI numbers, but they also suggest avoiding many healthy choices, including potatoes, carrots, and apples, that appear to cause as much of an insulin release as refined grain products and sugar.

While some studies show that consuming foods or meals containing foods that have a high glycemic index results in less satiety compared to eating other foods with a low GI number, many nutrition researchers warn that the *Glycemic Index* concept has been overly simplified. If you eat a potato on an empty stomach, it may break down quickly in your system, but when eaten as part of a well balanced, Mediterranean-like meal, the picture is much different.

The glycemic metabolic concept is complex, and may only lead to undue confusion. We, the authors of this book, are particularly fearful that *Glycemic Index* may become the next fat-free debacle—causing an almost panic response to avoid anything that's "high GI" in the same way many wonderful, healthful foods, such as nuts, seeds, and olive oil were avoided because they were deemed "high fat."

In general, if you are concerned about unstable insulin levels, which can lead to diabetes, not to mention binge eating and obesity, nutritionists suggest following a few basic principles.

- Choose carbohydrates in their whole forms: whole grains like whole wheat, oats, barley, whole corn, brown rice, whole-wheat pasta.
- Avoid added sugar.
- Eat vegetables and fruits in their whole form, rather than in processed juices and sauces.
- Eat a bit of protein and/or a little "good" fat along with your carbohydrates. A way to do this is to munch on a few nuts with whole grain crackers for an afternoon snack.
- Exercise daily.

Of course, these recommendations sound a lot like the very diet we've been telling you about in this book! The Mediterranean diet is a time-honored and time-tested diet, and research continues to explore it. In fact, a very large study out of Greece, which followed an impressive 22,000 men and women between the ages of twenty and eighty-six for almost four years, recently studied longevity, heart disease, and cancer rates as they correlated to how closely people followed a traditional Mediterranean diet. Those adhering most closely to a diet that included approximately a pound of vegetables a day cooked with olive oil, wine in moderation with meals, and approximately 30–40 percent of calories from primarily monounsaturated fat, had the longest lives and the lowest heart disease and cancer rates, and indeed, disease rates and longevity appeared to directly correlate with how closely study participants followed this traditional diet! This study, out of the University of Athens Medical School, was published in 2003.

Another recent study out of the Brigham and Women's Hospital Department of Nutrition in Boston compared the effects of a low-fat diet and a moderate-fat diet on long-term weight loss and maintenance. Both diets contained equal calories, but the moderate-fat diet contained 35 percent of calories from primarily monounsaturated fats, while the low-fat diet contained 25 percent of calories from primarily monounsaturated fats. The study showed that not only did the moderate-fat group lose more weight after two years, but had greater adherence to the diet. More people in the low-fat group dropped out of the study, and while both groups lost about the same amount of weight during the first year, a significant number of the low-fat-diet group gained much of that weight back by the two-year mark.

Remember the Lyon Diet Heart Study, which we mentioned in the first chapter? In this study of six hundred patients who had recently had heart attacks and were under the age of seventy, half the patients were placed on a Mediterranean diet with 30 percent calories from fat, while the other group was given general dietary and lifestyle counseling about a low-fat diet with physician instructions. The study was discontinued after just two years because the effects on the group following the Mediterranean diet were so dramatic compared to the other group that it was deemed unethical to withhold information on the Mediterranean diet from the low-fat diet group. Nineteen months after the study, the original Mediterranean diet group was still eating in a Mediterranean-style fashion, which is incredible considering that when it comes to nutritional studies, patient adherence to the study diets is one of the hardest factors to control and maintain.

But when it comes right down to your daily life, we don't want you to be thinking about this or that study. We want you to be living, enjoying good food, being a part of nature and community, active and full of energy. Remembering the simpler, more physically active, healthier life of the traditional Mediterranean can help to guide our choices. Staying healthy and achieving a desirable weight are best achieved not through extreme changes, complete elimination of certain food groups, or tricks, fads, or gimmicks. Staying healthy is a matter of achieving balance and making choices that healthfully feed our bodies, minds, and spirits.

Yet some of us may want more specific instructions because when faced with a choice between a doughnut and a bowl of cereal or a salad and a bag of chips, many people may find it difficult to make the right choice.

We think we can help. Knowing what we know about nutrition, weight loss, and healthy living, and knowing what we know about the time-tested Mediterranean way of life, we strongly believe that the very best way to proceed for the average American trying to improve health and drop excess weight is to use something all of us have access to, and something that doesn't cost a penny: common sense.

Should we eat lots of processed food filled with sugar, fat, and chemicals? Common sense will tell us no. Should we eat a lot of the foods we know contain high levels of vitamins, minerals, and health-promoting phytochemicals and fiber? Common sense says yes. Should we engage in sedentary lifestyles that promote weight gain and low energy? No. Should we maintain connections with friends and loved ones for emotional support? Yes. Should we use our bodies to move, work, run, and play? Yes. Should we eat food we enjoy? Of course! The trick is to balance all those messages that our common sense sends to us, while keeping up on the latest research regarding diet, nutrition, and good health, taking everything we read with just a grain of (Mediterranean sea) salt and always applying common sense.

To help you even further, we've provided two separate meal plans to get you started. The first is a week of meals in the Mediterranean spirit, specifically geared for those trying to drop excess weight. These meals include filling whole grains, healthy fats in reduced amounts, lots of fresh fruits and vegetables, low-fat and nonfat dairy, lean meat, and plenty of fish. They are satisfying, fulfilling, and inspirational.

The second meal planner is also Mediterranean in spirit, for those who are already at a healthy weight, or who have finally achieved their weight-loss goals. This second meal planner will help you to continue to live in the Mediterranean spirit and together, these planners can help you to form the basis for a lifelong habit of healthy eating and Mediterranean living.

☙ ONE-WEEK MEAL GUIDE TO HELP WITH WEIGHT LOSS IN THE MEDITERRANEAN SPIRIT

To help launch your new mode of eating in the true spirit of the traditional Mediterranean, we've provided a week's worth of meals. This is by no means a strict diet you must follow, but simply a menu plan to provide inspiration and a bit of guidance. *Please note that any eating plan should be individualized.* For weight loss, especially, we strongly recommend consultation with a dietitian or other qualified nutritionist to determine the optimal weight reduction plan for you. Remember that daily activity is as important as sensible eating for weight loss or weight maintenance, as well as time for rest, relaxation, and fun with family and friends.

We did not include beverages here, such as alcohol or coffee, because these are optional items in the Mediterranean diet plan. Including such foods in your diet is an individual decision, and should be based on your overall health status. Green tea has been given a lot of attention lately as a promoter of good health, and it can also be included if you wish. We suggest caffeine and alcohol in moderation, if at all, when trying to lose weight.

Many of the recipes listed here can be found in Part II of this book. Remember, always, these important guidelines when planning your Mediterranean-inspired meals:

- Enjoy your food! Savor the texture, flavor, and color of your food. This is good eating beyond nutrition. It is a feast for the senses. The more you enjoy your food, the more Mediterranean in character your meals will be.
- Watch portion sizes! Balance your caloric intake with your activity level. If weight loss is desired, aim to expend more calories than you consume. We know this may be easier said than done, especially in our society. But, if you are finding that losing

weight is difficult, consultation with a registered dietician or other qualified health care professional will help guide you in determining what your daily caloric intake and output should be. The following meal planner is just a guide; portion sizes must be adjusted to meet individual needs.

- Drink lots of water! Aim for six to eight 8-ounce glasses of good-quality water each day.
- Exercise, Rest, and Relax! These three important lifestyle components can greatly affect eating habits, and are shown outside of the Mediterranean Diet Pyramid. Get outdoors and move in any way that you can, and value the importance of rest and relaxation for overall health.

Recipes with an asterisk* are featured in the recipe section of this book.

☽ MONDAY

Breakfast
- 1 cup oatmeal made from whole oats topped with fresh blueberries and 1 tablespoon raw walnuts
- 1 cup low-fat, calcium-fortified soy milk

Lunch
- 1 whole-grain pita pocket filled with salad greens, mustard, and 2–3 ounces tuna
- 1 cup red grapes
- 1 cup nonfat or low-fat plain yogurt with 1 teaspoon honey or real maple syrup

Snack
- 6–12 whole almonds, 1–2 whole wheat breadsticks

Dinner
- 1 cup Tuscan Bean Soup* over ½ cup brown rice
- 2 cups green salad with tomatoes and 1 tablespoon Olive Oil Vinaigrette*
- 1 serving Cinnamon Oranges*

☼ TUESDAY

Breakfast
- 2 small Orange-Banana Muffins*
- 1½ cups low-fat, calcium-fortified soy milk
- ½–¾ cup berries

Lunch
- 1 serving Sweet Corn and Toasted Walnut Risotto*
- 1 serving Macedonian Salad*

Snack
- Baby carrots with 1–2 tablespoons Hummus Tahini*

Dinner
- Swordfish Steaks with Tomato-Caper Sauce*
- Greek Salad*
- Wine-Stewed Figs with Yogurt Cream*

☼ WEDNESDAY

Breakfast
- 1 egg plus 2 egg whites, scrambled with ¼ cup skim milk, black pepper, and fresh herbs
- 1 slice whole-grain toast
- ½ grapefruit

Lunch
- 1 serving Gazpacho*
- 1 serving Olive Oil Cheese Crisps*
- 1 apple
- 1 cup low-fat, calcium-fortified soy milk

Snack
- Caponata* on ¼ whole-grain pita pocket

Dinner
- Gingered Lamb Stew*
- Steamed broccoli tossed with olive oil, minced garlic, and a few hot pepper flakes
- ½ cup nonfat frozen vanilla yogurt topped with prune puree or berries

⊘ THURSDAY

Breakfast
- 1 cup whole-grain flaxseed cereal
- 1 cup low-fat, calcium-fortified soy milk
- 2–4 whole, pitted dates or dried plums (prunes), sliced into cereal

Lunch
- 1 serving Tabbouleh Salad*
- 1 serving Sautéed Shrimp with Chilies*
- ½–1 cup pineapple chunks

Snack
- 1 serving Broiled Tomatoes*

Dinner
- Mediterranean Salad Sandwich with Harissa*
- Stuffed Peaches*

☼ FRIDAY

Breakfast
- ¾ cup Almond Couscous*
- ½ cup mandarin oranges

Lunch
- Falafel with Tomato-Cucumber Relish*
- Green salad with shredded carrots and Olive Oil Vinaigrette*
- 1 pear
- 1 cup skim milk or low-fat, calcium-fortified soy milk

Snack
- Broccoli florets dipped in 1 teaspoon olive oil mixed with 1 tablespoon lemon juice

Dinner
- Mediterranean Citrus Chicken*
- ½ cup spinach sautéed with 1 teaspoon olive oil, 1 tablespoon balsamic vinegar, and minced garlic
- Apple slices dipped in 1 tablespoon almond butter

☼ SATURDAY

Breakfast
- 2 flaxseed or whole-grain waffles with sliced banana
- 1 cup low-fat, calcium-fortified soy milk

Lunch
- Moroccan-Spiced Cod*
- Beet Salad with Walnuts*
- 2 fresh apricots with 1 cup nonfat plain or naturally sweetened yogurt

Snack
- 1 slice sprouted-wheat bread with 1 teaspoon olive oil

Dinner
- Tuna Steaks with Green Sauce*
- 1 cup green beans steamed with minced fresh basil and ¼ cup crumbled feta cheese
- 1 fresh nectarine

⊛ SUNDAY

Breakfast
- Frittata (open-faced omelet) made with 1 egg, 2 egg whites, 1 teaspoon dill, ½ cup sliced portabella mushrooms, and ¼ cup skim milk or water, mixed together and cooked in a nonstick pan with olive oil cooking spray
- 1–2 slices whole-grain toast
- 1 cup low-fat, calcium-fortified soy milk

Lunch
- Mediterranean Vegetables with Walnuts and Olive Vinaigrette*
- ½ cup White Beans with Cumin*
- 1 small whole-grain roll

Snack
- 1 Serving Broiled Tomatoes*

Dinner
- 1 serving Chicken Raisin Stew*
- Green salad and Olive Oil Vinaigrette*
- ½ whole-grain pita pocket with 1 tablespoon Tapenade*

⏣ ONE-WEEK MEAL GUIDE TO HELP WITH WEIGHT MAINTENANCE IN THE MEDITERRANEAN SPIRIT

You've achieved a healthy weight and you are feeling great—full of energy and life. The longer you eat, move, and live in the Mediterranean spirit, the easier it becomes. Now you can begin to diversify your food choices even more, but keep your focus on plant foods, whole grains, whole vegetables and fruits, lean proteins, lots of fresh fish and shellfish, and healthy fats, primarily monounsaturated. By now, you may not even have a butter dish in your home anymore, and we hope that bottle of olive oil gets lots of action. Cooking and eating in the Mediterranean spirit is a lifelong adventure, so welcome to the next stage of your journey.

Feel free to substitute similar foods for each item, to add additional fruits, veggies, and whole grains if you are still hungry, or to adjust portion sizes according to need. Again, it is important to note that any eating plan should be highly individualized to take into account your age, height, weight, gender, activity level, and health profile. Consultation with a dietitian or other qualified nutritionist can help determine your individual needs. The point is to eat a variety of healthy foods corresponding to the Mediterranean Diet Pyramid, and to enjoy every bite.

The following menu will provide a guide for a well-balanced eating plan. While it is not designed for weight loss or gain, you might find you have so much energy and feel so good about yourself while eating it that you easily maintain your weight. We have been less specific about exact amounts and portion sizes in this section, trusting you to eat the amount of healthy food that satisfies your hunger. If you find yourself eating too-large portions, refer back to portion sizes on recipes, or to the above weight-loss meal planner for a reminder about portions.

☝ MONDAY

Breakfast
- 1 to 2 cups whole-grain cereal topped with a handful of dried fruit and ½ ounce dried or roasted nuts
- 1 cup low-fat, calcium-fortified soy milk

Lunch
- 2 slices whole-grain bread with 1 ounce part-skim mozzarella cheese, 3 (or more) large leaves of Romaine lettuce, 2 thick slices ripe tomato, a dash of olive oil, 3 ounces low-fat turkey breast, and a sprinkling of salt and pepper
- 1 fresh pear

Snack
- 6 to 12 whole almonds, with whole-grain crackers (amount depending on serving size)

Dinner
- Moroccan Vegetable Stew*
- Couscous
- Green salad with shredded carrots, drizzled with Olive Oil Vinaigrette*
- Fresh berries with ½ cup of vanilla soy ice cream

☝ TUESDAY

Breakfast
- Banana bread made with olive or canola oil and whole-grain flour (1 to 2 slices, depending on size of loaf)
- ½ ounce nuts or seeds (which may also be mixed into the banana bread)
- 1 fresh orange

- 1 cup warm or steamed low-fat, calcium-fortified soy milk, with a touch of vanilla extract mixed in, and topped with a dash of cinnamon

Lunch

- One cup pasta mixed with a bit of olive oil, topped with ½ ounce of walnut pieces, 1 tablespoon grated Parmesan cheese, and fresh parsley
- Green salad with Olive Oil Vinaigrette*
- Stuffed Peaches*

Snack

- Baby carrots with Hummus Tahini*

Dinner

- Tuscan Bean Soup*
- 1 to 2 slices whole-grain bread
- ½ to 1 ounce low-fat cheese
- Macedonian Salad*

☽ WEDNESDAY

Breakfast

- Oatmeal or other hot cereal (¾ to 1 cup dry mixed with 1 to 2 cups skim or low-fat milk to cook), then mixed with 1 to 2 heaping spoonfuls of pumpkin puree (or canned pumpkin), a tablespoon each of raisins, snipped dried apricots, and walnuts, and a sprinkle of brown sugar or maple syrup

Lunch

- Mashed white beans spread on whole-wheat pita bread
- Greek Salad*
- Citrus Compote*

Snack
- 1 slice whole-grain toast with 1½ tablespoons peanut or almond butter

Dinner
- Paella Valencia*
- Steamed broccoli tossed with olive oil, minced garlic, and a few hot pepper flakes
- ½ cup nonfat frozen yogurt topped with prunes or berries

⊛ THURSDAY

Breakfast
- Whole-grain bagel with 2 tablespoons almond or peanut butter
- 6 whole, pitted dates
- 1 cup low-fat, calcium-fortified soy milk

Lunch
- Mediterranean Vegetables with Walnuts and Olive Vinaigrette*
- ½ cup pineapple slices mixed in ½ to 1 cup of plain nonfat yogurt

Snack
- Green beans, steamed, chilled, and dipped in Olive Oil Vinaigrette*

Dinner
- Vegetable pizza topped with ½ to 1 ounce part-skim mozzarella cheese
- Stuffed Artichokes*
- Baked Apples and Pears*

⊛ FRIDAY

Breakfast
- 1 to 2 cups whole-grain cereal, dried fruit, and ½ ounce nuts, mixed in 1 cup plain, nonfat yogurt

Lunch
- Tapenade* on whole-grain sesame crackers
- Green salad with tomatoes, ¼ ounce sliced almonds, and Olive Oil Vinaigrette*
- 1 tangerine
- 1 cup low-fat, calcium-fortified soy milk

Snack
- Broccoli florets dipped in a plain nonfat yogurt blended with low-fat cottage cheese (half of each)

Dinner
- Seafood Risotto*
- ½ cup spinach sautéed with olive oil and minced garlic
- Grilled bananas

⊛ SATURDAY

Breakfast
- Whole-grain pancakes made from scratch with olive or canola oil and nonfat yogurt or buttermilk, topped with ½ to 1 cup fresh fruit, ¾ cup nonfat yogurt, and ½ ounce nuts such as pecans, almonds, or walnuts (you can also toss the nuts into the batter)
- 1 cup low-fat, calcium-fortified soy milk

Lunch
- Falafel with Tomato-Cucumber Relish*
- Green salad with fresh plum tomatoes and Olive Oil Vinaigrette*
- 4 whole dried apricots

Snack
- 1 slice whole-grain toast topped with peanut butter and sunflower seeds

Dinner
- Eggplant Parmesan
- 1 cup Italian green beans with oregano
- Fresh fruit salad

☉ SUNDAY

Breakfast
- Grapefruit broiled with a sprinkling of brown sugar
- 1 scrambled egg topped with 1 ounce cheese
- 2 slices whole-grain toast

Lunch
- Ratatouille*
- White beans tossed with olive oil, fresh lemon juice, and fresh or dried basil

Snack
- 1 ounce low-fat cheese on whole-grain crackers

Dinner
- French Cassoulet*
- Green salad and Olive Oil Vinaigrette*
- Homemade custard made with skim milk or low-fat, calcium-fortified soy milk and topped with berries

PART II

Recipes for Enjoying the Mediterranean Diet

Mediterranean Snack Food: An Art Form, a Meal

In the Mediterranean, snacking is a serious business. From the afternoon snack in the Italian trattoria to the elegant antipasti that precede the fanciest restaurant meals, from street fare of vendors working carts or bicycles or spreading their wares on a blanket on the street to the Spanish tapas bar where food and drink and fellowship can be found in equal parts, from the midafternoon meze of Greece or Turkey to a quick bite of skewed, spiced meat in Morocco, snacking in the Mediterranean serves many purposes: It fortifies the body and soul during that long stretch between the midday meal and the evening supper. It may accompany wine or ouzo or other alcoholic beverages, or it may be the perfect foil for a hot cup of tea. Perhaps most importantly, snacking brings people together, furthering a sense of community.

But snacking takes on a more insidious form in contemporary America. We eat our meals at our desks or in front of the TV or the newspaper, barely noticing the food as it passes from lips to stomach. Because we barely remember those meals, we find ourselves still seeking satisfaction, so

we snack between meals, all the while sitting at our computers or in front of our televisions. And then one day, we find
that the number on the scale is a lot higher than it used to be!
It's no wonder. We eat distractedly, so we neither taste nor
recognize how much we've consumed. Combined with a
sedentary lifestyle, such a method of eating spells disaster,
for health and for spirit, as we become further and further removed from a sense of appreciation for the food that nourishes us.

The first step may indeed be to cut down on the amount of
food we consume while upping the amount of attention we
pay to the eating process. Less food of higher quality can
help to nurture our palates and our appreciation for really
good food. For this reason, the Mediterranean snack can be,
for Americans, a quite adequate and delicious meal. A hard-
boiled egg sprinkled with cumin and a pinch of sea salt, a
wedge of rosemary foccacia, and a fresh piece of fruit make
a delicious breakfast. Who wouldn't be satisfied with a
lunch of capered fish cakes with olive-anchovy relish and a
salad of fresh greens dressed in olive oil and a splash of
vinegar? Or how about a plate of almond couscous and a
serving of white beans with basil and cumin for dinner?
Grilled stuffed portabella mushrooms perhaps? A lovely
plate of sautéed shrimp with chilies and broiled tomatoes on
crispy rounds of French bread toast?

In this section, we'll give you some ideas for
Mediterranean-inspired "snacks" in just a sampling of their
many wonderful incarnations. These meals are light, satisfying, portion-controlled, and best of all, fantastically memo-
rable.

✺ TAPAS (APPETIZERS)

In Spain, tapas are the snacks, usually served in bars, designed to accompany sherry. However, anyone can enjoy tapas, as a midday snack or as a light lunch—alcohol not required! Tapas can include any kind of Spanish-inspired hors d'oeuvres, so use your imagination. Add a dish of almonds lightly tossed with sea salt. Wrap slices of melon in paper-thin strips of proscuitto. Enjoy a few slices of Spanish goat cheese. Or serve a heaping plate of fresh, bite-sized vegetables with a shallow bowl of olive oil sprinkled with pepper and a pinch of salt, for dipping.

And of course, don't forget the plate of olives. Try green, black, speckled . . . experiment to see what you like, but please avoid the "California-style" black ones, which are green olives treated with lye to turn them black. These can't begin to approach the naturally brine-cured olives from Greece, Spain, Morocco, or elsewhere in the Mediterranean. The superiority of taste in these olives far outweighs the slightly higher cost.

(Serving suggestion: Invite friends! It would be a shame to deprive others of such a delightful eating experience!)

✺ CAPERED FISH CAKES WITH OLIVE-ANCHOVY RELISH

You've heard of crab cakes. This version is lighter, maintaining that "comfort food" quality, but with a Mediterranean flair. Depending on your calorie needs and taste preferences, they can be either quickly fried in olive oil for a delightful crispy texture, or baked in the oven—not as crisp, but plenty satisfying nevertheless. Either option is delicious, especially when topped with the briny, sparkling taste of olive-anchovy relish. You can almost see the Mediterranean when you taste this exquisite combination! If you can't find them or don't like them, you can leave the sardines out of the fish cakes and the anchovies out of the relish, but both add such a pleasant depth to the flavors that we hope you will choose to give them a try.

By the way, Eve's seven-year-old son/taste tester loved these, although he suggested that next time she "leave out the little green things" (i.e., the scallions). We suggest keeping the "little green things." The relish is strongly flavored and not particularly kid-friendly, but the fish cakes on their own (dare we say with a little ketchup?) make a pleasant supper for all ages.

Fish Cakes

1 pound cod fillet
½ cup vegetable broth
1 teaspoon extra virgin olive oil
3 scallions, finely chopped, including some of the green part
1 tablespoon capers, drained and minced
2 cloves fresh garlic, peeled and minced
2 sardines, drained and chopped
¼ cup whole-wheat or all-purpose flour
1 cup dried whole-grain bread crumbs
1 tablespoon grated Parmesan cheese
2 large eggs
1 tablespoon fresh dill (or 1 teaspoon dried dill)
2 tablespoons extra virgin olive oil
Lemon wedges

Heat a nonstick skillet over medium heat. Add the olive oil and vegetable broth and tilt the pan to coat. Add the cod fillet. Cook until the fish is cooked through and flakes nicely, about 15 minutes, flipping the fillet halfway through cooking. If the fish falls apart into the vegetable broth, that's fine—you'll be flaking it apart anyway.

Remove the cooked cod to a large mixing bowl and flake apart with a fork. Cod is a firm-fleshed fish, so if a fork isn't working very well, don't be afraid to get in there with your fingers and rub the fish to break up the big chunks. Add the scallions, capers, sardines, garlic, and flour.

In a small bowl, combine bread crumbs and cheese. Add ½ cup of the bread crumb mixture to the fish. Stir to combine. Mix the eggs with a fork in a small bowl or cup, then add the eggs and dill to the fish mixture. Stir thoroughly until the mixture resembles a thick paste.

Spread remaining ½ cup bread crumbs on a large plate. Dust your hands with a little flour, and take about ¹⁄₁₆ of the mixture in your hands. Shape it into a patty, then press the patty into the bread crumb mixture, coating both sides. Repeat with remaining mixture to make six patties.

To fry: Put 2 tablespoons of olive oil in a medium skillet, just large enough to hold the six patties (or a smaller one, doing the patties in batches, although if you do it this way, you may have to add more olive oil). Turn burner to medium, and heat until the oil releases its aroma, about 5 minutes. Place patties in pan and cook until golden brown and crispy, flipping once, about 5 minutes on each side.

To bake: Preheat oven to 425 degrees. Rub a thin layer of olive oil on a cookie sheet, or spray with olive oil nonstick cooking spray. Place patties on the cookie sheet so they don't touch one another. Bake for 30 minutes or until golden brown on both sides, flipping patties halfway through cooking time.

Serve hot, room temperature, or cold, with or without a salad, or stuffed in a pita with fresh spinach. If desired, top with olive-anchovy relish (recipe below).

Serves 6.

Olive-Anchovy Relish

½ cup black olives (not "California-style"), pitted and
 coarsely chopped

½ cup green olives, pitted and coarsely chopped
2 tablespoon capers, drained
1 clove fresh garlic, minced
2 anchovy fillets, drained and coarsely chopped
1 tablespoon extra virgin olive oil

Mix all ingredients. Spoon over fish cakes or other fish or meat.

Tip: To pit olives quickly, use a cherry pitter or press the flat side of a wide knife against the olive to crush it, then pick out the pit.

Makes 1 cup, or approximately 6 servings.

🌿 TAPENADE

This olive/caper/anchovy paste originated in France. It tastes great on pita, baguette, or your favorite bread. It's similar to the olive-anchovy relish above, but chopped down to be more of a paste. In fact, you can pulse the above recipe in a food processor (add a tablespoon of brandy if desired) for a version of tapenade. Or try this one, below. Pair it with bread for spreading and a Greek salad, and you've got lunch! To make this a vegetarian dish, just leave out the anchovies.

1 cup black olives (not "California-style")
¼ cup capers
12 anchovy filets
2 garlic cloves, minced
⅓ cup extra virgin olive oil
Juice of half a fresh lemon
1 tablespoon brandy (optional)

In a blender or food processor fitted with the metal blade, combine all ingredients and process to a grainy paste (tapenade is sometimes called the "caviar of Provence," so think caviar when determining the proper texture). Tapenade keeps in the refrigerator for about a week. If the paste is too dry or doesn't blend well, add another tablespoon of olive oil. Serve as a dip for raw vegetables or a spread for fresh bread.

✍ SAUTÉED SHRIMP TWO WAYS: WITH GARLIC AND CHILIES

Make this recipe a "Two-Way," as indicated, or double the garlic and eliminate the bell peppers and pepper flakes for an entire batch of Garlic Shrimp. Alternately, double the bell peppers to make an entire batch of Chili Shrimp.

1 pound medium raw shrimp
2 tablespoons extra virgin olive oil
4 large fresh garlic cloves, peeled and minced
½ red bell pepper, finely chopped
1 teaspoon hot pepper flakes

Peel shrimp and rinse in a colander. Set aside. In a large skillet, heat the extra virgin olive oil on medium until the oil releases its aroma, about 3–5 minutes. Add garlic and stir to coat. Cook until garlic begins to turn golden.

Add half the shrimp and toss with garlic, stirring until shrimp is pink and fully cooked and garlic is crispy and deep gold, about 5–8 minutes more.

Remove pan from heat and using a slotted spoon, remove shrimp from pan. Put shrimp on a paper towel and set aside.

Return pan to heat. It should still contain plenty of olive oil and some leftover garlic. Add the finely chopped red bell pepper and hot pepper flakes. Stir to coat and cook until red bell pepper begins to soften, about 3 minutes.

Add remaining shrimp and toss with peppers and garlic,

stirring until shrimp is pink, fully cooked, and coated with peppers.

Remove remaining shrimp from pan with slotted spoon to a double layer of paper towels to drain. Place garlic and chili shrimps in separate dishes, topping chili shrimps with any remaining sauce in the pan. Serve this dish with toothpicks for appetizers, or serve over a bed of fresh greens, or toss with pasta. Delicious hot, room temperature, or cold.

Serves 4 as a meal, 6–8 as appetizers.

ALMOND COUSCOUS

Couscous is easy to make and delicious, but never more so than with the addition of chopped raw almonds and Mediterranean spices. This recipe is quick, easy, and elegant, with a pleasing zing.

1 cup dry whole-grain couscous
2 cups water
½ cup raw almonds, coarsely chopped
½ cup currants
1 teaspoon each: ginger, cinnamon, cumin
Dash each: salt, red pepper, black pepper
1 tablespoon fruity olive oil

Put couscous in a bowl or large measuring cup. Add the boiling water and immediately cover with a lid or tea towel. Let stand for 5 minutes, or until couscous has soaked up all the liquid.

Stir in almonds, currants, and spices. When thoroughly combined, stir in olive oil. Allow to sit at room temperature or in the refrigerator for 2 hours, to allow flavors to blend and infuse the couscous.

This tastes even better the second day. My favorite way to eat this is as a next-day breakfast. On summer mornings, it's delicious straight out of the refrigerator! On chilly days, re-heat gently in the microwave or on the stovetop. (Reheating too quickly can scorch the currants.)

🌿 BACON-WRAPPED DATES

I make these at every party I have because they are always a favorite, surprisingly easy and incredibly delicious. The key is quality ingredients. If you can't find pancetta, you can use regular bacon, which will do in a pinch.

> 12 fresh dates
> 3 ounces Spanish goat cheese (or other goat cheese)
> ½ pound pancetta, or enough to make 24 four-inch
>   slices (might be slightly more than a half pound
>   depending on how thick the bacon is cut, so if buying
>   by weight, err on the heavy side, or just tell the
>   butcher how many 4-inch slices you need)

Cut dates in half with a sharp knife and remove seeds. Cut 24 one-inch slivers of goat cheese. Push a sliver of goat cheese into each date. Wrap each date with half a slice of pancetta or other bacon and secure with a toothpick.

Put dates on a broiler sprayed with nonstick cooking spray or rubbed with a little canola oil. Broil until bacon is crisp and goat cheese is golden brown and bubbly, about 12–15 minutes.

Serves 12 as appetizer, 6 as a light lunch when served with a salad.

🌿 MEZE

The meze table consists of a variety of appetizers for after-noon snacking. A common fixture along the eastern shores of the Mediterranean from Greece to Turkey to Syria, meze can consist of just a few dishes or a huge spread of food, which may or may not accompany alcohol. This collection of meze dishes is inspired by the cuisines of the eastern shores. What could be easier than a few chunks of pita bread dipped in a bowl of hummus? A few olives and chunks of goat cheese with grilled vegetables? Or a shish kebab to keep you fortified until dinner? Delicious!

In many areas, you can find hummus, baba ghanoush (eggplant dip), tabbouleh (a salad of bulgur wheat, tomatoes, and parsley), and other common dishes of the Mediterranean meze table freshly made in the deli or in the gourmet section of the store. They may not be quite as fresh as if you made them yourself, but for a quick lunch when time is short, they make a great alternative to drive-through fast-food!

🍃 HUMMUS TAHINI

This paste of chickpeas and sesame butter tastes delicious, is packed with protein and fiber, and will make you forget all about butter when topping your favorite bread. It's a staple in our house and a favorite at parties. Kids love it, too, as a welcome alternative to the peanut-butter-and-jelly rut.

Traditionalists make this with dried chickpeas and soak them overnight. If you have the patience, go for it, but for those of us who want to whip up a quick, spur-of-the-moment bowl of hummus, rinsed chickpeas from a can work just fine. Organic beans and organic tahini taste the best.

1 can chickpeas, drained and rinsed well in a colander
½ cup tahini (sesame paste)
2 cloves fresh garlic, peeled
Juice from ½ fresh lemon

1 tablespoon extra virgin olive oil
1 tablespoon chopped fresh parsley

Combine chickpeas, tahini, garlic, lemon juice, and olive oil in a food processor fitted with a steel blade. Process until smooth. Put hummus into a bowl and sprinkle parsley over the top. Serve with wedges of pita, slices of baguette, or even corn chips! Or spread on bread or even half a bagel and top with fresh spinach for a delicious, nutrient-dense sandwich.

🌿 WHITE BEANS WITH CUMIN

White beans are mild, filling, and satisfying. We eat them in our house often because family members of all ages enjoy them. This simple recipe combines canned, rinsed, organic white beans with fresh basil and cumin. The flavors are intense, and a bowl of these beans makes an excellent and practically effortless meal. You can also try these beans on top of greens for an interesting salad. Top with a dash of olive oil and a splash of vinegar.

1 can white beans (navy beans, great northern beans, or
*   any other white beans)*
1 tablespoon fresh chopped basil (or 1 teaspoon dried basil)
½ teaspoon cumin
1 teaspoon extra virgin olive oil

Drain beans and rinse well in a colander. Put in a bowl. Combine with basil, cumin, and olive oil. Enjoy at room temperature. These are also yummy the next day, straight from the refrigerator, especially when paired with crisp, chilled, fresh greens. To cut the calories and fat in this dish, just eliminate the olive oil. It's still delicious!

✍ SHISH KEBAB

The next time you fire up the grill, why not try shish kebab instead of the standard "burgers and hot dogs"? Shish kebab may be street food in the eastern Mediterranean, but here in America, it tastes like an extra special treat. Skewer meat and vegetables separately, as the meat will take longer to cook.

For the meat/fish marinade:

1 tablespoon olive oil
Juice of 1 fresh lemon
1 garlic clove, minced
1 teaspoon dried thyme, crushed
1 teaspoon dried cumin powder
½ teaspoon paprika
¼ teaspoon cayenne pepper
Dash black pepper

For the shish kebab:

1 pound either:
  - *lamb (for authenticity)*
  - *beef tenderloin (if you can't find or don't want to eat lamb)*
  - *cod or shrimp (for the coastal version)*
  - *or a mixture of the three, for variety!*
1 medium red onion
1 green bell pepper
1 red bell pepper
16 cherry tomatoes
4 cups fresh greens
4 pita loaves

Mix all the marinade ingredients in a bowl.
Cut the meat or fish into bite-sized cubes. Add to mari-

nade and stir to coat the meat. Cover and refrigerate for at least 2 hours, or overnight.

Cut the onion and bell-peppers into bite-sized chunks. Fill one or two long skewers with onion, one or two long skewers with bell peppers, and one or two long skewers with cherry tomatoes.

Put marinated meat/fish cubes on long skewers.

Spray grill or broiler pan with cooking spray or canola oil. Heat grill or preheat broiler.

Grill or broil meat or fish until done, turning as needed to cook all sides evenly. Lamb and beef take approximately 30 minutes, cod and/or shrimp about 15 to 20 minutes, or to desired doneness. About halfway through meat cooking time, add onion and pepper skewers to the grill or broiler. During final 5–10 minutes, add tomato skewers. Keep watching meat and vegetables, and remove at desired doneness. (Some people like their meat and vegetables well done, some less so.) During last 5 minutes, wrap pita loaves in foil and put on the grill to warm them.

When all meat and vegetables are cooked, remove meat to a plate and vegetables to a separate plate. Fill each pita with meat, vegetables, and greens, as desired.

Serves 4.

ANTIPASTI

In Italy, the fanciest of meals begin with antipasti, or a collection of Italian hors d'oeuvres made just for the purpose of announcing a grand feast and warming up the palate in preparation for the wonders to come. But antipasto can be a meal or midday snack in itself.

You don't need a recipe to concoct a pile of crudités and a bowl of fresh green olive oil topped with pepper for dipping, which can satisfy the urge to crunch in a way no potato chip ever could. A few marinated mushrooms, artichokes, and olives on a bed of greens make a luscious lunch, and you can buy these, imported from Italy, in any gourmet food store, and in many grocery stores, too. In the mood to cook? Try a few of these Italian-inspired recipes.

✤ CAPONATA

This traditional Sicilian vegetable relish is great as a sauce over meat, or as a chunky dip for slices of bread or crostini. Salt the eggplant first so it absorbs less oil. We like Nancy Harmon Jenkins's method of placing the eggplant cubes in a colander, salting them well, and covering them with a heavy plate weighted with a can of tomatoes to drain the juices from the eggplant. I like to sauté the eggplant first in a non-stick pan with olive oil cooking spray to further minimize the "oil-sponge" effect, before adding the eggplant to the rest of the caponata, but you can also cook it quickly in a little olive oil until golden if you prefer a heavier dish. You can use green peppers instead of the red and yellow, but the red and yellow make this relish look brighter and more beautiful. You can roast the peppers first, if you have the patience and love that melt-in-your-mouth effect, but since the peppers cook for so long in the caponata, we usually don't bother roasting them first. You can make this dish faster at a higher heat, but it won't be nearly as good! A long, slow cooking time results in a deep, rich, intense flavor that is well worth the wait, especially since it can cook while you are making dinner or cleaning the kitchen. Make it the day before you want to serve it as part of an antipasti or impressive party hors d'oeuvres surrounded by a ring of crispy crostini (bread toasted until crisp under the broiler) or Olive Oil Cheese Crisps (see recipe on page 264), bringing it to room temperature before serving. Or serve it hot or warm—also delicious, if less authentic.

1 medium eggplant
1 heaping tablespoon sea salt
2 tablespoons extra virgin olive oil
1 medium yellow onion, chopped
2 cloves garlic, minced
1 medium red bell pepper, chopped
1 medium yellow bell pepper, chopped
6 fresh tomatoes, blanched and peeled,
    or 1 large can tomatoes
½ teaspoon (or less) red pepper flakes (optional)
1 tablespoon red wine vinegar
2 teaspoons sugar
1 cup black olives (not "California style"),
    pitted and coarsely chopped
¼ cup capers, rinsed and drained
1 tablespoon chopped fresh Italian (flat-leaf) parsley
1 tablespoon chopped fresh basil (or 1 teaspoon dried)

Cut eggplant into dice-sized cubes. Put in a colander and toss with the sea salt. Place a paper towel over the eggplant, then put the colander in the sink. Top with a plate or bowl to weight down the eggplant (use a bowl if the colander is large and a plate doesn't put any weight on the eggplant. Weight the plate or bowl with something, such as a 1-pound can of tomatoes. Allow the eggplant about 30 minutes to drain into the sink.

Spray a nonstick skillet with olive oil cooking spray and heat over medium-high heat. Rinse and dry the eggplant well, then cook in the skillet until golden brown, tossing so all sides of the cubes are cooked. Remove the eggplant to a paper towel.

Return skillet to heat, lowering heat to medium-low. Add olive oil, onion, and garlic. Sauté until onion is soft and translucent, about 15 minutes. Add bell peppers, tomatoes, red pepper flakes, vinegar, and sugar, and cook until mixture thickens and breaks down into a more or less homogenous mixture (it should look more like a sauce than a stir-fry), about 30 minutes, then continue to simmer for an additional 30 minutes, stirring often to keep the caponata from sticking and burning.

Finally, add capers, olives, parsley, and basil. Stir thoroughly, and remove caponata from the heat. Allow to cool to room temperature, then serve or store in an airtight container in the refrigerator for up to 3 days.

Serves 6.

🌾 OLIVE OIL CHEESE CRISPS

These crostini-like crisps are the perfect thing for dipping into caponata, tapenade, or olive-anchovy relish, but they are also delicious on their own and make a crunchy, nutritious snack for kids.

*Six slices of your favorite whole-grain bread (try whole-
   wheat, multigrain, oat bread, pumpernickel, etc.)
¼ cup extra virgin olive oil
3 cloves garlic, peeled and halved
¼ cup grated Parmesan cheese
Dash sea salt*

Cut the bread slices into strips, about an inch wide. Brush strips lightly with olive oil on both sides and spread on a cookie sheet or broiler pan. Broil until light golden brown and crispy. Remove from broiler. Rub each crisp on both sides with the cut side of a garlic clove (about ½ per slice), then sprinkle crisps with the cheese and a light sprinkle of sea salt. Return to broiler just until cheese melts and begins to brown slightly. Remove from broiler and cool. Serve alone or with dip. Double the recipe for a party hors d'oeuvre.

Serves 6.

🌿 ROSEMARY FOCACCIA

Those puffy disks in the supermarket bakery labeled "focaccia" have nothing on the homemade variety, which takes more time but is well worth the effort. This is a nice project when you'll be home for the day, such as on a rainy weekend. Foccacia can be topped with anything before it is baked—a little cheese, a few paper-thin tomato slices, a scattering of anchovies, a few chopped olives, or your favorite fresh herb. This recipe replaces some of the flour with semolina, a traditional Italian ingredient in many types of bread.

> 1 packet active dry yeast
> ¼ cup warm water plus 1 cup warm water
> 2 cups unbleached all-purpose flour
> 1 cup whole-wheat, rye, or barley flour
> 1 cup semolina
> 1 tablespoon sugar
> 1 teaspoon sea salt
> 1 tablespoon extra virgin olive oil
> ¼ cup olive oil for rubbing over the dough
> Additional teaspoon or so of semolina for
>   the bottom of the pan
> Dash of cumin or paprika (optional)

Put the ¼ cup warm water in a glass measuring cup. Add 1 teaspoon sugar, and sprinkle the yeast over it. Let sit for about 15 minutes, or until frothy.

Put the flour in the bowl of a mixer fitted with a dough hook, or in a large mixing bowl. Make a well in the center of the flour and pour in the yeast mixture, sea salt, olive oil, and remaining water. Mix with the dough hook for five minutes, or mix the flour/yeast mixture with a wooden spoon to incorporate all the dry and wet ingredients until the dough forms a sticky ball and knead for about 5 minutes. Pour the ¼ cup olive oil over the top and smooth the dough with your hands, rubbing olive oil over the entire surface and forming into a ball by tucking under the edges. Cover with a tea towel and put in a warm place to rise until double, about 90 minutes.

Preheat oven to 400 degrees.

Turn out the dough on a floured surface and knead it for 2 minutes. Shape into a ball. Dust a pizza stone or pan with a few sprinkles of semolina, and place the dough on the stone, pizza pan, or 9×13-inch baking pan (foccacia are often rectangular, too). Pat down or roll into a disk the size of the stone or pan, as thin as possible. Brush the top of the foccacia with olive oil and sprinkle with rosemary leaves, pressing them into the dough. If desired, dust lightly with cumin or paprika.

Bake for approximately 30 minutes, or until the foccacia is a deep golden brown. Let the foccacia cool to room temperature, then cut into wedges or squares. Serve with olive oil for dipping, or use the foccacia to make sandwiches!

Serves 12.

🌿 BROILED TOMATOES

What better use for an overstock of summer tomatoes, fresh from the garden, just the way they are eaten in the Mediterranean? This recipe is a simple two-step process with fantastic results, especially if you use the best possible fresh tomatoes. To save on fat and calories, skip the searing-in-oil step and put raw tomatoes straight onto the broiler pan topped with salt, bread crumbs, cheese, and herbs. For this version, you won't need any olive oil.

6 medium, fresh, vine-ripened tomatoes
2 tablespoons extra virgin olive oil
½ teaspoon sea salt
¼ cup hard dry bread crumbs

2 tablespoons grated Parmesan cheese
2 tablespoons chopped fresh basil or
    2 teaspoons dried basil

Core the tomatoes, then cut them in half through the middle (not through the stem end).

Heat the olive oil in a nonstick skillet over medium-high heat until it releases its aroma (about 5 minutes). Place the tomatoes, cut sides down, into the hot oil and cook for 5 minutes, or until the cut sides are brown and look crispy. Scoop the tomatoes out with a spatula and place, cut sides up, on a broiler pan sprayed with olive oil cooking spray. Sprinkle tomatoes with salt, bread crumbs, cheese, and basil.

Broil the tomatoes on a broiler pan until the cheese melts and the tomato tops are a deep, crisp, golden brown. Serve hot or warm.

Serves 6.

STUFFED PORTABELLA MUSHROOMS

Portabella mushrooms practically beg to be stuffed. Those huge caps almost look like dinner plates! So why not heap them with bread, garlic, herbs, and just a little bit of meat? This is a filling entrée or an elaborate part of a pre-entrée antipasti. Feel free to leave out the sausage or replace it with vegetarian "sausage" crumbles for a meatless option.

7 portabella mushroom caps (6–8 inches in diameter)
4 slices whole-grain bread
4 ounces ground turkey sausage or
    ground spicy Italian sausage
½ teaspoon caraway seeds
½ teaspoon ground sage
1 teaspoon extra virgin olive oil
½ cup onion, finely chopped

1 stalk celery, finely chopped
1 clove garlic, minced
6 teaspoons grated Parmesan

Lightly rinse the mushroom caps and wipe dry. Set aside 6 caps. Finely chop the seventh and put in a large mixing bowl. Set aside.

Toast the 4 slices of bread in a toaster oven or on the broiler until crisp. Cut into small dice. Add the bread cubes to the chopped mushrooms.

Heat a medium skillet over medium heat. Cook the sausage until no pink remains. Drain. Stir in caraway seeds and sage. Add to bowl with mushrooms and bread cubes.

Add olive oil to skillet without rinsing it out. Heat over medium heat until oil releases its aroma, about 3 minutes. Add onion, celery, and garlic. Sauté until onion is translucent and garlic is golden, about 10 minutes. Add the vegetables to stuffing. Toss to thoroughly mix the dressing.

Preheat oven to 400 degrees.

Brush a cookie sheet or baking pan lightly with olive oil. Put remaining mushroom caps on the cookie sheet with the bottom sides up. Using a spoon, scoop stuffing evenly onto the 6 caps. Sprinkle each with a dash of sea salt and top each with 1 teaspoon grated Parmesan cheese.

Put mushrooms in the oven and bake for 45 minutes, or until mushrooms are tender and topping is nicely browned.

Serves 6.

🌿 MEDITERRANEAN CHUTNEY

This chutney is similar to the above recipe for caponata, except it doesn't include eggplant and it isn't cooked, so it retains a crisper texture, the small chunks of vegetables mingling but not melting into one another. Serve this with cut-up raw vegetables, thin slices of baguette, or pita triangles. It's a refreshing twist on the salad, and a pleasant way to get your fresh vegetables!

8 fresh tomatoes, cored, seeded, and chopped
6 scallions, chopped, including greens
2 stalks celery, chopped
1 green bell pepper, cored, seeded, and chopped
1 red bell pepper, cored, seeded, and chopped
1 cup green olives, pitted and chopped
¼ cup capers
1 tablespoon extra virgin olive oil
Handful Italian (flat-leaf) parsley leaves, chopped

Combine all ingredients, mixing well. Allow to sit for 2 hours to overnight to allow flavors to blend. Serve at room temperature.

Serves 8.

☞ SALADS

The Mediterranean salad is an entirely different animal
(vegetable?) than salad in America. We know the salad as a
first-course fixture of restaurant meals and an on-the-side
collection of iceberg lettuce, tomato wedges, and shredded
cheddar in a small bowl next to the dinner plate. Sure, we
have our variations: the ubiquitous chicken Caesar salad
slathered in rich dressing, the cured-meat and processed-
cheese-heavy chef's salad, the bacon-and-egg-rich Cobb
salad. However, in the Mediterranean tradition, salad is various and appears in many guises.

A tabbouleh salad featuring bulgur wheat, fresh parsley,
and tomato may form an integral part of a Middle Eastern
meze. A plate of ripe tomatoes in all their singular glory may
serve as an hors d'oeuvres or part of an antipasti, a simple
yet flavorful introduction to the tastes to come. But then
again, a bowl of fresh greens dressed in olive oil and a little
balsamic vinegar may end a meal, and collections of vegetables, fresh and marinated, with or without grains, alone or in
interesting seasonal (and ever-changing) combinations
could show up anywhere—on the breakfast table in
Provence, as part of a tapas bar in Spain, or as one link in a
long chain of delightful surprises served one after another—
or all at once!—in an Italian trattoria.

✤ OLIVE OIL VINAIGRETTE

Americans may love salad, but often select their salad dressings from a wide assortment of bottles on the supermarket
shelf containing an array of creamy, tangy, or vinaigrette-
type dressings in every color and flavor imaginable. In the
Mediterranean, the dressing of a salad is a much simpler
matter: a little lemon juice or vinegar, some salt and pepper,

and a good dose of extra virgin olive oil. Try mixing up this olive oil vinaigrette at home and you may find it is not only more economical but more delicious and fresh-tasting than bottled dressings. It's wonderful on fresh greens as well as drizzled over fresh raw or cooked vegetables.

*2 tablespoons balsamic vinegar, good-quality red wine
    vinegar, or fresh lemon juice
1 clove garlic, minced
1 teaspoon salt
Dash of freshly ground black pepper
½ cup extra virgin olive oil*

In a small bowl, combine the vinegar or lemon juice, garlic, salt, and pepper. Whisk in the olive oil until well blended. Serve immediately over fresh greens.

Makes about 8 tablespoons, or enough to dress salad for 4 to 6 people.

🌿 GREEK SALAD

A traditional Greek salad made with fresh produce and kalamata olives is a culinary experience not to be missed. What could be more Mediterranean? Served on a platter, it makes an impressive addition to the dinner table. We've chosen to leave out the traditional anchovies in this dish, but feel free to add a few anchovy fillets along with the olives if you fancy them. They add a seductively briny tang.

This salad is most transcendent if you purchase the best and freshest, locally grown, organic ingredients (just as they do in the Mediterranean). Savor every bite!

*2 cups bite-sized pieces romaine lettuce
2 medium tomatoes, cut into bite-sized wedges*

½ cup thinly sliced red onions
*½ cup thinly sliced cucumbers (cut them into half-
    circles if they are too large to be bite-sized)*
½ cup thinly sliced green bell peppers
½ cup thinly sliced red bell peppers
1 tablespoon minced fresh Italian (flat-leaf) parsley
½ cup crumbled good-quality feta cheese
10 pitted kalamata or other good-quality Greek olives

Dressing

¼ cup extra virgin olive oil
1 tablespoon fresh lemon juice
1 small clove garlic, minced
*½ teaspoon minced fresh oregano
    (or ¼ teaspoon dried oregano, crushed)*

Spread the romaine lettuce on a roomy platter. Arrange the tomato wedges over the lettuce. In a bowl, combine the onions, cucumbers, peppers, Italian parsley, and half the feta cheese, then spread over the lettuce and tomatoes. Top with the olives and remaining feta cheese.

To make the dressing, whisk together the oil, lemon juice, garlic, and oregano, then drizzle over the salad. Toss just before serving.

Serves about 4.

✍ BEET SALAD WITH WALNUTS

If you can find golden beets and don't care for that crimson color all over your salad, make this salad with that pale, delicious variety of beet. Or, if you love the vibrant hue of red beets, make this salad the more traditional way. You can also make this recipe with canned beets if you are in a hurry. It will still be good, but not quite *as* good. If you can't find walnut oil, replace it with olive oil.

1 pound fresh beets
¼ cup sweet white wine (such as an Italian Moscato)
1 tablespoon extra virgin olive oil
1 tablespoon walnut oil
1 tablespoon balsamic vinegar
1 clove garlic, minced
1 shallot, finely chopped
¼ teaspoon sea salt
½ cup walnut pieces
1 tablespoon chopped fresh tarragon

Preheat oven to 400 degrees.

Cut off the tops of the beets. If you like beet greens, reserve these for another meal. Wash the beets, then enclose them in a packet of tinfoil. Bake for 1 hour, or until tender.

Cool the beets, unwrap them, and when you can handle them, peel off the skins. Cut into bite-sized cubes. Set aside.

In a large salad bowl, add the wine, oils, vinegar, garlic, shallot, and sea salt. Stir to combine. Add beets and stir to coat. Cover and let the beets marinate for up to 1 hour, or put in the refrigerator overnight.

Just before serving, stir in the walnuts and sprinkle with fresh tarragon. Serve cold or at room temperature.

Serves 4.

✒ MACEDONIAN SALAD
(A "SPIRITED" FRUIT SALAD)

One of the most beloved ways to eat fruit in the Mediterranean, besides fresh, raw, and out of hand, is to macerate it in a little wine or other alcohol. Alcohol isn't always the norm, however. Soaking fruit in a little sugar syrup or citrus juice is also a Mediterranean tradition, so choose whichever suits your taste.

Feel free to substitute equivalent amounts of your favorite fruit for any of the fruits listed below. This "salad" could be dessert, or part of a tapas table, part of the main meal, or a beautiful meal in and of itself. Made with citrus juice instead of wine, it makes a delicious breakfast.

> 1 lemon, brought to room temperature
> 1 cup cubed peaches or nectarines
> 1 cup strawberries, halved, or other berries
> 1 cup seedless grapes (green, red, or a combination)
> 1 cup melon cubes or balls (cantaloupe, honeydew, or
>   watermelon)
> ¼ cup sugar (optional, but it brings out the juice)
> ½ cup red wine (try a Zinfandel for a rich, peppery
>   effect, a Pinot Noir for a lighter, flowery taste) or
>   2 tablespoons liqueur (Grand Marnier, kirsch, or
>   amaretto are all good choices) or ½ cup orange juice

Roll the lemon gently on the counter, then cut into quarters. Set aside.

Combine the remaining fruit gently in a large bowl and immediately squeeze each lemon quarter over the fruit, stirring gently to keep the fruit from breaking or getting mashed. Sprinkle with the sugar, then drizzle with the wine, liqueur, or orange juice. Toss gently.

Allow to sit at room temperature for 10 to 15 minutes (not more than 1 hour), then serve.

Serves 6.

🌿 MEDITERRANEAN VEGETABLES WITH WALNUTS AND OLIVE VINAIGRETTE

The purpose of this salad is to feature the freshest, most recently picked, seasonal produce available. Make it in the spring with the newest, crispest baby peas, beans, asparagus, and new lettuces. Or make it at the height of summer with all the bounty from the local farmer's market stands—tomatoes, zucchini, bell peppers. Then add a Mediterranean flair with a handful of walnuts and a vinaigrette dressing spiked with olives and capers.

This salad is ultimately flexible. Make it with one or two vegetables, or with ten! It all depends on what you can find at your local farmer's market, produce stand, or your own garden.

> 4 cups fresh, seasonal vegetables (use as many or as few at a time as desired: shelled peas, peapods, bite-sized bits of lettuce, radishes, sliced carrots, sliced summer squash and zucchini, chopped fresh tomatoes, sliced bell peppers . . . whatever is best and freshest and most irresistible at the moment)
> ½ cup walnut pieces, lightly toasted on a baking sheet in a 375-degree oven for about 10 minutes
> ¼ cup extra virgin olive oil
> ¼ cup white wine or white grape juice
> 1 tablespoon white wine vinegar
> ½ cup pitted, finely chopped green olives
> 1 tablespoon capers
> Freshly ground black pepper

Put the vegetables and walnuts in a large salad bowl, tossing lightly to mix them.

In a 2-cup glass measuring cup, pour the olive oil, wine or white grape juice, vinegar, olives, and capers. Stir to combine. Pour dressing over the vegetables. Top salad with freshly ground black pepper, and toss until thoroughly combined. Serve immediately.

Serves 6.

🌿 TABBOULEH SALAD

The ever-popular tabbouleh salad sticks to your ribs and makes you feel very, very good. Some versions have more or less bulgur, more or less parsley, more or less chopped vegetables. We like this version. Make it the day before you plan to serve it. You can peel, seed, and chop the tomatoes the day before and store in an airtight container in the refrigerator, to add before serving. Otherwise, the tomatoes get too mushy.

To peel and seed a tomato, put tomatoes in a sieve with a handle and plunge into vigorously boiling water. Keep submerged for about 30 seconds, then plunge into ice water. When tomatoes are cool enough to handle, slip the skins off. If they resist, return them for a few more seconds to the boiling water. Then cut the tomato in half through the stem end. Take each half in your palm, cut side facing out, and gently squeeze out the seeds. Chop the remaining tomato. Yes, this process gets easier with practice.

To seed a cucumber, after peeling, cut the cucumber in half lengthwise and scrape out the seeds in the middle of each half, then chop.

1 cup bulgur wheat
1½ cups finely chopped Italian (flat-leaf) parsley leaves
1 large, fresh romaine lettuce leaf, thick part of rib removed, coarsely chopped
8 scallions, chopped, including some of the green
1 medium cucumber, peeled, seeded, and finely chopped

1 tablespoon chopped fresh mint leaves or 1 teaspoon
    dried mint, crushed between your palms to release
    the flavor
¼ teaspoon ground black pepper
½ teaspoon cinnamon
¼ teaspoon nutmeg
2 tablespoons extra virgin olive oil
Juice and finely chopped zest from 1 lemon
3 tomatoes, peeled, seeded, and chopped
Sea salt, to taste

Put the bulgur wheat in a sieve and sift through it with
your hands to be sure it is free from extraneous material
(husks, small stones, etc.). Rinse thoroughly under cold water, letting the water run out through the bottom of the sieve.
Sift through to make sure all the bulgur is rinsed. Set over
the sink to drain.

In a large mixing bowl, combine parsley, lettuce, scallions, cucumber, mint, pepper, cinnamon, nutmeg, olive oil,
lemon juice, and lemon zest. Add the bulgur, mixing so all
the wheat is coated with vegetables and oil. Cover and refrigerate overnight, or for at least 6 hours.

Before serving, stir in tomatoes and add sea salt to taste.
Serve cold, or allow to come to room temperature first.

Serves 6.

⊛ SOUPS AND STEWS

Many Americans grew up on soup from a can, or those little packets of dried noodles and yellow powder that, when mixed with water, transformed into something resembling chicken noodle soup. What a far cry from the fresh soups and stews of the Mediterranean, infused with fresh herbs and vegetables just picked from the garden or plucked from the vendor, flavored with just a hint of savory lamb or chicken, egg, or fish, mussels, oysters, and shrimp straight from the sea. Get back in touch with nature's bounty with these Mediterranean-inspired recipes for soups and stews that make the most of the very best ingredients.

🌿 GAZPACHO

This Spanish favorite is hard for some to comprehend. Cold soup? And why not? Loaded with nutritious, fresh vegetables, gazpacho has a sparkling fresh taste with just a hint of spice—the perfect remedy for a torrid summer day, especially if you are feeling too lazy even to chew.

Traditional gazpacho often includes bread ground into the soup, but we prefer a more intense vegetable flavor and like to make this soup *sans* bread.

> 4 peeled, seeded, chopped ripe tomatoes (To peel,
>   immerse tomatoes for about 30 seconds in boiling
>   water to loosen the skins, plunge into ice water, then
>   peel when cool enough to handle. The skins should
>   slip right off. Cut in half and squeeze out the seeds,
>   then chop the "meat.")
> 2 cloves garlic, minced
> ½ cup chopped red onion
> ½ cup chopped bell pepper (any color)
> ½ cup peeled, chopped cucumber

¼ cup extra virgin olive oil
Juice of one freshly squeezed lemon
1 cup organic vegetable broth with enough ice cubes
    added to make 1½ cups liquid
¼ teaspoon ground cumin
Dash of cayenne pepper

In the bowl of a food processor fitted with the metal blade
or a blender container, combine all the ingredients and process until smooth. Chill at least 2 hours, or overnight. Serve
from a pitcher on the veranda, or take it to the beach!

Serves about 4.

TUSCAN BEAN SOUP

We love bean soup. Filling, warm, hearty, and soul-
nourishing, this bean soup, inspired by traditional recipes
from Tuscany, nourishes all year long but makes an especially nice supper on a chilly fall evening.

1 large yellow onion, chopped
2 ribs celery, chopped, including some of the greens
3 cloves garlic, minced
1 tablespoon extra virgin olive oil
1 tablespoon flour
1 tablespoon fresh rosemary leaves,
    or 1 teaspoon dried rosemary
½ teaspoon dried thyme
1 large bay leaf
Freshly ground black pepper, to taste
Four 14½-ounce cans reduced-sodium,
    organic chicken broth
One cup frozen baby lima beans, rinsed and drained
One 15-ounce can garbanzo beans, rinsed and drained
One 15-ounce can red beans, rinsed and drained

2 tablespoons tomato paste
1 cup barley
*1 medium red potato, unpeeled (cut out eyes and bad
    spots), cut into ½-inch cubes*
2 sliced carrots
1 cup packed, slivered spinach leaves

In a large saucepan, sauté the onion, celery, and garlic in
the oil 2 to 3 minutes; stir in the flour, herbs, garlic, and pepper, and sauté until the onions are tender, 2 to 3 minutes
longer. Add the chicken broth, beans (you can add the lima
beans, frozen), and tomato paste to the saucepan; heat to
boiling. Add the barley, potato, and carrots. Return to a low
simmer, and cook for 25 minutes. Stir in the spinach. Cook
for 5 minutes more. Remove from heat, fish out the bay leaf,
and serve hot with a good loaf of bread.
    Serves 8.

🌿 MOROCCAN VEGETABLE STEW

This vegetable stew is highly spiced with the flavors of
African cuisine. Make it for an elegant lunch, or serve it as a
first course at a dinner party. (Or any time!) This soup is
nutrient-dense and will fill you with energy and good feeling. Make it in the summer when you need a recipe for all
those tomatoes, zucchini, and other garden overflow and
serve it gently warmed, rather than piping hot. Or freeze
portions to reheat during the chillier days of fall.

1 medium eggplant, unpeeled, cut into 1-inch cubes
1 tablespoon sea salt
6 small onions, cut into quarters
4 cloves garlic, minced
2 tablespoons extra virgin olive oil

1½ teaspoons ground cinnamon
1 teaspoon ground cumin
¼ teaspoon ground turmeric
¼ teaspoon ground cloves
Pinch of red pepper flakes
Freshly ground black pepper to taste
3 fresh tomatoes, seeded and chopped (peel if desired)
3 medium zucchini, quartered lengthwise, then sliced
2 medium sweet potatoes, peeled and cut into
    1-inch pieces
1 green bell pepper, cored, seeded, and chopped
3 ribs celery, sliced
One 15-ounce can chickpeas, rinsed and drained
One 15-ounce can red kidney beans, rinsed and drained
1 cup organic chicken broth
2 tablespoons minced Italian (flat-leaf) parsley

Place the eggplant in a colander. Sprinkle with sea salt, cover with a paper towel, and then with a plate or bowl. Put the bean cans for this recipe on the plate or bowl to help press out the juices from the eggplant. Let stand for 15 to 30 minutes.

Meanwhile, heat a Dutch oven or large saucepan over medium heat. Add 1 tablespoon of oil and sauté the onions and garlic until onion becomes translucent but not brown, about 5 minutes. Add an additional tablespoon of oil, then add the eggplant. Sauté for an additional 5 minutes, or until the eggplant turns golden brown. Add cinnamon, cumin, turmeric, cloves, cayenne pepper, and black pepper. Stir to combine for 2 minutes.

Add the remaining ingredients except the parsley to the Dutch oven. Heat to boiling; reduce the heat and simmer, covered, until the vegetables are tender, about 20 minutes. Stir in the parsley and serve hot, with pita wedges.

Serves 8.

✒ SOUPA AVGOLEMONO

This famous Greek egg-and-lemon soup makes a delicious sauce over meat or vegetables, as well as a glamorous and beautiful soup that is surprisingly easy to prepare.

> 6 cups organic chicken broth
> ¼ cup short-grain white rice
> 1 tablespoon water
> 1 tablespoon cornstarch
> 3 large eggs
> 3 tablespoons fresh lemon juice
> 1 tablespoon chopped fresh Italian (flat-leaf) parsley
> Salt and freshly ground black pepper to taste

In a medium saucepan, heat the chicken broth over medium-high heat until it comes to a boil. Add the rice and allow to boil for about 20 minutes, or until the rice is cooked. Reduce the heat and allow to simmer gently (not boiling).

Meanwhile, combine the cornstarch with the water, stirring until dissolved. Set aside. In a small bowl, beat the eggs until light, whisk in the lemon juice, and stir in the cornstarch/water mixture. Quickly whisk in ¼ cup of the hot stock. Then slowly add the egg mixture to the simmering stock a little at a time, stirring briskly and constantly about 2 minutes until the soup thickens slightly. Stir in the parsley, season with salt and pepper to taste, and serve immediately.

Serves 8.

✒ GINGERED LAMB STEW

This delicious stew features tender bits of lamb in a rich, savory sauce. Traditionally, cooks would prepare this stew using homemade stock, but if you don't have the time to make your own stock (we never seem to!), you can buy many different varieties of very good organic beef, chicken, and vegetable broth. The stew will still be good, warming, and comforting. The long stewing time fills the stew with lamb flavor but the bulk of the ingredients are vegetables and herbs, each of which perfume the stew in its own unique way.

> *1 pound lean, boneless lamb shank*
> *1 tablespoon flour*
> *1 tablespoon cumin*
> *2 teaspoons ground ginger*
> *1 teaspoon cinnamon*
> *2 tablespoons extra virgin olive oil*
> *1 yellow onion, chopped*
> *2 cloves garlic, minced*
> *1 carrot, diced*
> *2 ribs of celery, diced*
> *1 small sweet potato, peeled and cut into 1-inch cubes*
> *3 cups homemade beef stock or purchased organic beef broth*
> *Salt and freshly ground black pepper*

Cut the lamb into 1-inch cubes.

In a small bowl, mix the flour, cumin, ginger, and cinnamon. Add the lamb and toss to coat all the pieces.

Heat the olive oil in a medium skillet over medium-high heat. When the oil releases its aroma, add the lamb along with any leftover seasoning mix, and sauté until the meat is browned on all sides. Remove the meat with a slotted spoon and set aside.

Turn heat down to medium. Add onion, garlic, carrot, celery, and sweet potato to the skillet. Cook, stirring constantly, until vegetables just begin to brown, about 10 minutes.

Add 1 cup beef stock to the skillet, scraping to release any bits of meat and vegetables stuck to the skillet. Add lamb and remaining stock. Bring stew to a boil, then turn heat down to low. Simmer the stew for 1 hour, adding more beef stock or water as necessary to keep the stew from drying out and sticking. Turn heat to medium-low, and simmer for 1 hour. Serve hot or warm, with pita bread.

Serves 8.

🌾 CHICKEN RAISIN STEW

The surprising addition of raisins to this stew adds depth and richness without adding any fat.

> *1 stewing chicken, 2–3 pounds, cut into parts*
> *½ teaspoon sea salt*
> *¼ teaspoon freshly ground black pepper*
> *1 teaspoon turmeric powder*
> *½ teaspoon saffron threads*
> *1 large onion, chopped*
> *3 tablespoons finely chopped fresh Italian*
> *   (flat-leaf) parsley*
> *1 cup water*
> *1 cup raisins*
> *1 cup orange juice*
> *2 teaspoons ginger*
> *1 teaspoon cinnamon*
> *1 teaspoon cornstarch*
> *4 cups cooked white or brown rice*

Rinse the chicken pieces and pat dry. Put in a Dutch oven or stock pot. Add salt, pepper, turmeric, saffron, onion, and parsley to the chicken, then pour in the water. Cover and heat over medium.

Meanwhile, in a small saucepan, combine raisins, orange juice, ginger, cinnamon, and cornstarch. Heat over medium-low heat, stirring frequently, until the raisins are plump, about 10 minutes. Carefully pour the raisin mixture into a blender and blend to a fine puree. Pour the raisin puree over the chicken, and re-cover. Simmer for 45 minutes, stirring often, until sauce is thick and chicken is fully cooked.

To serve, divide rice between 8 bowls (or 6, or 4, for the extra-hungry crowd). Put 1 or 2 chicken pieces on top of the rice, then ladle stew over the top of each.

Serves 8.

⊛ THE MAIN COURSE

These entrées and meat and fish dishes serve as the centerpiece to a meal . . . the part everyone anticipates, the driving force. The word *entrée* actually refers to a composed dish served between the fish course and the meat course, but in these days of single-course meals, entrée sometimes means the main course, even if it consists of meat or fish. Just as often, however, the entrée is indeed a composed collection of ingredients combined to make a satisfying and filling meal.

An entrée or main course needn't contain meat at all, and many of the recipes in this section are meat-free, or contain only small amounts of meat for flavoring. Others feature meat, fish, or chicken, but each is Mediterranean in character. Use the best, freshest organic ingredients to maximize the flavors of these dinner features.

🌿 RATATOUILLE

This traditional vegetable dish from the Provençal region of France combines eggplant, tomatoes, peppers, and zucchini in a brilliant mosaic of colors and textures, but feel free to substitute other fresh seasonal vegetables in your own kitchen. Seasonality is the key to authenticity. Ratatouille is often served as an accompaniment to meat or fish. We like it as a main course served with a rice (saffron-tinted yellow rice is perfect). It is so beautiful that all the other food goes unnoticed anyway!

We tried to keep this recipe relatively low in oil. A nonstick skillet will make it much easier to keep this dish lower in fat, and salting/draining the eggplant first will also help eliminate the eggplant "oil-sponge" effect. If veggies really start to stick, you may need to increase the amount of olive oil, but do so just a little at a time.

1 medium, fresh eggplant, peeled and cut into
    1-inch cubes
1 tablespoon sea salt
1 medium onion, coarsely chopped
1 large red bell pepper, diced
1 large green, yellow, or orange bell pepper, diced
4 cloves garlic, chopped
3 tablespoons extra virgin olive oil
1 medium zucchini, cut into 1-inch cubes
1 small hot chili pepper (such as jalapeño), chopped, or
    a dash of cayenne pepper (optional)
2 cups peeled, chopped, and seeded ripe tomatoes or one
    15-ounce can tomatoes
½ teaspoon sugar
¼ cup chopped fresh basil
¼ cup pitted ripe olives, sliced or chopped

Place eggplant in a colander, sprinkle with salt, toss to cover the cubes in salt, place a paper towel over the eggplant, and weight with a plate or bowl. Set over the sink so eggplant can drain into the sink.

Meanwhile, in a large nonstick skillet, sauté the onion, bell peppers, and garlic in 2 tablespoons of the olive oil until all are soft but not browned. Remove from the skillet and set aside.

Add another 2 teaspoons of the oil to the skillet, remove eggplant from the colander, and sauté the eggplant cubes until golden brown and tender (about 10 minutes). Keep stirring to prevent sticking. Remove the eggplant from the skillet and set aside with the onion-pepper mixture (you can combine them in a single bowl).

Add the remaining teaspoon of oil and sauté the zucchini and chili pepper, if you are using it (if you are using cayenne pepper, don't add it yet), until the zucchini is tender and golden. Remove from the skillet and set aside (again, you can add them to the bowl of other vegetables).

You should have some oil remaining in the pan. If you don't, add another teaspoon or less, then add the tomatoes and sugar, and the cayenne pepper if you are using it. Lower the heat and simmer, stirring frequently, for about 15 minutes, or until the tomatoes are reduced to a thick, jamlike consistency.

Gently add the cooked vegetables you have set aside, stirring them into the tomatoes. Warm through (about 5 minutes), then stir in the fresh basil and black olives. Serve over or beside rice.

Serves 4.

✐ STUFFED ARTICHOKES

This dish can be an entrée (one artichoke per person) or a side dish to accompany a pasta, rice, bean, or fish dish (one artichoke for two to share). This recipe may sound complicated, but once you are familiar with preparing artichokes, it really is easy. Sure to elicit "oohs" and "ahhs" from appreciative diners, this dish looks impressive. In Italy this is prepared in the fall, when artichokes are in season; make it when artichokes in the store look plump and fresh with bright green leaves.

> 2 cups fresh (not dry) whole-grain bread crumbs
> ½ cup grated Pecorino cheese (or substitute Parmesan)
> 1 medium onion, finely chopped
> 3 cloves garlic, minced
> ¼ cup minced fresh Italian (flat-leaf) parsley
> 4 large artichokes
> 1 lemon, quartered
> 4 tablespoons extra virgin olive oil
> 4 lemon wedges

In a large bowl, combine the bread crumbs, grated cheese, onion, garlic, and parsley. Set aside.

Rinse the artichokes and drain well. Prepare the artichokes by cutting off the top ½ inch with a very sharp knife. Cut off the stems so that the artichokes will sit upright in the pan. Snip off the sharp tips of the leaves with scissors and remove any very tough outer leaves. Squeeze a lemon wedge over each artichoke, covering all cut surfaces. Spread the artichoke leaves and, using a spoon or your fingers, stuff the bread crumb mixture among as many leaves as you can, dividing the mixture among the 4 artichokes.

Carefully place the artichokes in a saucepan or Dutch oven. Drizzle the olive oil evenly over the 4 artichokes. Boil some water in a teakettle or saucepan and add enough hot water to cover the bottom third of the artichokes, pouring carefully to avoid getting water on the filling (some filling is bound to spill out throughout the entire process, but do your best). Heat the artichokes until the water boils again, then lower the heat, cover the pan, and simmer about 30 to 40 minutes or until the artichokes are tender.

Remove the artichokes carefully to a platter and serve with lemon wedges.

Serves 4.

SWEET CORN AND TOASTED WALNUT RISOTTO

½ cup chopped walnuts
1 large onion, chopped
2 large cloves garlic, minced
1½ cups uncooked Arborio rice
1 quart organic chicken broth
4 ears fresh sweet yellow corn, husked, silk removed, and
    kernels cut from cobs
Salt and freshly ground black pepper, to taste
½ cup chopped fresh chives
6 teaspoons Parmesan cheese

In a dry skillet over medium-high heat, heat the walnuts for 1 to 2 minutes until slightly toasted. Set aside.

Coat a 12-inch round nonstick skillet with vegetable cooking spray and set over medium-high heat. Add the onion and sauté, stirring occasionally for 3 minutes. Stir in the garlic; sauté for 1 minute. Add the rice and stir often until it turns opaque, about 2 minutes. Stirring constantly, add the chicken broth, about a half cup at a time, adding more broth only when the rice has absorbed the previous amount. When adding the last half cup of broth, stir in the corn kernels. If the risotto seems dry, add additional chicken broth to achieve a creamy texture. When the rice is tender, the risotto is creamy, and the corn is cooked, remove from heat. Stir in the walnuts. Season with salt and pepper. Divide the risotto among 6 warm individual serving bowls and sprinkle with chives and Parmesan cheese.

Serves 6.

✒ MOROCCAN-SPICED COD

This simple and delicious fish recipe tastes exotic and very special. It is low in fat and high in protein, and looks beautiful. If the serving size appears too large, divide the fish portions in half and save the other half as a delicious treat the next day.

*4 cod filets, about 6 ounces each (total of about 1½
   pounds fish)*
1 tablespoon extra virgin olive oil
Juice from 1 fresh lemon
1 tablespoon ground cumin
1 teaspoon cinnamon
1 clove garlic, peeled and minced
¼ teaspoon sea salt
Dash red or black pepper
1 medium yellow onion, cut into thin slices

Preheat oven to 400 degrees.

Rinse cod and pat dry. Place a square of aluminum foil, approximately 12 × 12 inches, on a baking sheet, spray with nonstick cooking spray, and place fish filets on the foil.

In a small bowl, combine olive oil, lemon juice, cumin, cinnamon, garlic, sea salt, and pepper. Spread the mixture over the top of the cod filets. Cover filets with onion slices.

Cover foil with a second square of foil and roll up edges so fish are enclosed in a foil packet. Place packet (still on baking sheet) into preheated oven. Bake for 45 minutes, or until fish flakes easily with a fork. Serve over couscous or rice, or on top of a plate of fresh greens.

Serves 4.

✐ MEDITERRANEAN CITRUS CHICKEN

This recipe tastes as sunny as a Mediterranean beach with its tangy citrus flavors over tender chicken breasts. The hardest part is juicing and zesting the fruit, but that's not really so hard, is it? Use organic citrus fruit for this recipe. Because you will be using the zest, and commercial, nonorganic citrus tends to be not only sprayed but dyed, organic fruit is the healthiest choice.

Juice and zest from 1 large orange
Juice and zest from 1 large lemon
Juice and zest from 1 large lime
Juice and zest from 1 small grapefruit
4 boneless chicken breast halves, about 4 ounces each
   (totaling about 1 pound chicken breast); If you can
   find it, use free-range chicken
1 teaspoon olive oil
¼ cup chicken broth
1 tablespoon honey
1 teaspoon cornstarch

1 teaspoon water
2 cups fresh greens
1 additional lime, ends cut off, thinly sliced into disks
    (for garnish)
Italian parsley sprigs (for garnish)

Combine the 4 citrus juices in a 2-cup glass measuring cup. Combine the 4 zests in a small bowl. Place a gallon-sized zippered plastic bag in a small tray. Pour half the juice into the bag. Add the chicken. Sprinkle in half the zest. Seal the bag, and lay the bag on its side in the baking pan. Turn it over several times, to make sure the chicken is covered in juice. Place in the refrigerator and let marinate for at least 2 hours, or overnight. Store remaining zest and remaining juice in an airtight bag or bowl.

When ready to cook the chicken, remove from the refrigerator. Put olive oil and chicken broth in a medium, nonstick skillet and heat over medium-high heat until chicken broth begins to simmer. Add chicken breasts, discarding the remaining marinade in the bag. Lower heat to medium. Cook chicken until no pink remains, about 20–25 minutes, turning halfway through cooking time.

Meanwhile, in a small saucepan, combine reserved juice and honey. Heat over medium-low heat for 5 minutes. Combine cornstarch and water, mixing to form a paste. Whisk into the juice mixture, stirring constantly until mixture begins to thicken, about 15 minutes. Remove from heat.

Cover a platter with fresh greens. Place chicken breasts over greens. Drizzle with sauce. Sprinkle with remaining zest, and arrange lime slices and Italian parsley sprigs between chicken pieces for garnish. Serve warm.

Serves 4.

🌿 TUNA STEAKS WITH GREEN SAUCE

This fresh twist on tuna tastes delicious. The sauce adds brilliant color and a pleasing tang to the mild, meaty taste of tuna steaks. The sauce is almost a pesto. Choose tuna steaks about 1 inch thick, and grill or broil for approximately 5 minutes on each side, or until fish flakes easily. If the serving size appears too large, divide the fish portions in half and save the other half as a nutritious treat the next day.

Four 6-ounce grilled or broiled tuna steaks
½ cup walnut pieces
½ cup chopped cilantro
½ cup chopped fresh basil
1 teaspoon extra virgin olive oil
½ cup chicken broth (possibly a little more or less)

In the bowl of a food processor, combine walnuts, cilantro, basil, olive oil, and half the chicken broth. Process. Add remaining chicken broth 1 tablespoon at a time, processing between additions, until sauce is thick but can be poured. Drizzle over hot or cold tuna steaks.
Serves 4.

🌿 FALAFEL WITH TOMATO-CUCUMBER RELISH

This Middle Eastern classic never gets boring. When frying falafel in olive oil cooking spray, this dish is much lower in fat than its traditional preparation method, which is to fry it in lots of oil. We think it tastes better this way.

One 15-ounce can garbanzo beans, rinsed and drained
1 medium onion, coarsely chopped
¼ cup parsley, minced
2 cloves garlic, minced

½ teaspoon ground cumin
1 teaspoon dried oregano
1 tablespoon fresh lemon juice
Salt and freshly ground black pepper to taste
1 cup dry whole-wheat bread crumbs
1 large egg, lightly beaten with a fork
Olive oil cooking spray
Tomato-Cucumber Relish (recipe follows)

In a food processor fitted with the metal blade, process the garbanzo beans, onion, parsley, garlic, cumin, and oregano until smooth; season to taste with the lemon juice, salt, and pepper. Stir in ½ cup of the bread crumbs and egg.

Spread remaining bread crumbs on a plate. Using your hands, form the bean mixture into 16 round balls, rolling each ball in the bread crumbs to coat. Set the balls on wax paper until you have them all coated.

Spray a large nonstick skillet with the cooking spray; heat over medium heat until hot. Add falafel balls and cook, stirring, until balls are browned, about 10 minutes.

Arrange 4 falafel balls on each plate, and serve with the Tomato-Cucumber Relish, or stuff fresh greens and falafel in pita halves, topping with relish.

Serves 4.

Tomato-Cucumber Relish

½ cup chopped tomato
½ cup chopped cucumber
⅓ cup nonfat plain yogurt
¼ teaspoon dried mint (optional)
Salt and freshly ground black pepper, to taste

In a small bowl, combine the tomato, cucumber, yogurt, and mint leaves; season to taste with salt and pepper.

Serves 4.

✒ SWORDFISH STEAKS WITH TOMATO-CAPER SAUCE

Oh how we love fish! This recipe uses swordfish, a satisfyingly meaty fish that will make you forget all about fattier grill options. Cook swordfish steaks about 1 inch thick, and grill or broil for approximately 5 minutes on each side, or until fish flakes easily. The sauce is quick and simple. If the serving size appears too large, divide the fish portions in half and save the other half as a delicious treat the next day.

4 grilled or broiled swordfish steaks, about 6 ounces each
2 large tomatoes, seeded and chopped (you can peel
them if you like, but it isn't necessary—to seed,
quarter tomatoes and squeeze the seeds out into the
sink, then chop)
1 clove garlic, minced
¼ cup capers
1 teaspoon dried tarragon (or basil or oregano,
depending on which you prefer)
Sea salt and black pepper to taste
1 teaspoon extra virgin olive oil

Combine tomatoes, garlic, capers, tarragon (crush dried herbs with your palms before adding to release flavor), salt, pepper, and oil. Serve at room temperature over swordfish steaks (or any other fish, or chicken).
Serves 4.

✒ FRENCH CASSOULET

This elegant beans-and-pork casserole hails from the Languedoc area of France. Serve this in a glazed stoneware crock for an authentic touch. This is filling comfort food with a French twist. In France, cassoulet is supposed to contain 30 percent pork, mutton, or preserved goose and 70 percent beans, stock, and herbs. This recipe approximates this ratio, although if we err, it is on the side of less meat. Try this recipe in the crockpot. What could be easier?

> ½ pound boneless pork tenderloin, smoked or cooked, and cut into small dice
> ½ pound lean smoked sausage, preferably from Europe, cut into ½-inch slices
> 1 tablespoon extra virgin olive oil
> 1 large yellow onion, peeled and chopped
> 1 large red bell pepper, chopped
> 2 cloves garlic, minced
> Four 15-ounce cans navy beans, drained and rinsed
> One 14½-ounce can diced tomatoes
> 1 teaspoon dried thyme
> 1 cup chicken broth
> Sea salt and black pepper, to taste
> 2 cups whole-grain bread crumbs
> 1 additional teaspoon extra virgin olive oil

Preheat oven to 350 degrees.

Place pork and sausage in a casserole or crockpot. Set aside.

Heat olive oil in a medium skillet over medium heat until it releases its aroma, about 5 minutes. Add onion, red bell pepper, and garlic. Sauté, stirring often, until onions and pepper are soft but not browned, about 10 minutes. Add to casserole or crockpot.

Add beans, tomatoes, thyme, and chicken broth to casserole or crockpot and stir all ingredients to combine.

Sprinkle the bread crumbs over the cassoulet and drizzle with the remaining teaspoon olive oil. In the casserole, bake uncovered until topping browns and filling is thick and bubbly, about 90 minutes. Or cook in crockpot on low for 6–8

hours (in the crockpot, the topping won't brown the way it does in the oven, but the cassoulet still tastes delicious!).
    Serves 8.

🌿 PAELLA VALENCIA

Paella recipes are as various as paella cooks, and everyone is quite sure his or her recipe is the *only* way to make it! This rice, chicken, and shellfish dish originated in the Valencia area of Spain, and almost always contains saffron, giving the rice a sunny yellow color. We're happy to contribute our favorite version to the usually joyful and always animated international paella discussion.

    2 tablespoons extra virgin olive oil
    1 whole chicken, cut into pieces
    ½ pound chorizo or spicy Italian sausage
    2 onions, peeled and chopped
    1 leek, chopped (white part only)
    2 stalks celery, minced
    3 cloves garlic, minced
    2 red bell peppers, seeded and cut into thin strips
    1 teaspoon ground cumin
    Pinch of saffron
    2 cups white rice
    2 cups chicken broth
    One 15-ounce can diced tomatoes
    One 15-ounce can light red kidney beans,
        rinsed and drained
    1 cup green peas
    12 ounces peeled medium shrimp

In a large nonstick skillet over medium heat, heat the oil for about 5 minutes. Rinse chicken pieces and pat dry. Add chicken to the pan and sauté until chicken is golden brown. Remove to a plate and set aside.

Without cleaning the pan, add the chorizo or other sausage to the pan, and sauté until fully cooked, about 10 minutes. Remove to a bowl and set aside.

Again without cleaning the pan, add onion, leek, celery, garlic, and red pepper. Sauté over medium heat until vegetables are soft but not brown, about 5 minutes. Add cumin and saffron. Stir to combine. Add rice (uncooked) and stir until rice is coated with oil and spices and thoroughly incorporated with the vegetables.

Slowly pour chicken broth into rice mixture. Stir in tomatoes with their juice, kidney beans, and peas. Pour the entire mixture into a large casserole or oven-safe Dutch oven.

Arrange chicken pieces and shrimp on top of casserole in an attractive design. Cover casserole or Dutch oven and bake for 45 minutes. Remove from oven and allow to sit for 10 minutes, or until rice has absorbed all the liquid.

Serves 8.

ALMOND WALNUT LINGUINI

Nuts and pasta may sound like an unusual combination, but try them and you'll see how delicious they are! This almond walnut linguini packs a caloric punch as well as a nutritional punch, however, so keep servings small, and save this recipe for special occasions.

12 ounces dried linguine
1 tablespoon olive oil
1 cup chopped almonds
1 cup chopped walnuts
2 cloves garlic, minced
1 tablespoon fresh basil, minced, or 1 teaspoon dried basil

6 anchovy filets, finely chopped, or ½ teaspoon sea salt
¼ cup grated Parmesan cheese

Cook linguine according to package directions, until al dente.

Meanwhile, toss olive oil, almonds, walnuts, garlic, basil, anchovies or salt, and cheese in a large bowl. When pasta is done, drain, rinse, and immediately add to nut mixture. Toss to combine and serve right away.

Serves 4.

🌿 MEDITERRANEAN SALAD SANDWICH WITH HARISSA

In the streets of Tunisia, you can buy salad sandwiches from many street vendors. They are always served on baguettes and always topped with harissa, the ubiquitous, spicy Tunisian condiment. If you make the harissa ahead of time and keep it stored in your refrigerator (it will keep for months if covered with a thin layer of extra virgin olive oil), this recipe is almost effortless because you use whatever leftovers you already have in the refrigerator. A classic Tunisian sandwich on a baguette includes tuna, potatoes, and lettuce, but you needn't be limited to Tunisian tradition. As far as we are concerned, anything fresh and good from the sea or the garden belongs between two halves of a baguette!

One 16-inch baguette, cut into 4 pieces, each piece
*   halved lengthwise*
2 cups salad greens
Harissa, to taste (see recipe below, and remember, this
*   condiment can be very spicy, depending on what*
*   kind of chilies you use to make it)*

Leftover fish and vegetables, such as:

> *Cooked tuna*
> *Cooked salmon*
> *Cooked whitefish*
> *Cooked shrimp*
> *Sliced boiled potatoes*
> *Potato salad*
> *Cucumber slices*
> *Chopped tomatoes*
> *Relish, chutney, or salsa*
> *Chopped hard-boiled eggs*
> *Sliced red onion*

Spread insides of baguettes with harissa. Top each sandwich with ½ cup salad greens and leftover fish and vegetables. Enjoy!
Serves 4.

ꞯ HARISSA

½ pound dried chilies, medium or hot or a
*   combination, depending on your preference*
10 cloves garlic, peeled
1 teaspoon sea salt
½ cup caraway seeds
1 teaspoon ground cumin
1 tablespoon extra virgin olive oil, plus extra to cover
*   the harissa for storage*

Using rubber gloves to protect your hands (and anything they touch) from the hot chilies, pull off the stems and tap the sides to shake out the seeds. Discard stems and seeds. Place the chilies in a large bowl. Pour hot water over the chilies to cover, and set aside for approximately 30 minutes.

Put garlic cloves in a food processor and process until minced. In a small spice grinder or a well-cleaned coffee grinder, grind the salt, caraway seeds, and cumin until the caraway seeds are reduced to the consistency of coarsely ground black pepper. Pour this mixture into the food processor. Add the drained, softened chilies (discard soaking water), and 1 tablespoon oil. Process until the mixture forms a paste.

Store in a small bowl or crock covered with olive oil. Replenish olive oil whenever you use more harissa.

Makes 2 cups.

🌿 SPAGHETTI WITH MEAT SAUCE

When it comes to spaghetti, a little ground meat goes a long way. A sauce rich with vegetables and tangy tomatoes needs only a little meat to add depth and richness to its flavor. Some Italian meat sauces, such as those from Bologna, have a higher proportion of meat to sauce and also add bacon and chicken livers. However, according to Ancel Keys, the people in Bologna had significantly higher blood cholesterol levels than the Italian people living along the coast of the Mediterranean. We prefer to keep the meat content, and our blood cholesterol levels, a little bit lower!

1 medium onion, chopped
2 cloves garlic, minced
2 medium carrots, scraped and shredded
1 small stalk of celery, finely chopped
3 tablespoons extra virgin olive oil
4 ounces extra lean ground beef or lean ground pork
One 28-ounce can tomatoes with juice
2 tablespoons tomato paste
2 tablespoons chopped fresh Italian (flat-leaf) parsley
1 bay leaf

½ cup dry red wine or water
1 pound spaghetti, linguine, or vermicelli
Freshly grated Parmesan cheese (optional)

In a large saucepan over medium heat, sauté the onions, garlic, carrots, and celery in the olive oil. When the onions are translucent but not brown, add the ground beef. Break up the meat with a wooden spoon and cook until brown. Stir in the tomatoes, tomato paste, Italian parsley, bay leaf, and the wine, if you are using it. Reduce the heat and simmer about 30 minutes, until thick but not dry. (If the sauce gets too dry, add more water, a little at a time, to reach desired consistency.)

In the meantime, cook the pasta in boiling salted water according to the package directions, until al dente (tender but firm). Drain and return the pasta to the warm pan (do not return to the hot burner). Just before serving, add the sauce and toss well. Pass fresh grated Parmesan cheese.

Serves 6 to 8.

❧ SEAFOOD RISOTTO

Comfort food with the elegant addition of shrimp, crab, or lobster in an easy recipe? What's not to love?

10 large shrimp, peeled and cut into bite-sized pieces
½ pound crabmeat or lobster meat, cut into
*   small chunks*
2 tablespoons extra virgin olive oil
3 cloves garlic, minced
1 large onion, finely chopped
1 carrot, peeled and finely chopped
1 medium stalk of celery, minced
½ cup red bell pepper, finely chopped
½ cup green bell pepper, finely chopped

6 cups chicken or vegetable broth
2 cups uncooked Arborio rice
½ cup chopped fresh Italian (flat-leaf) parsley
¼ cup freshly grated Parmesan cheese

In a large nonstick saucepan over medium heat, gently sauté the seafood in the olive oil. Stir about 5 minutes. Remove the seafood to a paper towel. Without cleaning the pan, add the garlic, onion, carrot, celery, and bell peppers to the pan. Sauté the vegetables until they are tender but not brown, about 10 minutes.

In the meantime, set the water or broth on the stove to simmer.

Add the raw rice to the oil-vegetable mixture and mix to coat the rice with the oil, fully incorporating the vegetables. Then begin to add the simmering broth, ½ cup at a time, letting each addition become almost completely absorbed by the rice and vegetables before adding the next ½ cup. When the rice is tender and saucy-looking, stop adding broth (even if you haven't added it all) and stir in the cooked seafood.

Remove from the heat and stir in the Italian parsley and Parmesan cheese. Serve immediately.

Serves 6 to 8.

✤ EGGPLANT PARMESAN

A delicious, filling, meatless meal, eggplant parmesan is quintessentially Italian and a good example of how the Italians use cheese. This dish is at its best when the eggplant is cooked quickly to absorb the least amount of oil, and the ingredients are fresh.

1 small onion, finely chopped
2 cloves garlic, minced

2 tablespoons extra-virgin olive oil
One 28-ounce can diced tomatoes
2 medium firm and fresh eggplants (weighing about
    1 pound each)
¼ teaspoon sea salt
½ cup flour
2 large eggs, beaten lightly
1 cup dried whole-grain bread crumbs
1 pound mozzarella cheese (choose part-skim to save on
    calories)
1 cup freshly grated Parmesan cheese
1 tablespoon chopped fresh Italian (flat-leaf) parsley

Preheat oven to 400 degrees.

Prepare the tomato sauce: In a medium skillet over medium heat, sauté the onion and garlic in 2 tablespoons of the oil until the onion is translucent but not brown. Add the diced tomatoes and stir to combine. Simmer gently 15 to 20 minutes, until the sauce thickens slightly. Remove from heat.

Meanwhile, wash and slice the eggplants into thin slices (¼ inch thick at most). (You can peel it if you prefer, but it isn't necessary.) Dip the eggplant slices in the flour, then into the egg mixture, then into the bread crumbs to coat. In a large nonstick skillet, heat the remaining 2 tablespoons olive oil until a bread crumb sizzles on contact. Fry the eggplant slices quickly, until tender and golden. Drain on paper towels on a wire rack and sprinkle with the sea salt.

Slice the mozzarella cheese into thin slices.

Coat a 9 × 13-inch baking pan with ½ cup of the tomato sauce. Then layer the remaining ingredients as follows:

> one-third of the eggplant slices
> one-third of the remaining sauce
> half the mozzarella slices
> one-third of the eggplant slices

    one-third of the sauce
    half the grated Parmesan cheese
    remaining eggplant
    remaining sauce
    remaining mozzarella
    remaining Parmesan

Top with the chopped fresh parsley.

Bake 40 minutes at 400 degrees, remove from the oven, and allow to sit for at least 15 minutes before cutting into squares and serving.

Serves 6 to 8.

(Note: For a lower fat variation, halve the amounts of mozzarella and Parmesan cheeses.)

☺ DESSERTS

In the Mediterranean, dessert may come in the form of an afterthought, and sweets are more likely to accompany afternoon coffee or tea, if they appear at all. More common to follow a delicious meal is fruit, in its many incarnations: just-picked, baked, or cooked into stews, jams, tarts, and other variations. Fruit makes a sweet ending to a healthy meal, and for those who enjoy cooking, we've provided some sweet-but-nutritious, luxurious-but-sensible desserts, mainly featuring fruit and none featuring butter and white flour. (You'll never miss them.)

✒ BAKED APPLES AND PEARS

Baked apples have a reputation for being a homey, almost old-fashioned American dessert, but why don't we ever bake pears? Both fruits are superb for baking, which brings out their flavor and transforms them into tender, melt-in-your-mouth pleasures. Baked fruit will also perfume your house as it cooks, like fruit pie with all the flavor but without the high-fat crust!

For this recipe, if you scrub the fruit well, leave the peels on. The recipe will also work with peeled fruit. You can alter this recipe to suit the taste of those you are serving—all apples, all pears, double of each, whatever seems appropriate. (If you make only pears, serve with the stuffing sprinkled over and around the fruit.)

You can also use less sugar, or even none at all. If you choose to go without, you needn't alter the recipe in any way except to omit the sugar, or you can stir in a spoonful of honey where the sugar goes. Sugar brings out the taste of the baked fruit, but it isn't necessary.

This is an excellent cold-weather or winter holiday dessert.

½ cup brown sugar
¼ cup chopped walnuts, almonds, or a combination
¼ cup raisins or dried currants
4 medium to large apples
4 medium pears, still firm
1 to 2 tablespoons fresh lemon juice
2 cups red wine, apple cider, or apple juice
½ teaspoon ground cinnamon
¼ teaspoon ground nutmeg
Rind from 1 small well-washed, organically grown
    orange or lemon, cut in strips

Preheat oven to 300 degrees.

In a small bowl, combine ¼ cup of the brown sugar, the nuts, and the raisins. Set aside.

Core the apples from the top, leaving about a ½-inch of apple at the base. Don't core the pears, but slice off the very bottoms so they stand up straight. Leave their stems intact. Brush any peeled or cut fruit surfaces with lemon juice, then set the fruits upright in a 1- to 1½-quart baking pan or casserole. Stuff the apples with the nut mixture.

In a saucepan, combine the wine, cider, or juice; cinnamon; nutmeg; the remaining brown sugar; and the citrus rind. Heat to boiling, then pour carefully over the fruit. Cover the pan with a lid or aluminum foil, then bake for 30 to 45 minutes, until the fruits are soft when pierced with a fork. Baste occasionally with the wine sauce during baking.

Serve each piece of fruit in a shallow bowl or small dish with the wine sauce spooned over the top. These also look pretty served in wineglasses or stemmed glass sundae dishes.

Serves 8.

✎ STUFFED PEACHES

This luxurious dish is impressive and easy to prepare, not to mention delicious. Choose very fresh, large, juicy peaches for this recipe. If you really want to make this but can't find good peaches, canned peaches will work, but because they are softer, they require more delicate handling and only about 15 minutes of cooking time. Buy canned peaches packed in juice, not sugar syrup.

Peaches and almonds are closely related, so they make a natural pairing here. Both are also grown extensively in Italy, where baked peaches are a perennial favorite.

> 4 large whole ripe peaches or 8 canned peach halves
> ½ cup almond or other cookie crumbs (amaretto cookies or almond macaroons are best, but you can substitute any nonchocolate cookie—even vanilla wafers will work, if you can't find fancier cookies or don't have time to make your own)
> ¼ teaspoon ground cinnamon
> 2 tablespoons chopped almonds
> 1 tablespoon amaretto liqueur or ¼ teaspoon almond extract (optional)
> 1 egg yolk
> 1 tablespoon sugar or honey (optional)
> Citrus peel or sliced almonds for garnish

Preheat the oven to 400 degrees.

Cut the peaches in half. Remove all traces of pits, then scoop out the centers so they are about the size of a tablespoon. Reserve any scooped pulp. Put the peaches, hollowed sides up, in a baking pan sprayed with nonstick cooking spray.

Combine scooped pulp, if any, with the cookie crumbs, cinnamon, almonds, liqueur or almond extract (if using), and egg yolk. Fill each peach with one-eighth of the mixture. Sprinkle the peaches lightly with brown sugar or drizzle with a little honey, if desired.

Bake about 20 minutes, until the peaches are tender and the filling is golden. Garnish with curls of citrus peel or sliced almonds (or both).

Serves 4.

CITRUS COMPOTE

Citrus trees adorned the Mediterranean long before they adorned the southern shores of the United States. Citrus fruits are available all year round but are particularly seasonal during the winter, making this dessert a refreshing fall, winter, or early spring finish to a warm, hearty meal. Served extra cold in chilled glass dishes, it is also a cooling summer dessert.

An alternative to bringing the lemon and lime to room temperature is to pierce each with a knife and microwave 30 seconds each (do them one at a time) to release the juice.

This recipe is too tart for some, hence the optional sugar. You may not want to use it if you like a good pucker!

2 medium tangerines
2 medium oranges
1 medium red grapefruit
1 medium lemon at room temperature
1 medium lime at room temperature
1 to 2 tablespoons sugar (optional)
Fresh coconut slivers or chopped almonds
    for garnish (optional)

Peel the tangerines, oranges, and grapefruit. Segment, and trim the white pith. (You don't have to cut it all off, as pith is loaded with fiber and phytochemicals. Too much pith adds a bitter taste, however.) Halve or quarter any segments that are larger than bite-sized.

Remove any seeds with a sharp knife. Combine the segments in a large bowl.

Quarter the lemon and lime and squeeze over the citrus segments. Or halve and use a citrus juicer to extract the juice, then drizzle over citrus segments.

If desired, sprinkle with sugar and mix gently. Chill at least 1 hour and serve cold.

Serve in glass bowls. Garnish with slivers of coconut or a sprinkling of chopped almonds, if desired.

Serves 6, depending on appetites.

✒ CINNAMON ORANGES

This dessert couldn't be simpler, or more delicious, if you use the freshest, juiciest, in-season oranges.

*2 fresh, ripe oranges, in season (in the U.S., in season for
    citrus means wintertime)*
1 teaspoon cinnamon
1 tablespoon sugar

Halve the oranges. Put each orange half in a pretty bowl. Combine cinnamon and sugar. Sprinkle over oranges. Serve with a spoon for scooping out the sections.

Serves 4.

✒ LEMON ALMOND CAKE

This cake has Majorcan origins and uses ground almonds in place of flour, for a dense, luxurious cake.

1½ cups blanched almonds
¼ cup honey
4 large eggs
Zest from 2 organic lemons
¼ teaspoon nutmeg

Preheat oven to 375 degrees. Spray a 9-inch springform pan with nonstick cooking spray.

Put the almonds in a food processor or blender and grind to a fine meal.

Separate the eggs, putting yolks into a large mixing bowl and the whites in a separate, clean mixing bowl. To the yolks, add the honey, zest, and nutmeg. Beat on medium until the yolk mixture begins to thicken, about 3 minutes.

Clean the beaters completely, and beat the egg whites on high until soft peaks form.

Stir almonds into the yolk mixture, then fold in the egg whites. Gently scoop the batter into the springform pan.

Bake until a toothpick inserted in the center of the cake comes out clean, 30–40 minutes.

Cool for 5 minutes. Using a sharp knife, loosen the edges of the cake from the sides of the pan. Cool an additional 25 minutes, then remove sides. Serve at room temperature with ice cream.

✤ ORANGE-BANANA MUFFINS

This recipe is more Mediterranean in spirit than in actuality, but it makes a delicious breakfast, so we'll include it. These muffins are full of good fruit and grain flavor and nutrition.

3 cups rolled oats
½ cup almonds
1 tablespoon baking powder

1 egg
1 very ripe banana, mashed
1 cup mandarin orange slices, drained and mashed with
    a fork
1 cup unsweetened applesauce
½ cup canned pumpkin puree (not pumpkin pie mix)
½ cup brown sugar
1 tablespoon vanilla
½ cup nonfat plain yogurt

Preheat oven to 375 degrees.

Put oats and almonds in a blender and grind to a flour. Pour into a large mixing bowl. Stir in baking powder. In another bowl, beat the egg with a fork. Add banana, oranges, applesauce, pumpkin, and sugar. Mix well with a fork, until thoroughly combined.

In a 2-cup glass measure, stir vanilla into yogurt.

Add one-third of oat mixture to banana mixture. Stir just until combined. Add half the yogurt, stirring until just combined. Repeat with another third of the oat mixture, the remaining yogurt, and the remaining oat mixture.

Spray 12 muffin cups with nonstick cooking spray, or use muffin liners. Fill muffin cups with batter. Bake 20 minutes, or until middles are set. Remove from the oven, cool 15 minutes, and remove from muffin tin. Allow to cool completely before serving.

Serves 12.

✍ WINE-STEWED FIGS WITH YOGURT CREAM

Wine lends figs an elegance, making them a perfect finish to a fancy dinner for guests, or a private indulgence just for you. You can also skip the chilling step and serve this warm, as a dessert on a winter evening.

½ cup brown sugar
1 bottle red table wine (or 4 cups cranberry juice)
Juice and zest from 1 organic lemon
2 cinnamon sticks
3 cloves
2 pounds fresh figs
2 cups plain low-fat or nonfat yogurt
1 teaspoon vanilla
1 tablespoon honey
Ground cinnamon for garnish

In a large stainless steel or nonstick saucepan, combine brown sugar, wine or cranberry juice, lemon juice and zest, cinnamon sticks, and cloves. Heat over medium-high heat until the liquid comes to a boil. Lower the heat to medium and cook, stirring constantly, until mixture begins to thicken slightly and sugar is completely dissolved.

Lower heat to medium-low and add figs to wine mixture, stirring gently to coat figs. Simmer in wine mixture for 5 minutes, stirring constantly to keep figs moving and coated. Remove figs to a glass or ceramic bowl.

Continue cooking the wine until it has been reduced by about half and looks like a thin syrup. Fish out the cinnamon sticks and cloves, and discard them. Ladle the wine syrup over the figs. Chill in the refrigerator for at least 1 hour.

When you are ready to serve the figs, put them in 4 individual dessert dishes or bowls. Drizzle any remaining syrup over the figs.

Put the yogurt in a medium bowl. Add vanilla and honey. Stir gently to combine. Top each dish of figs with some of the yogurt cream. Sprinkle each with ground cinnamon and serve.

Serves 4.

✍ HONEY-SWEETENED BROILED FETA

This recipe may sound strange, but it is delicious! The combination of the tangy, creamy cheese with the crisp, broiled, sweetened coating is irresistible. The aniseed and honey give this dessert a real Greek flavor.

> *12 ounces feta cheese cut into 3 × ½-inch sticks*
> *1 tablespoon extra virgin olive oil*
> *¼ cup honey*
> *½ teaspoon aniseed*

Preheat broiler. Divide cheese sticks between four broiler-proof ceramic ramekins. Brush cheese with oil. Set ramekins under the broiler, about 6 inches from heat source. Broil until the cheese is golden brown and bubbly, about 2–4 minutes. Watch it carefully, because this will happen fast and you don't want to burn the cheese. Remove ramekins and set aside.

Combine honey and aniseed in a small saucepan and heat over medium heat until hot, or combine in a glass measuring cup and heat in the microwave on 50 percent power for 90 seconds. Top each serving of cheese with equal portions of the honey mixture. Serve immediately.

Serves 4.

✍ ESPRESSO GRANITA

Sometimes it's just too hot to drink an espresso, but it's never too hot for an espresso granita, that sweet icy Italian concoction that is low in fat and high in flavor—perfect for ending a light summer lunch, or as a morning or afternoon refresher when temperatures rise. Granita is like ice cream without the cream, coarser in texture than a sorbet, and satisfying to crunch. If you are watching your caffeine intake, use naturally (chemical-free) decaffeinated espresso. It tastes just as good, and no jitters! You can also substitute strong brewed coffee for the espresso, for a coffee granita. (This is a good way to use the rest of that pot nobody drank, but make the granita within an hour after the coffeepot warmer has been turned off.)

½ cup water
½ cup sugar
2 cups espresso
½ teaspoon real vanilla
Whipped cream for topping (optional)

Put water and sugar in a small saucepan and heat over medium heat until boiling, about ten minutes, stirring occasionally. Don't be tempted to speed this up by heating on high, as the sugar can burn. Boil the sugar mixture for 5 minutes without stirring, then remove from heat. Stir once and allow to cool completely.

Combine espresso, sugar syrup, and vanilla in a shallow casserole or baking pan (not aluminum). Put in the freezer. After 30 minutes, remove and stir the crystals around the edges into the middle with a fork. Put back in freezer. Every 30 minutes, remove pan and stir up crystals with a fork. If you forget and wait too long, use the side of a spoon to shave down the larger chunks. When completely frozen (4–6 hours), the granita is done. You can store it for a day or two, covered, in the freezer, but stir it occasionally to keep it from freezing into a hard chunk. When ready to serve, spoon granita into wineglasses or champagne glasses. Top with whipped cream if desired.

Serves 6.

Resources

For more information on the Mediterranean diet, landscape, and lifestyle, take a look at these books and web sites.

BOOKS

American Heart Association. *The New American Heart Association Cookbook: Twenty-fifth Anniversary Edition.* New York: Times Books, 1999.

Barrenechea, T., and Goodbody, M. *The Basque Table: Passionate Home Cooking from One of Europe's Great Regional Cuisines.* Harvard Common Press, 1998.

Boyle, M., and Zyla, G. *Personal Nutrition.* 3d ed. Minneapolis: West Publishing Company, 1996.

Cloutier, M., Romaine, D., and Adamson, E. *Beef Busters: Less Beef, Better Health.* Avon, Mass.: Adams Media, 2002.

Gollman, B., and Pierce, K. *The Phytopia Cookbook: A World of Plant-Centered Cuisine.* Dallas: Phytopia, 1999.

Hazan, M. *Marcella's Italian Kitchen.* New York: Alfred A. Knopf, 1987.

Helou, A. *Mediterranean Street Food.* New York: Harper-Collins, 2002.

Jenkins, N. H. *The Essential Mediterranean.* New York: HarperCollins, 2003.

Jenkins, N. H. *Flavors of Tuscany: Traditional Recipes from the Tuscan Countryside.* New York: Broadway Books, 1998.

Jenkins, N. H. *The Mediterranean Diet Cookbook: A Delicious Alternative for Lifelong Health.* New York: Bantam Books, 1994.

Jodice, M., and Matvejevic, P., *Mediterranean.* New York: Aperture, 1996.

Keys, A. B. *How to Eat Well and Stay Well the Mediterranean Way.* New York: Doubleday, 1975.

Lovatt-Smith, L. *Mediterranean Living.* New York: Whitney Library of Design, 1998.

Mackley, L. *The Book of Mediterranean Cooking.* New York: HPBooks, 1996.

Mahan, K., and Escott-Stump, S. *Krause's Food, Nutrition, & Diet Therapy.* 9th ed. Philadelphia: W. B. Saunders Company, 1996.

Ornish, D. *Program for Reversing Heart Disease, the Only System Scientifically Proven to Reverse Heart Disease Without Drugs or Surgery.* New York: Ivy Books, 1996.

Pawlak, L. *A Perfect 10: Phyto "New-trients" Against Cancers*. Berkeley, Calif.: Biomed General Corp., 1998.

Pennington, J. *Bowes & Church's Food Values of Portions Commonly Used*. 17th ed. Philadelphia: Lippincott, 1998.

Randall, Otelio S., and Donna Randall. *Menu for Life*. New York: Broadway Books, 2003.

Rogers, J., ed. *Prevention's Quick and Healthy Low-Fat Cooking: Featuring Cuisines from the Mediterranean*. Rodale Press, 1994.

Rosso, J. *Fresh Start: Great Low-Fat Recipes, Day-by-Day Menus—The Savvy Way to Cook, Eat, and Live!* New York: Crown Publishers, 1996.

Rothfeld, G., and LeVert, S. *Folic Acid and the Amazing B Vitamins*. New York: Berkley Books, 2000.

St. Paul's Greek Orthodox Cathedral, ed., *The Complete Book of Greek Cooking: The Recipe Club of St. Paul's Orthodox Cathedral*. New York: HarperPerennial Library, 1991.

Schlesinger, S., and Ernest, B. *The Low-Cholesterol Olive Oil Cookbook: More Than 200 Recipes*. Villard Books, 1996.

Shulman, M. R. *Mediterranean Light*. New York: William Morrow, 2000.

Simopoulos, A. P. and Robinson, J. *The Omega Diet: The Lifesaving Nutritional Program Based on the Diet of the Island of Crete*. New York: HarperCollins, 1999.

Uvezian, S. *Recipes and Remembrances from an Eastern Mediterranean Kitchen: A Culinary Journey Through Syria, Lebanon, and Jordan*. Texas: University of Texas Press, 1999.

Weir, J. *From Tapas to Meze: First Courses from the Mediterranean Shores of Spain, France, Italy, Greece, Turkey, the Middle East, and North Africa.* New York: Crown Publishers, 1994.

Weir, J. *Joanne Weir's More Cooking in the Wine Country.* New York: Simon & Schuster, 2001.

Wells, P. *Trattoria: Healthy, Simple, Robust Fare Inspired by the Small Family Restaurants of Italy.* New York: William Morrow, 1993.

Wolfert, P. *The Cooking of the Eastern Mediterranean: 215 Healthy, Vibrant, and Inspired Recipes.* New York: HarperCollins, 1994.

Wolfert, P. *Couscous and Other Good Foods from Morocco.* New York: HarperCollins, 1987.

Wolfert, P. *Mediterranean Cooking.* New York: Harper Perennial, 1994.

Wolfert, P. *Mediterranean Grains and Greens: A Book of Savory, Sun-Drenched Recipes.* New York: Harper-Collins, 1998.

Wolfert, P. *Mostly Mediterranean: More Than 200 Recipes from France, Spain, Greece, Morocco, and Sicily.* New York: Penguin USA, 1996.

Woodward, Sarah. *Classic Mediterranean Cookbook.* New York: Dorling Kindersley, 1995.

Wright, Clifford A. *A Mediterranean Feast: The Story of the Birth of the Celebrated Cuisines of the Mediterranean from the Merchants of Venice to the Barbary Corsairs.* New York: William Morrow, 1999.

Young, D. *Made in Marseille: Food and Flavors from France's Mediterranean Seaport.* New York: Harper-Collins, 2002.

WEB SITES

American Dietetic Association: http://www.eatright.org/

American Heart Association: http://www.americanheart.org/

American Journal of Clinical Nutrition: http://www.ajcn.org/

Cucina italiana.com, "The virtual home of Italian cuisine and the Mediterranean Diet": http://www.cucinaitaliana .com/index.shtml

DotPharmacy's "Life of the Med": http://www.dotphar macy.com/upmed.html

Dr. Andrew Weil's Self-Healing (contains newsletter subscription information): http://www.drweilselfhealing.com/

Gourmed: Journey to the Big Blue (Greek recipes and culture): http://www.gourmed.gr/

Mediterranean recipes from arabicnews.com: http://www. arabicnews.com/recipes/recipes.html.

Oldways Preservation and Exchange Trust: http://www.old wayspt.org/

Paula Wolfert's website: http://www.paula-wolfert.com/ recipes.html

Tufts University Health and Nutrition Letter (includes subscription information): http://healthletter.tufts.edu/

Tufts University Nutrition Navigator (reviews nutrition-related web sites): http://navigator.tufts.edu/

U.S. Food and Drug Administration, "Internet FDA": http:// www.fda.gov/

Index

Recipes denoted by *italic* page references

THE MEDITERRANEAN DIET NUTRIENT SCORE CARD

Food Item	Calories	Protein (g)	Fat (g)	Sat Fat (g)	Fiber (g)
VEGETABLES					
Artichoke, boiled, 1 medium	150	10	5	0	16
Asparagus, boiled, 6 spears	22	2.3	0	0	1.5
Broccoli, boiled, 1/2 cup	22	2.5	0	0	2.5
Carrots, boiled, 1/2 cup slices	35	1	0	0	2.5
Cauliflower, boiled, 1/2 cup pieces	14	1	0	0	1.5
Eggplant, boiled, 1/2 cup	13	0.5	0	0	1
Endive, raw, 1/2 cup chopped	4	0.5	0	0	1
Green beans, boiled, 1/2 cup	22	1	0	0	2
Romaine lettuce, raw, 1/2 cup shredded	4	0.5	0	0	0.5
Mushrooms, boiled, 1/2 cup pieces	21	2	0	0	2
Onions, raw, 1/2 cup	16	1	0	0	1.5
Peppers, sweet, raw, 1/2 cup chopped	14	0.5	0	0	1
Radicchio, raw, 1/2 cup, shredded	5	0.5	0	0	0
Spinach, raw, 1/2 cup, chopped	6	1	0	0	1
Zucchini, boiled, 1/2 cup slices	14	1	0	0	1.5
Squash, summer, crookneck, boiled, 1/2 cup	18	1	0	0	1.5
Tomato, red, raw, 1 medium	26	1	0	0	1.5
Tomato, red, sun-dried, 1/2 cup	70	3.5	0	0	3.5
BEANS, LENTILS, PEAS					
Broad beans, 1 cup, boiled	187	13	0	0	9
Chickpeas (garbanzo beans), boiled, 1 cup	270	14.5	0	0	12.5
Hummus, 1/2 cup	210	6	10	1.6	6
Northern beans, boiled, 1/2 cup	105	7	0	0	6
Kidney beans, red, boiled, 1/2 cup	110	7.5	0	0	7.5
Lentils, boiled, 1/2 cup	115	9	0	0	7.5
Lima beans, boiled, 1/2 cup	108	7	0	0	6.5
Navy beans, boiled, 1/2 cup	228	8	0	0	5.5
Peas, green, boiled, frozen, 1/2 cup	60	5	0	0	2
Peas, split, boiled, 1/2 cup	215	8	0	0	8
White beans, boiled, 1/2 cup	125	8.5	0	0	5.5
FRUITS					
Apple, raw with skin, 1 medium	80	0.5	0	0	2.5
Apricots, raw, 3 medium	50	1.5	0	0	2.5
Pear, raw, 1 medium	100	0.5	0	0	4.5
Cherries, sweet, 10 raw	34	1	0	0	1.5
Dates, 4 dried	100	0.5	0	0	3

Food Item	Calories	Protein (g)	Fat (g)	Sat Fat (g)	Fiber (g)
FRUITS					
Figs, 2 dried	125	2	0	0	4
Plums, raw, 1 medium	36	0.5	0	0	1
Raspberries, raw, 1/2 cup	30	0.5	0	0	4.5
Orange, navel, raw, 1	60	1.5	0	0	3
Peach, raw, 1 medium	37	0.5	0	0	1.5
Strawberries, raw, 1 cup	45	1	0	0	3.4
GRAIN PRODUCTS					
Whole grain bread, 1 slice	70	3	1	0	1.5
Whole wheat pita, 1/2 large	100	4.5	0.5	0	2.5
Brown rice, long grain, cooked, 1/2 cup	108	2.5	1.4	0	1.5
Spaghetti, whole wheat, cooked, 1 cup	175	7.5	1	0	6.5
Macaroni, whole wheat, cooked, 1 cup	175	7.5	1	0	4
NUTS, SEEDS					
Almonds, dried, 1/2 oz (12 nuts)	82	3	7.5	0.5	1.5
Cashews, dry roasted, 1 oz (9 nuts)	82	2	6.5	1	0.5
Chestnuts, European, raw (2 1/2 nuts)	60	0.5	0.5	0	2.5
Pistachios, dried, 1/4 oz (12 nuts)	40	1.5	3.5	0	0.5
Pumpkin seeds, 1/3 cup	110	5	5	1	2
Sesame seeds, whole, dried, 1 tablespoon	52	1.6	4.5	0.5	1
CHEESE, YOGURT, MILK, EGGS					
Mozzarella, part skim, low moisture, 1 oz	80	8	5	3	0
Ricotta, part skim, 1/4 cup	135	7	10	6	0
Romano, 1 oz	110	9	7.5	5	0
Provolone, 1 oz	100	7	7.5	5	0
Feta, 1 oz	75	4	6	4	0
Cottage cheese, 1% fat, 1/2 cup	82	14	2.5	1.5	0
Yogurt, plain, 1.5% milk fat, 4 oz	115	5	1.5	1	0
Milk, 1% fat, 8 fl oz	102	8	2.5	1.5	0
Egg, chicken, 1 large, boiled	80	6	5.5	1.5	0
POULTRY, FISH					
Chicken/Turkey, light meat, w/o skin, roasted, 3.5 oz	175	30	4.5	1.5	0
Scallops, sea, raw, 3.5 oz	60	11	1	0	0
Haddock, dry heat cooked, 3 oz	95	21	1	0	0
Halibut, dry heat cooked, 3 oz	119	23	2.5	1	0
Snapper, dry heat cooked, 3 oz	110	23	1.5	0.5	0
Salmon, Atlantic, wild, dry heat cooked, 3 oz	155	22	7	1	0